AMERICAN

MEDICAL BIOGRAPHY

OR

MEMOIRS OF

EMINENT PHYSICIANS

A MILFORD HOUSE REPRINT

The figure impressed on the volume's
cover, is the silhouette, by MASTER HANKES,
of Dr. E. A. HOLYOKE, 1728-1829,
of Salem, Massachusetts.

The special typography of the introductory
pages, the box & the binding has been designed
by Schuyler Watts, in rare type-faces of
Eric Gill and Jan van Krimpen.

AMERICAN MEDICAL BIOGRAPHY

OR MEMOIRS OF EMINENT PHYSICIANS

EMBRACING PRINCIPALLY THOSE WHO
HAVE DIED SINCE THE PUBLICATION
OF DR. THACHER'S INITIAL WORK
IN 1828 ON THE SAME SUBJECT.
GREENFIELD, MASSACHUSETTS, 1845

BY STEPHEN W. WILLIAMS, M. D.

NEW YORK
MILFORD HOUSE Inc.
MCMLXVII

PREFACE.

MORE than fifteen years have elapsed since the venerable Dr. Thatcher, of Plymouth, Massachusetts, published his inestimable work upon American Medical Biography, which was most favorably received by the medical public. This space of time embraces nearly one half of a generation. During this period great numbers of the most eminent men in the profession in America, have descended to the tomb. The memorials of many of these have been only published in the ephemeral journals of the day, like many of our newspapers; some have been published in more valuable and durable medical periodicals. Many of these have had so limited a circulation that they are not seen by the great mass of the profession. Of others, no published biographies have appeared.

It has been my object in the present work to collect these scattered materials, and place them in a more condensed and durable form. There are abundance of facts scattered throughout the country, to form in-

teresting volumes upon this subject, but the grand
difficulty is to draw them forth and present them to
the public eye. Most men are so much occupied in
their own pursuits that they can find but little time to
write biographies, even of their dearest friends, however well qualified they may be for the task. The
labor of a work of this kind must, therefore, be extremely onerous. The work has been delayed for
several months on this account, and even now I am
obliged to commit it to the press with the omission of
the names of several very distinguished physicians. I
regret this the less, as it is already sufficiently large for
an octavo volume. I shall still be happy to receive
communications for another volume, which will, probably, succeed this.

The work is necessarily, in a great measure, a com-
pilation. Biographies must almost, as a matter of
course, be so. No one man can grasp all the materials of extended biographies in his own mind, be it
ever so capacious. The facts at least, if not the very
expression of them, must come from others. And who
are better qualified for this than those who are most
intimately acquainted with the deceased? In many
instances I have taken the liberty to abridge and alter
the language of my correspondents, and the writers to
whom I am indebted for many of the facts in this work,
for which I hope they will excuse me. Indeed, the

most laborious part of the undertaking has been the
collecting, condensing, and compiling the work.   Had
I not taken this liberty, which some of my correspondents have granted me, the volume might have been
enlarged to an unwieldy and cumbersome size.   I
hope I have done justice to the writers, and given
them due credit for their productions.

Some of the memoirs were written by myself on
different occasions, such as those of Drs. Allen, Church,
Hamilton, Haynes, Goodhue, Prentiss, Stone, Wing,
Thomas and William S. Williams, Henry Wells, John
Lee, and several others.   I feel under great and lasting obligations to my friends Drs. Sewall, of Washington ; Coxe, Hays, Randolph, Wood and Hodge, of
Philadelphia ; Charles A. Lee, Francis, Mott, &c., of
New York ; Jackson, J. V. C. Smith, Thatcher, Alden,
Woodward, Baylies, Haskell, and others, in Massachusetts ; Menzo White and Amasa Trowbridge, of
Western New York, and to very many others, who, I
trust, will pardon me for not enumerating their names,
for the aid they have given me in the prosecution of
the work, and for the assurance which they have given
me, that such a publication from me was very desirable.   The encouragement of such men is a guarantee
that a production of this kind will meet the approbation
of the public.

To a medical man no species of writing is more

interesting than medical biography. The republic of medicine contains but few ambitious aspirants for fame, beyond the immediate circle of their practice. Physicians are called to move in a humbler sphere than clergymen, lawyers, and statesmen. Hence they are much less noticed by the great body of the people than these more prominent actors on the theatre of life. But we deny that they are less learned, useful, and good. This is not the place to discuss the priority of the learned professions; but it is acknowledged by those who have investigated the subject that the profession of medicine is more philosophical and learned than either of the others, and that in its ranks have ever been found some of the most scientific men the world has ever produced. This is not to be wondered at, when we reflect that " the science of medicine is related to every thing."

It has been truly said that " history is philosophy teaching by example." With how much greater force and truth does this assertion apply to biography, which has been termed the " very heart of history." The examples of the wise and good, as shown in their lives and characters, in their written memorials, must ever present most worthy patterns for imitation. Whose bosom is not animated by the description of the glowing fires of medical lore, which burned within the breasts of such men as Smith, Post, Hosack, Todd,

Dewees and Physick, and their more youthful but not less zealous and worthy followers, Godman, Jackson, and Trowbridge? These, and many more whose memoirs are recorded in this work, will ever stand as pole stars to direct the course of the future traveller on the road to medical honor, distinction, and usefulness.

Deerfield, Mass., Sept. 1st, 1844.

AMERICAN MEDICAL BIOGRAPHY.

Dr. Joseph Allen, of Buckland, in the county of Franklin and Commonwealth of Massachusetts, was born on Long Island in the year 1764. He came to Hardwick, Massachusetts, when only two years old, and resided there till he was old enough to study the profession of medicine. I know little or nothing of his early education, but I believe it was sufficient to qualify him for entering on the study of the healing art. At least, it was so considered at that early day. He studied the profession of medicine with Dr. William Kittredge, then residing in the town of Conway, in this state. Dr. Kittredge was considered by the public to be an eminent bonesetter and surgeon. Dr. Allen commenced his professional career in Coleraine, in the county of Franklin, where he continued one year, when he removed to Buckland, about twelve miles from Coleraine, where he had a great run of business till the time of his death, which occurred in 1823, at the age of fifty-nine. His health for many years had been feeble, being troubled with dyspeptic complaints, but by a rigidly abstemious, and principally a milk diet, he was enabled to bear up under his

3

complaints, and even to perform a great amount of business, in a rough and hilly country. He joined the Massachusetts Medical Society in 1812, and resigned in 1818. He made considerable property by the practice of his profession, and he was well thought of by his professional brethren. I believe he performed some capital operations in surgery, and he was thought by many to be a superior bonesetter. *Vide my Medical History of Franklin County.*

DR. MILTON ANTONY. This gentleman was a distinguished Professor of Obstetrics in the Medical College of Georgia. The Southern Medical and Surgical Journal thus speaks of him, while announcing his death. " It is with feelings of the most poignant sorrow that we have to announce the death of Dr. Milton Antony, Editor of this Journal. He expired on Thursday afternoon (Oct. 18, 1839) after an illness of five days." The editor of the Boston Medical Journal observes, that " his loss is indeed a public calamity, and greatly to be deplored by the profession throughout the country. He retained the entire possession of his mind to the last, and the closing hours of an honorable and useful life were brightened by the hopes of a glorious immortality."

DR. NATHANIEL WALKER APPLETON was born at Boston, in the year 1755, and received his degree at Harvard College, in 1773. He was a grandson of

Nathaniel Appleton, D. D., of Cambridge, who died in the year 1784, in the 91st year of his age. He studied the profession of medicine with the venerable Dr. Holyoke, of Salem, and established himself in Boston as a practitioner of medicine, not far from the year 1777. He was one of the founders of the Massachusetts Medical Society, and of the American Academy of Arts and Sciences.

He was very highly estimated as a physician. He was very active in promoting the interests of the Massachusetts Medical Society, and published several valuable papers in the transactions of that Society. He was the first Secretary of ·that Institution. He resigned his fellowship about the year 1794, with the intention of moving from the state, and as a token of his great regard for the Society, he made a donation to it of a part of his library and anatomical cabinet. He resided for a few years at Marietta, in Ohio, when he returned to Boston, about the year 1798, where he died, at the age of 43.—*Alden's Notices of the Founders of the Mass. Med. Society.*

DR. WILLIAM ATCHERSON, of Windham County, Vt., died on the 26th of January, 1823, in the meridian of life, and in the midst of extensive business. I am indebted to an address delivered before the Vermont Second Medical Society at their semi-annual meeting in June, 1833, by Dr. John H. Wells, extracts from which were published in the 8th vol. of the Boston Medical Journal, for the following notice of his life and death.   I regret that I am not able to obtain more particulars concerning him.   The remarks contain more of eulogy than narrative.   ' An afflictive providence has deprived this Society of one of its most valuable members.   Long had he been a Fellow of it, and his loss will be lastingly felt.   As a practitioner of medicine he was respectable, and a careful investigator of cause and effect, judicious in his prescriptions, consequently successful.   He possessed abilities, and he was ever ready modestly to use them for the benefit of his fellow men.   His integrity was unsuspected, his character liberal, and he was, we humbly hope, a friend of that God in whose immediate presence he now appears.   At the very zenith of his prosperity and usefulness he was cut down, and will rise not till the last trump shall summon him.   The forebodings of approaching dissolution awaken the keenest sensibilities of our nature ; the stoutest heart trembles at the prospect, and would fain yet linger a little longer on these mortal shores.   ' O how mysterious and inscrutable are the ways of Providence !' ' Surely it is not in man to direct his steps.'   But a few days since, as high a glow of health sat on his cheeks as that which flushes ours ; but a few days since that lifeless pulse could beat as well, those unstrung muscles could bound as high as ours ; prospects of health and long life, were as bright and flattering as ours.

' Dissolution, too, reigns throughout the world inanimate.   Summer's green and verdant livery, in sickly yellow, pines away before the chilling breath of Autumn. The flowery tribes will scarce live out a summer's sun. The stately oak which has endured the rude blasts of ages, threatening a kind of vegetable immortality, in rottenness dissolves, and lies unnoticed from the dust it shaded. The hills, by perpetual washing, and by gravitation of looser particles, are sinking to a level with the valley. Yea, the great globe itself (with awe I name it), and these material heavens, shall dissolve, and like the unsubstantial fabric of a vision leave not a wreck behind.'

' The same unerring law of nature pervades universal creation. What myriads of insects flit and buzz away their lives in a summer's sun. What hecatombs of beasts are sacrificed to one revolving year! And is man mortal too?—man, who measures the earth, counts the stars, subjects nature? Yes, my friends, immortal man is mortal. His life is swifter than a weaver's shuttle, and cradles do but rock him towards his tomb. What countless millions in successive generations have chased one another through the long annals of time to their common home! How soon will this assembly, should all the hopes in it be realized, moulder in the silent mansions of the dead! How soon the mighty myriads, who now swarm on the face of the whole earth, surfeiting in unthinking mirth, or teeming with wise projects of future wealth, pleasures or honors, lie undistinguished from the dust they tread on! No age, sex, or condition is privileged against the King of Terrors. The tender infant—the youth whose cheeks are flushed with health, whose tide of life runs high, who never thought of death but in distant prospect—the middle aged, and the old, may at an unexpected moment yield to the dread summons.'

Dr. Wells then gives an account of his last sickness and death. 'He was taken unwell last September, immediately after a fall from his carriage, by which he was much hurt at the time; but he did not then, nor indeed ever after, appear to attach much consequence to the circumstance.

'In consequence of my own ill health, and that of my family, I did not see him until some time in the month of November. From that time till his death, which took place on the 26th of January, the symptoms in his case were those, and only those, which usually accompany inflammation and suppuration of the liver. These have been so accurately described by authors who have devoted their time and talents to the subject, and they are so well understood by this audience, that it would be trespassing upon your time and patience for me to attempt a delineation of them. The remedial means made use of, were such as are usually resorted to in like cases. Yet suffice it to say, the disease progressed slowly, but steadily, to its fatal termination.'

Dr. Samuel Baker. This highly respectable physician was born at Baltimore, Oct. 31st, 1785. He was son of William Baker, who emigrated, when quite young, from Germany, and married a lady of Irish descent. He obtained his early education at an academy at Baltimore. At the age of fifteen he entered Chestertown college, a celebrated seminary of learning, under the superintendence of Dr. Ferguson. At the close of his pupilage here he entered an apothecary's store owned by Dr. Henry Wilkins, for the purpose of obtaining a practical knowledge of pharmacy. At the conclusion of his course with Dr. Wilkins, he commenced the regular study of medicine, under the direction of Drs. Littlejohn and Donaldson. During the courses of 1806–7 and 1807–8 he attended the medical lectures of the University of Pennsylvania, and was elected an honorary member of the Medical Lyceum and of the Medical Society of Philadelphia. He received the degree of Doctor of Medicine from the University in the year 1808. The subject of his dissertation was Chorea. In the spring of this year he returned to Baltimore and commenced the practice of medicine there. He was elected Professor of Materia Medica in the Medical College of Baltimore in the year 1809. He held this appointment till the spring of 1823, when he resigned the office and devoted himself exclusively to the practice of his laborious profession. Dr. J. Fonerden, an intimate friend of Dr. Baker, thus speaks of him in the Baltimore Atheneum for January 2nd, 1836. ' As a lecturer, Dr. Baker maintained to the period of his retirement, an undiminished reputation for a comprehensive knowledge of the branch of knowledge which he taught. He made no parade of learning, and never attempted to amuse by fanciful and idle speculations. He culled the facts and opinions of the older writers with judicious skill, and he diligently searched the numerous

volumes of his cotemporaries, for the results of the labors of a more enlightened age.   The fruits of his
own observation and judgment, added to the useful
matters thus collected from books, both ancient and
modern, were delivered in a plain and lucid style.
His criticisms were always flavored with modesty and
respect, however erroneous he regarded the opinions
against which they were directed; and his award of
praise to those whom he esteemed successful cultivators of science, was frank and honorable.   During
the mention of medical facts that had come under his
own notice and when giving expression to the original
reflections of his own mind, there was often in the
lecture room a breathless silence, which indicated the
profound respect entertained by the class for the judgment of the preceptor.   He was a universal favorite
with the students.   The facts seen by himself and
narrated to them, they believed as implicitly as if they
had themselves been the observers, and his process of
reasoning was rarely opposed by them in their conversational debates, without a serious mistrust of their
own logic.'

Dr. Baker for many years held the office of Secretary to the Medical and Chirurgical Faculty of the
state of Maryland, and was one of the censors for
granting licenses.   He was also President of the Baltimore Medical Society, and he was the originator of
a motion for the establishment of the Library of the
Medical and Chirurgical Faculty of Maryland, and he
was the chairman of its board of directors as long as
he lived.   He was also one of the founders of the

Baltimore Medico-Chirurgical Society, and he was President thereof at the time of his decease. The following extract from the writer of his biographical memoir, published in the 36th No. of the Am. Medical Journal at the commencement of the last session of the Medical Department of the University of Maryland, will show the estimation in which Dr. Baker was held by the writer, as well as by the public :

' I cannot conclude this contemplation of frail mortality without alluding to the loss which we in common with this community have recently sustained in the death of one whose office it was, year after year, to fulfil the duty which now devolves so unworthily upon me. Yes ! gentlemen, from this very place has the young investigator of the animal economy annually heard the precepts of experience from his lips, which are now hushed in the silence of the grave. Associated with the Medical Department of the University of Maryland, almost from its first inception, as the Professor of Materia Medica ; largely concerned with the plan and execution of this fair fabric ; liberal indeed in his pecuniary advancements, at a time when embarrassment existed to such an extent as to throw difficulties in the way of its completion, Dr. Baker has left behind him a monument which will endure, I trust, for ages. But this is a small part only of the gratitude that we owe him. What proposition has there been made for the improvement of medicine which did not receive his zealous support ? Where was the occasion on which he was not ready to extend the hand of courtesy to a professional brother, and to do justice—

4

courtesy to a professional brother, and to do justice—
more than justice, in one case, at least—to the professional merits of another? It was mainly, in consequence of the noble and disinterested conduct of our
lamented friend, that I have now the honor of addressing you. In a manner most complimentary to his
successor, and with a self-denial most honorable to
himself, he relinquished the emoluments and advantages of his chair to another, and that other at the time
personally almost unknown to him. How rare for us
to meet with such superiority to regards of private
advantage! and how highly ought we to cherish and
commemorate it. I know, gentlemen, that there is a
feeling of an amiable, but I think unfortunate, nature,
which is as prevalent as it is injurious, and is embodied in the old maxim, that of the dead we should
say nothing but what is favorable; and accordingly,
we are constantly doomed to find that many who have
spent their worthless lives, disregarded and despised
by all who knew them, receive after their decease
commendations which they merit not; or have their
vices slurred over and mitigated whenever they become the topic of animadversion. It is a fault which
originates in estimable feelings, but when ethically regarded, it cannot be esteemed free from objections.
The prospect of future rewards and punishments is
confessedly an incentive to correctness of conduct;
and the transmission of a fair name to posterity must
enter largely into the consideration of the good, as
one of those rewards; but if the wicked and the trifling are to receive equal posthumous commendation

with the upright and the distinguished, one great incentive to distinction, intellectual or moral, is rendered nugatory.

Very different from this—and much more in accordance with morality—was the practice of the ancient Egyptians. When any one of their fellow men died, an opportunity was afforded to every accuser to step forward; and if it was proved that the conduct of the deceased had been dishonorable, his memory was made infamous, and his body was denied sepulture. If, on the other hand, he remained unscathed, the body was honorably interred. Even their kings were subjected to this ordeal, and some were deprived of inhumation by reason of an unfavorable verdict. When the judgment was propitious to the deceased, a funeral panegyric was passed on his merits; and in this panegyric, titles, dignity, birth, possessions, were set at nought, because they are the gifts of fortune, whilst the orator dwelt in eulogy, on piety towards the gods, justice towards his fellow men, and all the virtues which constitute the good man. These ancient funeral orations might, indeed, be a model for those *oraisons funebres*, which are so common in some countries, where the rank of the deceased has often more to do with the eulogium than exalted personal merit.

How brightly would our departed friend have issued from such an ordeal as this! His life was, indeed, a beautiful model of all the virtues that can adorn a man. Throughout his laborious and useful career, the breath of calumny could not soil the bright mirror of his reputation. As a member of the Medical Faculty of the University, his connection with his colleagues, during the many years of his association with them, was one of unalloyed courteousness, and of strenuous co-operation in every proposition for the advancement of the institution. As a member of his profession, he was unwearied in the application of his talents, and the benevolent feelings of his nature to the relief of his fellows; and as a man, his motto was, ' peace and good will towards men.' I need not, in this community, dwell upon the many benevolent acts of this exemplary individual—how many bleeding hearts he has consoled in their distresses—what expense of time, talent, and comfort, he generously appropriated to the relief of suffering humanity, without expectation of pecuniary reward. The scene doubtless witnessed by many of you, on the day when his mortal remains were consigned to the tomb —of the multitudes who crowded to exhibit their respect, and ere the grave closed over him, to obtain one last look of their friend or their benefactor, testified in deep toned and affecting language to the excellence of the man, and to the value and extent of his services. He was eminently the attentive and benevolent physician, the untiring philanthropist, the pattern of religion and moral goodness. Can I, young gentlemen, present a fairer model for your emulation? Can I conclude with a more suitable aspiration than that, at the termination of a long, and, I trust, successful career, you may merit the same honorable eulogy ?'

For several of the last years of his life, Dr. Baker was attacked with several severe paroxysms of disease. The complaint of which he died was illusory, and no one apprehended that he was near his end until a day or two previous to his decease. He died on the 16th of October, 1835, aged fifty years.   R. D.

Am. Med. Jour.

DR. EBENEZER BARNARD was born at Deerfield, Massachusetts, in the year 1745. He was son of Ensign Joseph Barnard, whose ancestors came to America about the year 1630, and settled at Salem, or somewhere in the neighborhood of Boston. Soon after the first settlement of Deerfield, in 1672, some of them removed to this place, and permanently established themselves here, amidst all the horrors and dangers of savage warfare. His grandfather, Mr. Joseph Barnard, was killed by an Indian in Deerfield south meadows in 1695, and his is the earliest grave stone which can be found in our ancient burying yard. The descendants of this man were the most wealthy in this section of the country for many years. Ebenezer was bred a scholar, and an affluent one. He graduated at Harvard University in 1765, at the age of 20. He then studied the profession of medicine for two years, the customary period at that time, with a relative, Dr. Lemuel Barnard, of Sheffield, Mass., a highly respectable practitioner. He then returned to Deerfield, and established himself in the practice of his profession here. He enjoyed the con-

fidence of his brother practitioners, and was highly
esteemed by them, as well as by his numerous patrons.
His business was extensive, and he gave great satisfaction to his employers. He performed some of the
capital operations in Surgery, such as amputation of
the leg, &c. He kept pace with the important improvements in his profession, as was evinced by his
library, which contained the principal modern works
which were then extant. I have several of these volumes in my library, and they are all of standard merit.
Unfortunately I can procure none of his papers. He
died in the year 1790 at the age of 45, the year that
I was born, and his widow, or some of his friends, disposed of his papers, or deposited them in so obscure a
place that I have never been able to obtain them,
much to my regret.

Dr. John Bartram was a grandson of Richard
Bartram, who came from England to America with
the friends of William Penn, towards the close of the
seventeenth century. He settled in the town of Marpole, Chester Co., Pennsylvania, about twelve miles
from Philadelphia. Richard had two sons, John and
Isaac. The father of the subject of this memoir
was John, who inherited the paternal estate at Marpole. John, the son, the celebrated naturalist and
botanist, inherited an estate in Darby, a few miles
from Marpole, which descended to him by his uncle
Isaac. The country was then comparatively new,
and John had but few advantages from the learning

even of common schools or literature. Such, however, as the common schools afforded he availed himself of; and as opportunities presented, he studied such of the Latin and Greek grammars and classics as his circumstances enabled him to procure. He was always fond of and courted the society of the most talented and worthy men.

There can be no doubt of the propriety of noticing him among the eminent physicians of our country, as he devoted much of his time and attention to the study of physic and surgery. He obtained some celebrity in the practice of surgery, and he was somewhat useful in it, and he often administered relief to his indigent neighbors, who were too poor to apply for medicines and advice to the physicians of Philadelphia, where the nearest practitioners resided. Most of his medicines were derived from the vegetable kingdom, and it is highly probable that this circumstance might indicate to him a wish for the cultivation of the science of Botany. He is spoken of by Dr. Haller in his Bibliotheca Anatomica, as a physician.

I am indebted to his son, Mr. William Bartram, of Kingsessing, near Philadelphia, who was also one of our most celebrated naturalists, for the following notice of his worthy father, published in the first volume of Barton's Medical and Physical Journal, in the year 1804. Dr. Bartram seemed to have been designed for the study and contemplation of nature and the culture of philosophy. Although he was bred a farmer, or a husbandman, as a means of procuring subsistence, he pursued his avocations as a philosopher, being ever attentive to the works and operations of nature. While engaged in ploughing his fields and mowing his meadows, his inquisitive eye and mind were frequently exercised in the contemplation of vegetables ; the beauty and harmony displayed in their mechanism ; the admirable order of system which the great author of the universe has established throughout their various tribes, and the equally wonderful powers of their generation, the progress of their growth, and the various stages of their maturity and perfection.

He was, perhaps, the first Anglo-American who ever conceived the idea of establishing a Botanic Garden, for the reception and cultivation of the various vegetables, natives of the country, as well as of narcotics, and of travelling for the discovery and acquisition of them. He purchased a convenient piece of ground, on the banks of the Schuylkill, at the distance of about three miles from Philadelphia, a happy situation, possessing every soil and exposure adapted to the various nature of vegetables. Here he built, with his own hands, a large and comfortable house of hewn stone, and laid out a garden containing about five acres of ground.

He began his travels at his own expense. His various excursions rewarded his labors with the possession of a great variety of new, beautiful and useful trees, shrubs, and herbaceous plants. His garden at length attracting the visits and notice of many virtuous and ingenious persons, he was encouraged to persist in his labors.

Not yet content with having thus begun the establishment of this school of science and philosophy, in the blooming fields of Flora, he sought farther means for its perfection and importance by communicating his discoveries and collections to the curious in Europe and elsewhere, for the benefit of science, commerce and the useful arts.

Having arranged his various collections and observations in natural history, one of his particular friends, Joseph Brentnal, merchant of Philadelphia, undertook to convey them to the celebrated Peter Collinson, of London. This laid the foundation of that friendship and correspondence which continued uninterrupted, and even increasing, for near fifty years of the lives of these two eminent men. Collinson, ever the disinterested friend, communicated, from time to time, to the learned in Europe the discoveries and observations of Bartram. It was principally through the interest of Collinson that he became acquainted and entered into a correspondence with many of the most celebrated literary characters in Europe, and was elected a member of the Royal Society of London, of that of Stockholm, &c. Dr. B. S. Barton observes: It is believed that there have been but two or three native Americans whose correspondence with the learned men of Europe was so extensive as that of Mr. Bartram. The mere catalogue of his correspondents would fill a page. A few of the principal ones are mentioned: Linnæus, Gronovius, Delibard, Sir Hans Sloane, Caterby, Dillenius, Collinson, Fothergill, George Ed-

wards, Philip Miller, and Targioni. He likewise lived
in habits of intimacy and friendship, or corresponded
with most of the distinguished literary characters at
that time in North America, among whom I may
mention Dr. Franklin, Dr. Garden, Mr. Clayton, and
Governor Colden. His large collection of letters to
these and other celebrated men, is in the possession
of the editor. Extracts from some of them have
already been printed in this Journal, and many more
will be given in subsequent numbers. It is much to
be regretted that many of the letters are so injured
by the ravages of time that they cannot in many
places be read at all; at least not without extreme
difficulty. Parts of them are irrecoverably lost.

He employed much of his time in traveling
through the different provinces of North America, at
that time subject to England. Neither dangers nor
difficulties impeded or confined his researches after
objects in natural history. The summits of our highest mountains were ascended and explored by him.
The lakes Ontario, Iroquois, and George; the shores
and sources of the rivers Hudson, Delaware, Schuylkill, Susquehanna, Alleghany and St. Juan, were visited by him at an early period, when it was a truly
perilous undertaking to travel in the territories, or
even on the frontiers of the aborigines.

He traveled several thousand miles in Carolina
and Florida. At the advanced age of nearly seventy
years, embarking on board of a vessel at Philadelphia, he set sail for Charleston, in South Carolina.
From thence he proceeded by land through part of

Carolina and Georgia to St. Augustine in East Florida. When arrived at the last mentioned place, being then appointed botanist for the king of England, for exploring the provinces, he received his orders to search for the sources of the great river St. Juan.

Leaving St. Augustine, he traveled by land to the banks of the river, and embarking on board a boat at Picolata, ascended that great and beautiful river (near 400 miles) to its sources, attending carefully to its various branches, and the lakes connected with it. Having ascended on one side of the river, he descended by the other, unto the confluence of the Picolata with the sea.

In the course of this voyage, or journey, he made an accurate draught and survey of the various width, depths, courses, and distances, both of the main stream, and of the lakes and branches. He also noted the situation and quality of the soil, the vegetable and animal productions, together with other interesting observations, all of which were highly approved of by the Governor, and sent to the Board of Trade and Plantations in England, by whose directions they were ordered to be published, for the benefit of the new colony.

Mr. Bartram was a man of modest and gentle manners, frank, cheerful, and of great good nature; a lover of justice, truth and charity. He was himself an example of filial, conjugal, and parental affection. His humanity, gentleness, and compassion, were manifested upon all occasions, and were even extended to the animal creation. He was never known to be at enmity with any man. During the whole course of his life, there was not a single instance of his engaging in a litigious contest with any of his neighbors, or others. He zealously testified against slavery; and that his philanthropic precepts on this subject might have their due weight and force, he gave liberty to a most valuable male slave, then in the prime of life, who had been bred up in the family almost from his infancy.

He was through life a striking example of temperance, especially in the use of vinous and spirituous liquors; not from a passion of parsimony, but from a principle of morality. His common drink was pure water, small beer, or cider mixed with milk. Nevertheless he kept a good and plentiful table. Once a year, commonly on new year's day, he made a liberal entertainment for his relations and particular friends. His stature was rather above the middle size, and upright. His visage was long, and his countenance expressive of a degree of dignity, with a happy mixture of animation and sensibility. He was naturally industrious and active, both in body and mind; observing that he could never find more time than he could employ to satisfaction and advantage, either in improving conversation, or in some healthy and useful bodily exercise; and he was astonished to hear men complaining that they were weary of their time, and knew not what they should do.

He was born and educated in the sect called Quakers. But his religious creed may, perhaps, be best collected from a pious distitch, engraven by his own hand, in very conspicuous characters, upon a stone placed over the front window of the apartment, which was destined for study and philosophical retirement :

> ' 'Tis God alone, Almighty Lord,
> The Holy One, by me adored.' J. B., 1770.

This may show the simplicity and sincerity of his heart, which never harbored, or gave countenance to, dissimulation. His mind was frequently employed, and he enjoyed the highest pleasure in the contemplation of nature, as exhibited in the great volume of Creation. He generally concluded the narrations of his journies with pious and philosophical reflections upon the Majesty and Power, the Perfection and Beneficence, of the Creator. He had a high veneration for the moral and religious principles of the scriptures, both old and new. He read them often, particularly on the Sabbath day; and recommended to his children and family the following precept, as comprehending the great principles of moral duty in man: "Do justice, love mercy, and walk humbly before God."

He never coveted old age, and often observed to his children and friends that he sincerely desired that he might not live longer than he could afford assistance to himself; for he was unwilling to be a burthen to his friends, or useless in society; and that when death came to perform its office, there might not be much delay. His wishes in these respects were grati-

fied in a remarkable manner; for although he lived to
be about 80 years of age, yet he was cheerful and
active to almost the last hours. His illness was short.
About half an hour before he expired, he seemed,
though but for a few moments, to be in considerable
agony, and pronounced these words: " I want to
die." '

DR. WILLIAM BAYLIES was born at Uxbridge, in
the county of Worcester, December 5, 1743. His
father was Nicholas Baylies, a native of Colebrook
Dale, Shropshire, England, who early in life came
with his father, Thomas Baylies, to this country, and
settled at Uxbridge, where he resided several years,
but subsequently removed to Taunton. ' He represented the town of Taunton several years in the General
Court, was much engaged in the transactions of the
Revolutionary period, and was Chairman of the County Committee of Correspondence.

William Baylies graduated at Harvard College in
1760. He studied medicine with Dr. Elisha Tobey of
New Bedford, (then Dartmouth) a physician of more
extensive business than any other practitioner in the
county. At the completion of his medical pupilage
he married the daughter of the Hon. Samuel White
of Taunton, Speaker of the House of Representatives in 1759, 1764, and 1765. He was also a member of the Council.

Dr. Baylies, after residing a short time in Taunton,
finally established himself as a physician in Dighton,

where he remained till his death, with the exception of
a few years towards the conclusion of the Revolutionary war, when he resided in Taunton. His practice here was very extensive. He entered with great
zeal into the political controversies of the times. He
represented the town of Dighton in the General
Court, and was a member of the three Provincial
Congresses of Massachusetts, and also of several important committees. He was a member of the State
Convention that adopted the Federal Constitution.
He was a Judge of the Court of Common Pleas for
the county of Bristol for several years, and for a long
time Register of Probate for that county. He was
one of the Electors of President and Vice President
of the United States in the year 1800.

His principal pursuit, however, was his profession,
the practice of which he never abandoned till a short
time previous to his death. As a physician he enjoyed an extensive and permanent popularity, arising
from the confidence reposed in his skill and integrity.
He was much employed in consultation, for his professional brethren throughout the wide circle of his
practice placed great reliance on his judgment and
discretion. He disdained all that parade and artifice
under which the impostors of the profession endeavor
to hide their ignorance and deceive the people, and
to which even physicians otherwise of fair reputation
are sometimes, in their desire to gain practice and
popularity, too ready to yield themselves. Applying
his strong sense, aided by reading and observation, to
the investigation of disease, he was seldom mistaken

in his *prognosis*. He was a prudent and cautious, but
not a timid, practitioner. He pondered much on
his cases, and when his deliberations had convinced
his judgment, he laid down his course of practice,
from which he seldom found it necessary to deviate.
When danger was imminent he acted with promptitude, decision, and energy. He was well acquainted
with the sciences which had an immediate relation to
that of medicine. He read much, and reflected
much on what he read ; but he acknowledged no
master. His discriminating mind enabled him to
detect the sophistries of plausible theories, and to
separate them from the sound and scientific principles
with which they were blended ; and when the test of
experience was applied, his judgment was seldom
found to have been erroneous. He was never daz-
zled with splendid novelties, nor bewildered with
systems, nor led away from the maxims of sound
practice, by the authority of great names.

Notwithstanding his almost incessant labors in his
practice, he found time for other studies than those
immediately connected with his professional pursuits.
He was well versed in metaphysics and theology.
The science of government he had studied with
much attention, and the fallacies of rash and daring
innovators never lured him from the path of rational
liberty. Though pleased with the originality and
eloquence of " that self-torturing sophist, wild Ros-
seau," he rejected those extravagant and visionary
notions which could find no liberty for man but in
the practical equality of savage life. He was for a

government of laws—laws sufficiently strong to protect person and property, and *to give a consciousness of security.* He was familiar with the works of the best English poets. He was an original member of the Medical and Historical Societies of Massachusetts, and also a member of the American Academy of Arts and Sciences. In 1807 he received from Harvard University the honorary degree of M. D.

For social pleasures and enjoyments, when not pushed to excess, he had a keen relish, and delighted in every species of genuine wit. In all the relations of life his conduct was exemplary. Though some of the physical infirmities of old age came upon him, the vigor of his mind remained but little impaired, until the sudden and brief illness that terminated his life on the 17th June, 1826.—*Hon. William and Francis Baylies, in Alden's Collections.*

Dr. Lemuel Whittlesey Belden was a native of Wethersfield, Connecticut, where he was born in September, 1801. He was son of Dr. Joshua Belden of that place, a highly respectable physician and worthy man, who died of the malignant spotted fever, in June, 1808, in the midst of his usefulness. Dr. Lemuel W. Belden, the subject of this notice, was left an orphan, with three younger brothers, in the care of a judicious and sensible mother, at the age of seven years. She bestowed great attention upon his early education, allowing him all the advantages which the best teachers could bestow. He

entered as a Freshman in Yale College in the year
1817, at the age of sixteen.

The following notice of him was first published in
the Boston Medical and Surgical Journal, and afterwards appended in a note to the excellent address of
Dr. A. L. Pierson of Salem, before the Massachusetts Medical Society, at their annual meeting in
1840. It was written by a friend who was amply
qualified to do justice to his memory.

'The loss which a community sustains in the death
of an intelligent and beloved physician is severe, and
often irreparable; not so much that one of equal
skill cannot be substituted, as that the confidence
reposed in the *one*, cannot be immediately transferred
to the *other*. Such a physician is not only the medical adviser, but also the friend and confidant of the
sick; he sympathizes with them in their sufferings,
enters into all their feelings, and is a comforter in all
their trials. His presence and encouragement are
often as beneficial as the medicines which he pre-
scribes. When death removes him, they feel that
their security is gone; that life is less valuable,
because more uncertain, and because one of the
sources of enjoyment is removed, and that a severe
trial awaits them in selecting another in whose knowledge and judgment they can place the same confidence, and on whose integrity and friendship they
can safely rely.

These reflections have been awakened by the
wide spread sorrow and lamentation occasioned by
the death of that excellent man and estimable phy-

sician, Dr. Lemuel W. Belden, of Springfield, Mass.
who recently fell a victim to the malignant typhus
fever, which has prevailed somewhat extensively in
that vicinity.

During his minority, and before he entered college, young Belden was a modest, reserved youth,
fond of his books, which had greater attractions for
him at this early age than the sports and amusements
of his associates. The traits of character most prominent in his childhood were, *love of truth, sobriety,
and consistency of conduct ;* and these were no less
conspicuous in all his after life. His reputation in
college was always good, both for diligence as a
scholar and for exemplary and discreet deportment.
If he did not acquire as rapidly as some others, he
was always prepared for what was expected of him—
always ready, and acquitted himself with honor. He
was scrupulously regardful of all college duties, was
never absent from prayers, and rarely, if ever, from
recitations, during the whole of his college life.
One of his most respectable classmates and constant
friends, writes thus of him : ' He was a diligent
student; I think peculiarly so. It was evident that
he never lost sight of the object for which he came
there, and he attended to every study prescribed, with
steady perseverance. I can look back now and see
evidence of maturity and soundness of judgment in
this respect, which was uncommon at that age. His
college course did not present much of incident, as
it partook of the stability and steady attention to the
object for which he came, which was afterwards so

prominent a trait of his character. The loss of his sound judgment and growing attainments to the medical profession, you can better appreciate than I can.'

He received the honors of college at his graduation, and the part assigned him on this occasion shows the estimation with which he was regarded by the authorities of the University, placing him among the most distinguished scholars of his class. After obtaining his first degree in September, 1821, he took charge of a respectable Academy at New Canaan, in his native state, where he continued two years, a very respectable teacher. In the autumn of 1823 he relinquished the employment and commenced the study of medicine with Dr. Woodward, then of Wethersfield, his native state, now the Superintendent of the State Lunatic Hospital at Worcester, Mass. As a student of medicine, he was a close applicant, and made rapid proficiency; he availed himself of every means of acquiring professional knowledge; he was not only a diligent scholar, but was careful to watch the progress of such cases of disease as he could witness in a circuit of extensive country practice.

His first course of medical lectures was attended in Boston in the winter of 1825. The succeeding spring and summer he spent with his former preceptor, and devoted much time in visiting the sick, to ascertain the character and progress of disease. The following winter was spent in New Haven, attending to the Medical Lectures in Yale College. In March,

1826, he received the degree of Doctor of Medicine. In both these institutions he obtained a high reputation as a scholar, and at his graduation he acquitted himself so well as to take the very first rank in his class.

Returning from college he again entered the office of Dr. Woodward as assistant in his practice, where he continued more than a year, attending extensively to the sick, and teaching the preliminary branches of study to a class of medical students. During this long intercourse a warm friendship was formed between preceptor and pupil, which continued until his death.

Dr. Belden pursued the study of his profession with the ardor of a scholar and the spirit of a philanthropist. He loved his profession because he considered it honorable and useful; he felt the responsibility that awaited him, and he was too conscientious to commence the practice of it without a thorough knowledge of its principles, and a faithful improvement of all the advantages for clinical knowledge and experience.

In the autumn of 1827 he took up his residence in Springfield, where he soon gained a respectable practice, and became the favorite physician of many of the best families in the town.

Dr. Belden had none of those shining qualities which commend themselves at first sight to the fancy of the many. He was not destined to be the popular man. He was peculiarly diffident and retiring; his manners were simple, but his deportment was digni-

fied and reserved. He could obtain friends and
business only on substantial merit. His success was
not rapid, but permanent—those who once employed
him rarely failing to adhere to him; the more extensive their acquaintance, the more they respected and
loved him. To many he was 'the beloved physician;'
rendered no less so by the amiable qualities of his
heart, his upright and honorable deportment amongst
men, than by his sagacity and tact as a physician.
He made no bustle in his business, and no display in
the community in which he resided; but now that he
is dead, they will realize that a man is gone from
amongst them, whose influence, though quiet and
gentle as the evening zephyr, has been wide and
salutary, diffusing intellectual light and moral beauty
wherever it was felt and known—that a physician has
departed from their midst, in whose skill there was
safety, in whose integrity there was confidence, in
whose character there was rectitude unwavering, and
in whose countenance ever beamed benevolence and
philanthropy.

Unlike many young men, Dr. Belden continued
the habits of study through life which he had early
formed. In the intervals of his business he was
rarely found absent from his 'study.' Here he
applied himself closely to professional reading, literature and general intelligence. He was a thorough
scholar the *last* as well as the first year of his
professional life. The readers of your Journal cannot have forgotten his lucid history of Jane C. Rider,
well known as the 'Springfield Somnambulist,' which

occupied two weekly numbers of your periodical, and detailed with great accuracy and precision the wonderful phenomena of that remarkable case. This, with a popular work, published somewhat previously, on the same subject, constitutes all the writings from his pen which have been given to the public. There are many things, however, in manuscript, which show his diligence in recording facts no less than his ardor in the pursuit of knowledge.

During the last year, Dr. Belden had interested himself in effecting a change in the Medical Society of this State. At their first annual meeting in the spring he presented his views to the Society in person, in so clear and perspicuous a manner as to induce those present to consider the subject seriously. A large and respectable committee was appointed to act upon it, of which Dr. Belden was a member. Their report is just published, which recommends such changes as to meet the views of all who have interested themselves in it, retaining many of the old, and adopting some of the new, principles proposed by their author.

Dr. Belden was married in May, 1829, to Miss Catherine Chester, daughter of Stephen Chester, Esq., late Sheriff of the county of Hartford, Conn., an amiable and accomplished lady, who survives him to mourn the loss of one of the best of husbands, and kindest and most indulgent of men. He left no children, having lost an only son in early childhood.

Few men are better situated to enjoy life, than was Dr. Belden at the time of the attack of his fatal disease. His domestic relation was peculiarly felicitous; he was in the midst of an intelligent and enterprising population, who justly appreciated his medical attainments and moral worth. Beloved by his friends, respected by all who knew him—rising in reputation in his profession by the surest of all means, knowledge of his business and devotion to his patients, he had gained a character of sterling value in an extensive circle of practice. In the midst of this prosperity came the withering hand of disease and cut him off.

Of the character of Dr. Belden, we may justly say it had no shades, no dark spots which his friends would desire to conceal or remove, no eccentricity which gave it the slightest irregularity. From his childhood he loved truth, simplicity and virtue, and these were his eminent qualities. His well balanced mind led him to right views of every subject; he discriminated well and judged correctly. His acute moral sense kept him in the strictest path of rectitude. A motive to do wrong never actuated him for a moment; his integrity was above suspicion. His mind was more distinguished for solid than for brilliant traits; he had no dazzling qualities. He loved to investigate the truths of science and philosophy. His knowledge was of the substantial kind; he made no display of it, but it came to his aid when and where he needed it. As a physician he had few equals of his age. He was a ripe scholar in the principles of his profession, and he made the best use of his experience. His Index Rerum

shows how careful he was to note facts and references, and what stores of medical knowledge he
was amassing. He was useful no less as a scholar
than as a physician, and he was preparing for still
greater usefulness and distinction.

How desirable that such a man should live! And
now that he is gone, how desirable is it to the living
as well as to the dead that he was such a man! A
long and intimate acquaintance with him left us
ignorant of his faults; if his character had blemishes,
they were invisible, surrounded and swallowed up
as they were in estimable and amiable qualities.
We love to contemplate the man, to look upon one
so pure and blameless in life, fulfilling the relations
of son, husband and father, brother and friend, in a
manner so acceptable to all. His life was exemplary
and well spent, his death a dignified and calm departure from scenes less congenial to his pure spirit, to
the blessed fruition of an heavenly inheritance, prepared by his Redeemer above.

His loss is great to us all; to his family and
relatives irreparable; but hardly less deeply to be
felt by that circle of friends, whose physician he was,
whose affections he had secured, and who, on every
return of affliction and suffering, will lament, with
renewed sorrow, his premature departure.'

DR. CHAUNCEY BREWER. From the pen of the
Rev. Doctor Osgood of Springfield, Massachusetts.

The subject of this memoir was the son of Dea-

7

con Nathaniel Brewer, and grandson of Rev. Daniel Brewer, the third minister of the First Congregational Church in Springfield, Massachusetts. The Rev. Mr. Brewer was a native of Roxbury, was graduated at Harvard University, and was settled in Springfield in 1693. His wife was the daughter of the Rev. Nathaniel Chauncey, the second President of Harvard University. Thus it appears that the ancestors of Dr. Brewer were among the most respectable citizens of this Commonwealth, both as to talents and moral worth.

Dr. Chauncey Brewer was born at Springfield, April 21, 1743. He graduated at Yale College in 1762. Though he was young he maintained a very respectable standing in his class, and was highly esteemed for his sobriety and good conversation in general. He commenced and completed his medical studies under Dr. Charles Pynchon, of Springfield, who was for many years one of the most eminent physicians in this section of the state, and died at an advanced age, respected and beloved by a large circle of friends.

Dr. Brewer commenced the practice of physic in West Springfield, where he remained several years, and was highly esteemed both as a physician and a citizen. The people of West Springfield manifested their confidence in his talents and integrity by choosing him to represent them in the second and third Provincial Congress of Massachusetts, at a period when the best and most prudent men were selected to manage the public affairs of the Commonwealth, which were every day becoming more perplexed by collision with the mother country.

He was appointed Justice of the Peace in 1775. This appointment gave great satisfaction to the people of West Springfield, and when he soon afterwards removed to Springfield they felt that they had lost a valuable physician and a wise and faithful magistrate, at a time when talents, and probity, and firmness, were necessary in public men.

Dr. Brewer was a firm friend to the cause of his country in the struggle which terminated in the establishment of its independence, and although his growing reputation as a physician, and the wider field of usefulness which was opened to him by the death of Dr. Pynchon, prevented him from engaging in his professional character in the scenes of the revolution, yet he was ever ready to sustain and encourage the authorities of the town in any measures which were deemed necessary to push forward an enterprise which he considered to be founded in justice, and so justly connected with the cause of human rights.

For many years Dr. Brewer was regarded as one of the first in his profession in all this section of the country. He was consulted in all difficult cases, and he was so highly esteemed for his good judgment, and at the same time for his carefulness, that his opinion was received with great deference by all his brethren of the profession.

He was a man who was possessed of great tenderness of feeling, so much so that he was often reluc-

tant to perform difficult surgical operations where
firmness of nerves was necessary, and he even preferred that such business should be given to others.
This trait in his character rendered him very popular
in his profession. He readily entered into the feelings of his patients, and by the gentleness of his
manners he won universal estimation. His judgment
held out to extreme old age, so that when his infirmities induced him to decline all applications to take
the entire charge of the sick, his brethren were anxious to obtain his advice, and the writer of this article has heard more than one physician speak with
admiration of the soundness of his opinions in difficult cases, even in extreme old age.

Dr. Brewer had no enemies, not even among his
competitors in the profession. No one, perhaps, ever
carried out the injunction "speak evil of no man,"
more thoroughly than he did. If he did not approve
of the method of practice by any of his brethren, he
never attempted to injure their reputation by severe
animadversions. Young physicians ever found him
easy and affable in his conversation, and ready to
communicate any information within his power.
Long before he relinquished the business of his profession, which he retained much longer than his own
inclinations prompted, he candidly discussed the prospects which the town afforded for any new candidate,
whenever such person called upon him. He never
tried to discourage any new applicant by darkening
the prospects for success, but gave his views with

great sincerity and left the person to decide for himself. Hence he always retained the respect and confidence of his brethren.

Dr. Brewer had very little selfishness. Though his practice was extensive, and he possessed the patronage of the most wealthy citizens of the town for many years, he was so moderate in his charges that he did not roll up a great estate. He ever seemed contented with a competence. He reared a numerous family, and ever provided for them liberally. Had he possessed the eagerness to acquire property which characterizes mankind in general, he might have been rich. But he seems to have prized "a quiet and peaceable life in all godliness and honesty," to a bustling and anxious one connected with great wealth. He was anxious to relinquish the business of his profession long before his friends were willing that he should do it. The writer of this article, when he came into Springfield, applied to him to become his family physician, and although then in good health, he replied, "I am an old man, and am not able to go abroad in the night, and you had better engage the services of a younger physician." This shows that he had nothing of that selfishness which is ever "seeking its own," or that jealousy which regards with evident dissatisfaction the prosperity of others who may be its competitors.

Dr. Brewer was a man who "lived peaceably with all men." Though he was no time server, but formed his opinions upon all subjects with great deliberation and maintained them with firmness, yet he was so mild in his manner that he rarely excited the displeasure of an opponent. He sometimes administered rebuke, yet it was with such gentleness that it gave no offence. On one occasion he was called to a family, the head of whom was very impatient under his hands. He had already lost two children with a malignant fever which then prevailed, his wife was then dangerously sick, and a third child was dangerously seized. This was too much for the unsubmissive father. He exclaimed, "we may as well send for a butcher and have them killed at once." Dr. Brewer replied in a manner which made him feel his impiety, "I should think the work of death is going on fast enough without any additional help."

He was very pleasant and interesting in social life. He had a fund of anecdote which he knew well how to apply, and no person could be long in his society without being delighted and profited by his conversation.

It remains for us to say something of him as a Christian. At what period of his life he became particularly interested in the subject of religion as a personal concern, we have no means of ascertaining. He had the advantage of early education from pious parents, and "from a child he knew the holy scriptures." He was admitted to the church in West Springfield, under the ministry of that eminent servant of Christ, the Rev. Dr. Lathrop. His views were decidedly evangelical, embracing all those distinguishing doctrines which were held by the Puritans. He loved to converse upon subjects which were connected with the prosperity and progress of the church in the world. He was eminently a holy man, and spent a considerable portion of his time during the last twenty years of his life in reading the scriptures. He was particularly fond of the writings of Baxter, Flavel, and Doddridge, and when the commentary of Dr. Scott was published, he manifested great delight in perusing it. He was also much interested in the cause of missions. The publication of Dr. Buchanan's sermon entitled "The Star in the East," inspired his benevolent heart with fervent desires for the conversion of the heathen, and he manifested the greatest interest in those communications which came from our missionaries in the East, and the Isles of the Sea. Dr. Brewer enjoyed uninterrupted health till the day of his death. He possessed a robust constitution, which was never weakened by excess or irregularity. He was early elected a deacon of the First Church in Springfield, and he continued to serve in this office until within a few years of his death. He enjoyed as much of life as falls to the lot of man.

He was more free from corroding care and anxiety than almost any man. He always had a competency of worldly goods, and some to spare for the repeated calls which were made upon his benevolent heart, and having made the Lord his trust he appeared to be fully satisfied, and to feel that a "man's life does not consist in the abundance of the things he possesses, but in righteousness and peace and joy in the

Holy Ghost." His mental as well as bodily powers
continued strong and bright to the end of his life,
which was prolonged to the period of eighty-seven
years. The day previous to his death he walked
abroad, and seemed as vigorous as usual, spent the
evening in cheerful and pleasant conversation with
his children, several of whom lived with him, and he
retired to rest about the usual hour. During the
night his son, who slept with him, thought he heard
an unusual noise, as if his respiration was difficult;
he immediately raised him up, and found him expiring
without a struggle or a groan. Of him it might be
literally said, " having served his own generation, by
the will of God he fell asleep "

Doct. Thomas Brown was an eminent physician
of Charles county, Maryland. He received his medical education at Edinburgh, and graduated at that
University in 1768. The inaugural thesis which he
wrote and defended was on Animal Heat. On his
return to America, he settled in his native place, and
through the whole of his life he had an extensive
practice. Dr. Rush, who was cotemporary with Dr.
Brown at Edinburgh, used to say of him, that he was
not second to any student of the University at that
period. Dr. Brown was not only a well read physician, and an able practitioner of medicine, but a
good classical scholar, and indulged his taste for
general reading during the whole course of his laborious practice. It is said that he used but few reme-

dies in his practice, and those of a most efficient character.

DRS. GUSTAVUS BROWN and WILLIAM BROWN were nephews of the preceding, and were educated at Edinburgh at nearly the same period. They were both eminent practitioners of medicine, the former in St. Marys county, Maryland, and the latter in Alexandria. It is not known that either of these gentlemen left any medical writings behind them, except the inaugural theses, which they defended at the time of their graduation.—*Letter from Dr. Causin, in Sewall's Lecture.*

DR. PETER BRYANT, father of the poet, William Cullen Bryant, was born at Bridgewater in the State of Mass., in the year 1767. He was an eminent physician and surgeon, and established himself in early life in his profession at Cummington, in the county of Hampshire and State of Massachusetts. Here he soon attained the highest reputation among his employers and professional brethren. His library was the most select and extensive in the interior of the state, and all his leisure hours were spent in the retirement of it; storing his mind with the rich legacies of his fathers and cotemporaries in the profession of medicine. This is the only way to establish a lasting and well founded reputation in the science,

8

and without a resort to this course the applause of
any physician, however popular he may be for a little
period, must be evanescent and ephemeral. Dr.
Bryant thus obtained his reputation, which will not
soon be forgotten. His townsmen frequently elected
him their representative in the state legislature, and
while at the emporium of the state he became intimately acquainted with the most eminent physicians
in the capital. Here, as elsewhere, he was always
strenuous in his exertions for promoting the cause of
science and literature, particularly of medical science.
Dr. Warren says of him that he was "as remarkable
for a modest and reserved demeanor as for his
acuteness, love of study, and profound knowledge of
his profession." He was elected a Fellow of the
Massachusetts Medical Society in the year 1806, and
continued his fellowship till his decease in the year
1820. He was often elected a counsellor and censor
in the Society. The appointment of delivering the
annual dissertation before that Society was twice conferred upon him, and while he was making preparations to go to Boston for this purpose in June, 1819,
he was seized with the complaint of which he died,
after a lingering illness, in the year 1820, at the age
of fifty years. Dr. Bryant was fourth son of Dr.
Philip Bryant, who practiced physic in North Bridgewater, Mass., for more than sixty years. Dr. Abiel
Howard, the first native of Bridgewater, educated at
Harvard University, was his maternal grandfather,
and in the well furnished library of this gentleman

he found the means of gratifying an early and a predominating passion for study. After a preparatory education he entered upon the study of medicine with his father, and subsequently became a pupil of Laprilete, a French surgeon, settled in Norton, in Bristol county, and a man of great dexterity and knowledge in his art. He completed his studies in 1790, and the next year went to Hampshire county, where he married, and continued for the most part of the practice of his profession to the time of his death. In the early part of his professional life he went in a surgical capacity to the Indian Ocean, visiting on his way the Cape of Good Hope, and remaining for some months in the Isle of France, where he learned the French language and laid the foundation of that familiarity with the French literature which he afterwards attained. He was for many years a member of the Massachusetts House of Representatives, where he exerted himself in conjunction with several of his friends to procure the enactment of certain regulations, the object of which was to raise the standard of education and knowledge among the members of the medical faculty.

After many unsuccessful attempts they prevailed, and in the year 1813 a system of rules was adopted in relation to the examination and licensing of practitioners of physic and surgery, which has continued with very little alteration to this day. Dr. Bryant was chosen a member of the electoral College of Massachusetts, on the election of President and Vice President of the United States in 1816. The next year he was returned to the Senate of his native State. He was an early member of the Massachusetts Medical Society, and for many years held the place of Counselor in that body. While preparing to deliver the anniversary discourse before the Society, he was attacked with the disease which put an end to his life. He died of consumption on the 10th of March, 1820. Dr. Bryant was profoundly versed in the learning of his profession, the authors of which he collected with diligence and studied with eagerness, seldom sitting down without a book in his hand, and making that a recreation which most men regard as a labor. In surgery he was a delicate and dextrous operator. He was the author of many compositions, both in prose and verse, which appeared in the publications of the day. They were mostly on professional and political subjects, and of a humorous cast, and were distinguished for their point and polish. His manners were modest and retiring, and he was not less beloved for his private virtues than respected for the qualities of his intellect.—*Wm. Cullen Bryant, in Knapp's Am. Biography.*

Dr. Thomas Bucklin, of Hopkinton, was born in Rehoboth, Bristol county, Mass., Sept. 28, 1772. His father, Mr. John Bucklin, was a respectable farmer of that town. His advantages for an education were ordinary for that day. He commenced his professional studies when about 18 years old, with Dr. Humphrey of Pawtucket, R. I., and continued with him about one year. He then put himself under the tuition of the late Dr. Thurber of Mendon, with whom he continued two years.

In May, 1793, Dr. Bucklin commenced his professional life in Hopkinton, Mass., where he pursued the practice of medicine fifty years. He was admitted a member of the Massachusetts Medical Society in 1812, and was a Counselor of that Society more than twenty years.

Few physicians have reached a more eminent standing in the community, than the late Dr. Bucklin. When young in the profession he gave evidence of promise. He was naturally zealous and enthusiastic, and followed up his investigations of disease with great industry and earnestness. Prompt to his business, attentive to his patients, and happy in his results, he soon became a noted physician in his town and vicinity. During the last forty years of his life, no medical man was more devoted or more laborious in his pursuits. He was emphatically a student during his whole life, and his strong powers of perception and retentive memory made him rich in facts, which he had been accumulating during a long life of experience. His urbanity, his hospitality, and his love for a social hour, will not soon be forgotten.

Dr. Bucklin's manners in the sick room were most benignant and affable; he seemed always to be in unison with the sick man's feelings. No one sympathized more readily, more actively, with the suffering; and his sympathy could not be restrained—it was impulsive.

His moral sensibilities were exalted and refined. But if there was any one quality of his heart that prevailed—that seemed to act as a presiding divinity over the man—it was his benevolence. The community in which he lived will not forget or cease to feel the influence of his generous acts. In every public improvement, in every effort for moral elevation, or intellectual advancement, or for enhancing the interests and comforts of the community, the heart and hand of Dr. Bucklin were readily enlisted. The loss of so worthy a man, and so able a physician, must be felt by the public, and especially by those who depended upon him in sickness.

We make no attempt to represent the value of such a man as Dr. Bucklin in the family relationship. Those who enjoyed his company daily, must realize how difficult this would be. His example as a husband, a parent, and neighbor, will have the deepest impression on those who knew him most intimately.

That Dr. Bucklin had no faults, we would not say—for we cannot say that of any man. We knew him to have one sin—but it was an amiable one— the sin of tolerating an opinion differing from his own, especially if that difference was of no practical advantage ; and if his view of it had an important bearing upon results, his manner of correcting that opinion was most lenient and christian.

Thus briefly we have alluded to our deceased friend; and if what we have written should serve to retain in a more compact form the elements of his character, or prove an humble tribute of respect to his memory, it will be sufficient for our purpose.

Bost. Med. and Surg. Jour., Jan. 1844.

DR. JOHN APTHORP BULFINCH was born at Boston on the 26th of March, 1806. He commenced his education, and studied the classics in the Latin school in that place until the year 1818, when he removed with his father to the city of Washington, where the latter was appointed architect of the Capitol of the United States. Here he continued his studies, under an able teacher, until the year 1821, when he entered Columbia College in the city of Washington. After finishing his collegiate course reputably, he commenced his professional studies in the medical school of the same college, under the instruction of Dr. Thomas Sewall, the distinguished Professor of Anatomy, and after three years of devoted attention received the degree of M. D. He now visited his friends in Boston, intending to commence the practice of his profession there, but finding the field so much crowded he returned to Washington, where he remained for a few months. He afterwards went into Virginia, where he took charge of a family of children in a respectable house, with the privilege of attending occasionally to medical practice, where he remained a year. Another year he acted as Principal of a large Academy at Warrenton, Geo., near Augusta, where his brother, the Rev. S. G. Bulfinch, was settled as pastor of the Unitarian Church. Thus with the usual alternations of hope and disappointment, which so commonly attend the young practitioner, without abandoning his profession he availed himself of temporary occupations, till a favorable opening for professional practice should be presented. At the close of his engagement at Warrenton, he declined renewing it for another term, though solicited to do so by the trustees ; but urged by a fondness for his profession, removed to Augusta, and became connected with Dr. Alexander Cunningham, an eminent physician in full practice. While at Augusta, the situation which he accepted and continued to hold for the short remainder of his life, presented itself at Hebron, a small town situated seventy miles from Augusta, and twelve from Milledgeville, the capital of the state of Georgia. To this place he removed in 1834, and found himself among intelligent and friendly people, with a sphere of usefulness opening upon him. The writer of this notice, which is taken from the Boston Medical and Surgical Journal, has received an interesting letter from the

Rev. Mr. Bulfinch, from which he has permitted him to make the following extracts:

'My brother had mentioned in one of his letters that he had been unwell; but spoke of it so slightly that I considered it an attack which had passed over. He fell a victim to his professional fidelity. The sickness of which he wrote me had confined him to the house about three days, and was undoubtedly brought on by over exertions. He was looking forward to some relaxation, and preparing for a promised visit to Augusta, when he was seized with the sickness which cut him down, in the prime of his opening usefulness. On the day when he showed symptoms of a return of his sickness, he went the distance of half a mile to visit a patient, and could hardly be persuaded to go back. A physician was sent for, who came and passed the next night with him. He says that when he first saw him he made those convulsive motions with his arms, which are the indications of the most fatal kind of typhus fever. A degree of delirium, or rather a condition of dreamy forgetfulness, continued to the last. His last struggle was easy. He could of course give no indications of a religious character, beyond those exhibited by an exemplary life of energetic, self-sacrificing usefulness, always sustained by professed Christian principles. He was buried on Sunday, and a very large number attended. His host undertook the arrangements, which were highly respectable. He was buried near the Baptist meeting

9

house, about half a mile from his place of residence.

I found that my brother had been engaged in practice far beyond my expectation. He was conscientiously attentive to all, remaining with the sick sometimes through the night; and never sparing himself when it was possible to relieve a fellow being. To use the words of a neighbor, ' he always seemed more attentive to a person that could not pay, than to one that could.' His success in the cases he had was great. The most entire confidence was reposed in him by all around, and the deepest feelings of respect and affection that could exist towards one almost a stranger, exhibited by all with whom I have spoken of him. He had been solicited to remove to Saundersville and to Milledgeville, but he felt under obligations to the kind people of the neighborhood, and wisely, as far as he could foresee, determined to remain among them, or at least against any immediate change.'

Dr. Bulfinch was one of those who have not their reward on earth. This was to him a scene of trial and discipline for heaven; but I thank God he was permitted to live thus long, to give convincing proofs of his talents and energy. I forego, then, with something like resignation, the course of extensive usefulness, reputation and earthly happiness, which he appeared to have entered upon, for he has a better inheritance on high. Dr. Bulfinch was about thirty-one years of age when he died.—*Boston Med. and Surg. Jour., Jan.,* 1836.

DR. ASA BURBANK was born in Williamstown, Massachusetts, in the year 1773. He devoted his early life to study, and graduated at Williams College in the year 1797. In the year 1798 he was appointed a tutor in that college, which office he held two years. In the year 1800 he commenced the study of medicine in the office, it is believed, of the celebrated Dr. Towner, a distinguished surgeon in Williamstown. He attended one or two courses of medical lectures in the medical school of the city of New York, under the direction and instruction of the eminent Dr. Post and other distinguished Professors in that celebrated institution, then connected with Columbia College. He then commenced the practice of his profession in Lanesboro' in the county of Berkshire and State of Massachusetts. Here he continued in extensive and lucrative practice, not only in this, but in most of the neighboring towns, giving universal satisfaction to all his numerous patrons and employers. In 1824 he removed to Albany, the capital of the State of New York, where he remained four years, till he was attacked with dropsy of the brain, which was probably brought on by a fall, and injury of the head, in 1824, and which induced him to leave the theatre of his active usefulness at Albany, and return to Williamstown, the place of his nativity, the last year of his life. Here he became blind, and remained so for nine months, when death terminated his sufferings in the year 1829, at the age of fifty six.

Dr. Burbank stood high in the estimation of his professional brethren, as well as of the public. In the year 1822, about the time of the establishment of the Berkshire Medical Institution connected with Williams College, he was appointed Professor of Obstetrics in that celebrated school, and continued his useful labors there for two years, giving great satisfaction to the students, when he resigned, and removed to Albany. I was intimately acquainted with him in this institution, where I was a fellow laborer with him in the department of medical jurisprudence, and I can bear ample testimony to his worth and usefulness. He was one of the most companionable and facetious of men, and his happy turn of relating anecdotes, of which an abundance was stored in his capacious mind, often kept an assemblage of his friends in a roar of laughter. He had a most happy and enviable faculty of cheering up the minds of his patients, even in the most desponding cases, and often of smoothing their pillows in their descent to the grave. No one can doubt that he was both a moral and a highly religious man.

DR. JAMES P. CHAPLIN. Dr. Chaplin was born at Groton, in the county of Middlesex, Mass., twenty miles from Boston, where his father, a venerable clergyman, is still living. He studied medicine as a pupil of the late Dr. Warren, in Boston, took the degree of Doctor of Medicine in Harvard University, and settled as a practitioner in that part of Cambridge called Cambridgeport. After obtaining a high reputation and extensive business in this town, he added to his other labors the formation of an establishment for the reception and care of insane persons. The number of patients received was for some years small. But his success with them was so remarkable that he was induced to enlarge his buildings, and to place his asylum on a more extended plan, so as to afford all necessary accommodations for the comfort and cure of those put under his care. His reputation increased and spread so widely that he had applications for many more than he could receive, from every part of the United States; and his success kept pace with his reputation. Probably no institution of the kind in any country ever presented a greater number of cures. His method was a moral one. In common cases he used no medicines but occasional purgatives. Coercion and confinement were but little employed, and violence made no part of the system. It was by his peculiar, calm, commanding manner, and admirable judgment in conversing with his patients that he succeeded in softening the obstinate, and controlling the violent. To moral modes of treatment he added careful regimen and great exercise.

Dr. Chaplin's private character was highly amiable and interesting. His friends knew where to find him.

He united himself with the Massachusetts Medical Society in the year 1803, and for many years he was an officer in that institution. In that Society his opinion was received with great respect, and he was therefore generally called on to assist in arranging and deciding on the most important concerns of the Society. Of late years he took a deep interest in the subject of religion, and became remarkable for his devotion to pious and benevolent objects. Cut off in the full career of his exertions, and in the vigor of his experience, his loss will be deeply felt and with difficulty supplied. He died in 1828, at the age of 46. A long account of his complicated complaints and death may be found in the Boston Medical and Surgical Journal, from which the above notice was taken, in 1828.

DR. SAMUEL CHURCH was born at Amherst in the county of Hampshire and State of Massachusetts, about the year 1756. He graduated at Harvard University in 1778, and studied the profession of medicine with Dr. Coleman of Amherst, a man of a good deal of celebrity in those days. Soon after, he commenced the practice of his profession in Sunderland, an adjoining town, where he resided much esteemed to the time of his death, which occurred in the year 1826, at the age of 70 years. He was admitted a Fellow of the Massachusetts Medical Society in 1816, and he resigned in 1823.

Dr. Church was always a judicious, but rather a timid, practitioner of medicine. His judgment in relation to diseases was discriminating and very correct, but he never administered his remedies with so bold and unsparing a hand as many of his professional brethren. He nevertheless enjoyed the confidence of his professional brethren to a great extent, and he was on terms of great intimacy with such men as the venerable Dr. Wells of Montague, Dr. Hunt of Northampton, Dr. William S. Williams of Deerfield, and many others. In his manners he was affable and polite, but modest and retiring. He never sought business, but was always ready to attend his calls, whenever they were made. In size he was about the middling height and proportions. He was very plain in his dress as well as in his manners. He was considered to be a very good and correct writer, but he never published many of the productions of his pen. I understand he kept some manuscript volumes of medical notes, but I have also been informed that they were probably lost with an only son, who perished on board the ill-fated Lexington on Long Island Sound, in January, 1840. He was a poet of no mean abilities. I have before me three manuscript volumes, the productions of his pen, in poetry, which fully justify the truth of the above assertion. In addition to these a pamphlet was published a good many years ago, containing a humorous controversy between himself and the former minister of Shelburne, in poetry. The doctor's poem was considered to be very witty and ingenious. I am sorry my limits do not allow me to extract from it.

Doctor Church had always a great vein of humor, which he sustained to the day of his death. I had the charge of him during his last sickness, and I shall never forget his cheerfulness and good spirits, although laboring under a distressing complaint which he bore with christian fortitude. Suffer me to relate an instance of his good humor, and his apt reply to a witty attack. Dr. Hunt of Northampton, who kept a drug store there, and of whom Dr. Church procured his medicine, was also a man of unbounded humor. He once called upon Dr. Church for the settlement of a bill in the following words:—" Dr. Church, Dear Sir: I am in want of a fat hog; please send it, or—Ebenezer Hunt." Dr. Church replied as follows :—" Dr. Hunt, Dear Sir: I have no fat hog; and if I had—Samuel Church."

Dr. Church for many years held the office of Justice of the Peace, and was considered a most able and upright magistrate. In a few of the last years of his life he did much more business in his legal than in his medical capacity, though most of his old patrons continued to employ him as a physician as long as he lived.—*See my Address before the Mass. Med. Society, May,* 1842.

Dr. NEHEMIAH CLEAVELAND of Topsfield, Mass. The following biographical notice of this distinguished physician, was forwarded to the Boston Medical and Surgical Journal, and published in the No. for

June, 1839, by Dr. A. L. Pierson of Salem. It was written by his son, Mr. N. Cleaveland of Byfield. It was read by Dr. Pierson before the Essex South District Medical Society, of which Doct. Cleaveland was a much respected member. Doct. Pierson remarks of him previous to giving the notice of him by his son, that 'No man amongst us set a better example of professional integrity and honor, and his son has drawn his character in colors, which from the natural fear of being charged with filial partiality, are the reverse of being extravagant. The few who could boast of his friendship, will long remember with pleasure the virtuous, kind hearted old man, whose influence was uniformly and efficiently exerted in supporting good order and the true advancement of society.

He died on the 25th of February, 1837, of a most painful disorder. Inflammation and slow ulceration attacked the stomach, and after occupying the superior third of the mucous ,and muscular coats, finally, a few days before his death, penetrated the diaphragm, and opened a communication with the thorax. The whole of this process occupied about a year, during every day of which his character beautifully developed the results of religious training and cheerful resignation to the will of God. Our American patent of nobility is *to come of a good stock*, and this inheritance the late Nehemiah Cleaveland, M. D., both received and transmitted.'

Mr. Cleaveland observes: 'My father was born

10

at Ipswich, on the 20th of August, 1760. His father, the Rev. John Cleaveland, was for more than fifty-two years minister of the parish then known by the ancient Indian name Chebacco, and since incorporated as the town of Essex. I have no recollection of my grandfather, who died when I was but four years old. But his image, derived from oft repeated description, is vivid before me: a clergyman of the old school—of erect port—urbane, yet dignified—an ardent, animated preacher —a faithful pastor, and a christian patriot. In the French war he served as chaplain at Louisburgh, and at Ticonderoga. In the war of the Revolution he again became attached to the army; and at Cambridge, in New Jersey, and New York, was heard imploring blessings on a cause which he believed to be that of justice and of God.

Catching his spirit and following his example, three of his sons enlisted in the army. John, the eldest, had a commission as lieutenant. After his term of service expired, he devoted himself to theological studies, became an exemplary minister of the gospel, and died lamented, about twenty-two years ago.

Parker, who was about two years younger, studied medicine, and had commenced the practice in Rowley (Byfield parish) before the revolutionary war broke out. He then obtained the appointment of assistant surgeon in the army. After serving a few months in that capacity he returned to the more quiet scenes of domestic life and a country practice.

He had a mind uncommonly active and discriminative. Besides being a most observant, judicious and skillful physician, he was a thorough politician and sound theologian. He certainly had the ability and merit to have filled a sphere wider and more brilliant than that in which it was his lot to move. But he lacked the tact and worldly wisdom which enables one to make the most of his advantages, natural or acquired. It was a common remark in regard to Dr. Parker Cleaveland, that as a physician he was too honest. He was by no means the only instance in the annals of medical men, where solid merit has been left to pine in neglect and poverty, while the ignorant and empirical, by flattering the caprices and indulging the whims of patients, have secured the business and enjoyed its emoluments. Dr. C. died eleven years ago, at the age of seventy-four. Two sons survive him, who inherit his talents, and stand high in public estimation : Parker Cleaveland, Professor of Chemistry and Mineralogy in Bowdoin College, and Rev. J. P. Cleaveland, President elect of a College in Michigan.

Nehemiah was in his sixteenth year when he enlisted as attendant on his father in the army, then investing Boston. At a later period he served as a common soldier in New Jersey and at West Point. The remaining years of his minority were passed at home. Stripling though he was, on him devolved at that critical and distressing period the almost entire support of the family. He restored to good order the little farm which had suffered from ab-

sence, neglect and mismanagement. He devised
ways and means—he labored hard with his own
hands, and formed those habits of order, frugality
and industry, which he maintained through life.

It was his father's wish and conditional promise
that he should have a college education. But the
formidable expense—the *res angustæ domi*—and the
importance of his services at home, concurred to
prevent. His early opportunities for instruction
were extremely limited. The extent to which, amid
cares and business, he supplied these defects in
later life, strikingly exhibited the energy of his mind
and character.

As soon as he was at liberty to do so, he entered
his name as a student in medicine with Dr. John
Manning of Ipswich, a good physician, at that time
enjoying an extensive practice. He remained with
Dr. Manning somewhat more than a year, and then
completed his medical studies with his brother at
Byfield. Just as he got ready to practice, a vacan-
cy was made in Topsfield, by the death of Dr.
Dexter. He removed to that place at the close of
the year 1783. Dr. Dexter left a handsome estate,
the fruits of a practice somewhat extensive and lucrative. His library and stock of medicines were sold
at auction. My father purchased them. The library—hear it, ye ill starred doctors, of later times, who
must toil through many a wearisome tome, and
whose shelves groan under a weight of medical lore
—the library of this popular and successful physician consisted of just *two* books.

My father soon found employment. He early secured, and ever retained, so long as his health permitted him to attend to it, the larger and better part of the medical practice of the place. He was likewise often called into the neighboring towns, Ipswich, Hamilton, Wenham, Middleton, Boxford, and particularly Danvers.

Very soon after coming to Topsfield he received a commission of Justice of the Peace, at that time a distinction of some value. This appointment opened to him an additional field of labor. He turned his attention to those points of law and statute which come within the jurisprudence of the civil magistrate, and soon qualified himself to discharge his duties with accuracy and fidelity.

In 1787 he married Lucy, eldest daughter of his instructor, Dr. Manning. She was a lady of great excellence, but died in 1791 without issue. In the following year he was married again to Experience, daughter of Dr. Elisha Lord of Pomfret, Connecticut.

By this connection he had nine children. Three died in infancy. The others with their mother survive.

At this period of his life he was often employed as a referee ; often on committees for laying out roads and other matters of the kind, which require a knowledge of business and a sound judgment. In 1811 he was chosen into the Senate of this Commonwealth. In 1812 he was ousted by the operation of the Gerrymander law. But the change in public sentiments produced by that high handed measure restored him in 1815. He retained his seat by successive elections until 1819, when he declined being a candidate. I am not aware that while a member of this body he ever engaged in debate. In this respect he felt probably an unnecessary diffidence. In comparing himself with others, he thought too much of his early disadvantages. But his weight of character, his knowledge, judgment and good sense, were felt and acknowledged by his associates at that board. Among them there were some of the first men in the State—men whose approbation was *praise*—and who then, and ever after, when occasion offered, evinced that he had secured their esteem and regard.

In 1814 he was appointed a Session Justice of the Circuit Court of Common Pleas. From 1820 to 1822 he was Associate Justice of the Court of Sessions, and in 1823 he was appointed Chief Justice. For this station he was well fitted by his knowledge of business, his sound discretion, and his unyielding firmness on all questions of principle and duty. This station he held until 1828. From that time he was engaged in no public business.

In 1824 he received from Harvard University the honorary degree of Doctor in Medicine. This attention was not less pleasing, in that it was equally unsought and unexpected.

Dr. Cleaveland was just six feet in height. His form was erect, dignified, and commanding. Until past thirty, he was spare and slender. He afterwards became corpulent, weighing at one time two hundred and sixty-five pounds. Yet such were the height and proportions of his frame that his corpulence never materially injured its symmetry. His health until about fifty years old, was uncommonly firm. He shrunk from no exposure, sunk under no hardship. His first severe sickness he supposed at the time to be an attack of colic. A repetition of the attack, attended by clearer symptoms convinced, him that his sufferings arose from urinary calculi. The debility and emaciation produced by these attacks of excruciating pain were very great. He felt that his constitution was broken up, and that his lease of life had probably dwindled to a span. Though he at length recovered in a good degree his strength and resumed attention to business, he never afterwards regained his former firm health. He continued to be subject to attacks of severe pain and confinement and scarcely ever rode without feeling more or less uneasiness. A sulkey, which he used constantly for the last twenty-five years, was the only vehicle in which he could ride with tolerable comfort. Whether this was owing to its greater easiness, or the peculiar nature of its motion, may be a question of some interest with medical men.

A brief allusion to some of his personal traits will not, I trust, be deemed unbecoming. A slight acquaintance with my father would suffice to identify him with a school which has passed or is fast passing away. He was nursed in the puritan strictness of earlier times. His character, early formed and invigorated under the pressure of hardship and stern necessity, and amid the thrilling scenes of the revolution, exhibited in his maturer years the strength and firmness which might be expected from much training. There was no effeminacy about him. He regulated his life with the closest regard to principle. If his strictness sometimes bordered on severity, his severity was of the wholesome kind. With all this, his natural sensibilities were quick and tender.

In public affairs and political questions, he took from his first entry into active life a lively interest. Of his political opinions his children will never feel ashamed, for they can say that they were those of Hamilton, Jay, and Washington. In politics his course was decided and unwavering. With the class so numerous of late years, who fashion ‘their doctrines to the varying hour,’ he had neither fellowship nor sympathy.

As a physician he was much esteemed by those who had an opportunity to learn his worth. He made, indeed, no pretensions to extensive medical lore—he attempted no difficult surgical operation. But he had—what all the schools of medicine cannot of themselves supply—an observing mind, a retentive memory, a good judgment, and a high sense of responsibility. Nor did he, like too many country physicians, neglect the reading of medical books and journals. His practice was always prudent and cautious—qualities which young and ardent physicians are not apt sufficiently to admire. He was punctual in attending to calls, and kind and cheerful in the sick room. He possessed in a high degree the qualities which ensure to the physician the confidence and attachment of his patients. These feelings were often and very strongly manifested. Amid the strife of parties and the collision of rival interests, a man so decided and active could not be without opponents. These he had, and bitter ones. Yet it was no uncommon thing to hear even the bitterest say that Dr. Cleaveland was a *good physician*—while they gave every proof of sincerity by employing him still.

The position of a medical man in a small country village is, in some respects, very different from that of a city practitioner. The division of labor in large towns very naturally shuts the physician up to his chosen, appropriate sphere. But the country doctor will find many opportunities and calls to do good, for which the faculty, as such, give no prescriptions. Happy he who has the power and disposition to meet such calls. During the fifty years of my father's practice in Topsfield, few days probably passed when his opinion or assistance was not sought in some matter aside from his profession. I believe, too, that I shall be borne out by those who knew him best and longest, in saying that there were few occurrences or questions incident to common life in regard to which he had not formed an opinion, or could not give judicious advice. Indeed, the mere fact that through so long a series of years confidence continued undiminished—the oracle being consulted even to the last—proves that the responses had not been found unsafe or fallacious. The happy influences of

11

so long a course of beneficent actions are not to be estimated. How many quarrels have been arrested— how many law suits prevented—how much needless expense and trouble saved, in a thousand instances, by the timely and un-feed advice of a judicious and peace-making neighbor.

Dr. David Cobb, late Lieutenant Governor of Massachusetts. I am indebted to the Hon. Francis Baylies, of Taunton, Mass., for the following just eulogium upon the character of this distinguished man, pronounced at Taunton, soon after the decease of General Cobb.

David Cobb was born at Attleborough, in Mass., in September, 1748; his father, Thomas Cobb, Esq., having at that time a temporary residence at Attleborough, although he generally resided at Taunton. His paternal grandfather was Morgan Cobb, of Welch descent. His mother was a daughter of James Leonard. Paternally and maternally he was descended from the ancient settlers of Taunton.

Being a favorite son of his father he was designed for a liberal education, and very early in life was placed under the instruction of Mr. Marsh, an eminent schoolmaster at Braintree, (now Quincy). In 1766 he was graduated at Harvard College. His chum, or room-mate, was that celebrated, popular orator, Dr. Charles Jarvis. He married a daughter of Ebenezer Bradish, Esq., of Cambridge, and prepared himself for the profession of a physician under the direction of Dr. Perkins, an eminent practitioner in Boston.

An industrious student, and possessing a peculiar, practical aptitude for the several branches of his profession, when he left his instructor he was accomplished in his art; knowing in its ancient lore and modern improvements. His excellent education, native sagacity, and quickness of mind, enabled him in the outset of life to compete with those whose skill had been perfected by years of practice and long experience.

His first essay in his profession was made at Boston under flattering circumstances, and with hopeful prospects of success; but at the urgent solicitation of his father he returned to the county of Bristol, and pursued his profession in the country.

He returned at a period when the controversy between the British Parliament and the Province of Massachusetts Bay began to assume an alarming aspect. His father was an Episcopalian, advanced in years, and possessed of a large estate; and although no Tory, was of moderate principles, and dreaded a convulsion. The son threw himself into the very front rank of the revolutionists, and led on by an ardent temperament, he brought to the controversy all the energies of youth, and a deep knowledge of the principles on which the rights of the Province were based, and from the outset was determined to try the worst. Young as he was the eyes of the people were turned to him, for this was

not the period for impudent and superficial dema-
gogues to operate upon the public mind. In the
hour of danger and distress, talent and wisdom
and energy assume, as a matter of course, their
appropriate place at the head of political society,
and in the primary assemblies of the people he took
the lead because he was fitted for it.

In 1774 he represented Taunton in the first Provincial Congress of Massachusetts, as the colleague
of his brother-in-law, Robert Treat Paine, one of
the Signers of the Declaration of Independence,
and when the resort to arms was made, he went
through the Roxbury campaign in his calling as a
surgeon.

But it was not for him to be satisfied with supporting a good cause merely by his services as a
civilian. He was impatient to share the perils and
the glory of the field, and when the opposition assumed the character of regular resistance on military principles, he assumed the sword and entered
the army as Lieutenant Colonel of a Continental
Regiment, commanded by Colonel Henry Jackson.
In this regiment he encountered some hard service,
particularly in New Jersey, and on Rhode Island,
where he led what might be called a Forlorn Hope
—to delay, with twenty men, the progress of a Hessian regiment of cavalry.

His activity, talent, and high military qualities,
attracted the attention of the Commander-in-Chief,
and he was invited into his military family as an
Aid-de-Camp. In that station he remained till the

termination of the war, although he was appointed to the command of the regiment in which he had entered the service. When the army was disbanded he was a full Colonel, and a Brigadier General by brevet.

He was with Washington during all the greater operations of the war, and during many of those periods of trial in which that great Commander was placed. He was with him at the time of the treason of Arnold, the capture of Cornwallis, and when the army, maddened by neglect, had resolved with their own arms to redress their own wrongs.

The councils which were holden in Washington's tent were no petty caballings for offices and distinctions. His counselors applied themselves to their mighty tasks with the wisdom of sages, the purity of patriots, and the energy of heroes.

Washington had that rare discrimination which could select from amongst his followers the very person best adapted to the service to which he was designated, and under his vigorous administration of army affairs, no talent was suffered to be wasted which could be profitably employed in the public service. To Colonel Cobb the duty was assigned of entertaining and doing the honors to the French officers, to whom, from the gaiety and vivacity of his manners, and his martial bearing, he was peculiarly acceptable, and to him he entrusted the negotiation with Sir Guy Carleton, the British commander, for the evacuation of New York.

On one occasion Colonel Cobb exposed himself

to the hazard of giving mortal offence to the French officers at Yorktown. When Lord Cornwallis invaded Virginia, he seized upon a beautiful and valuable horse called Black-and-all-Black, which belonged to one of the back settlers. On his surrender, the French officers, without any particular understanding, appropriated Black-and-all-Black to themselves, and Colonel Cobb, whose taste and judgment in horses were duly appreciated, was called upon by them daily to admire his lofty bearing and symmetric proportions, and consequently he knew his place of concealment, and from frequent visits had gained an accurate knowledge of its localities. The owner came down from the upper country to reclaim his horse, but his entreaties were in vain. It was decided that Black-and-all-Black should visit France. In his despair the poor Virginian endeavored to obtain access to General Washington, but he having some intimation of his purpose, and unwilling to embroil himself with the French officers, avoided him. The love of the Virginian for his horse was like the love of an Arab, and the horse constituted his whole property. In his distress he applied to Colonel Cobb, told the story of his misfortune with all the eloquence of grief, and with streaming eyes entreated him to obtain for him an interview with Washington. Cobb was always moved with the sight of distress, but he knew that it would be unpleasant to Washington to interfere. 'My good fellow,' said he, 'don't apply to the General, and I will put you in the way to get your horse.' He then informed him of the place of concealment, described the localities with so much accuracy, and devised such an ingenious plan for the abstraction, that the Virginian, profiting by his counsel, was enabled during one dark night to steal his own horse. Dire was the commotion in the French camp, and dire were the execrations against the fugitives from the British army, to whom the theft was imputed. Colonel Cobb kept his own counsel, and was unsuspected by all, save one. Several days after the occurrence, when Black-and-all-Black was safe amongst his native hills, Washington, with his peculiar, cold and significant smile, said to his Aid— ' Colonel Cobb, can you inform me where Black-and-all-Black is stabled ?'

During his military life Col. Cobb formed some close and intimate friendships, particularly with Generals Greene and Knox, and Colonel Jackson. He had been associated not only with the great and heroic men of his own country, but with the warriors of Frederic the Great, the fiery spirited Polanders, and the splendid chivalry of France ; with men who afterwards acquired immortal names, and convulsed Europe with revolutions.

Early in 1784 he resumed his profession. He had now seen life in all its varieties—in the city— in the country—and in the camp ; in the highest circles of fashion, and in the obscurest recesses of poverty. By this extensive acquaintance with every variety of the human character, he had attained some knowledge which he soon had occasion to use.

Soon after his return he received from Governor Hancock an appointment to the bench of the Court of Common Pleas, and from the Legislature the office of Major General of the Fifth Division of Militia, and in both his civil and military capacity he was called upon to encounter the tempests of 1786, and to uphold the civil institutions of the State, threatened with subversion by an insurgent populace. He met this crisis with manly firmness. The escutcheon of the State had heretofore borne none but honorable emblems, but there was danger that it might be stamped with bankruptcy and fraud. The government had been stable, but the foundations were loosened; and there was danger that the whole fabric might fall. Men rose to resist the laws, to besiege—not hostile fortresses, but Court Houses—to direct their arms, not against armed men, but against the Judges who adjudicated on the laws.

In June, 1786, a mob appeared on Taunton Green for the avowed purpose of preventing the sitting of the Court of Common Pleas. General Cobb, acting as a Judge, had devised a plan to save the laws from violation, satisfy the people, and preserve peace. He proposed that the Court should be opened, the actions entered to preserve attachments, and that the Court should adjourn without entering the judgments. By this means the debtors might gain time, and possibly save their property from ruinous sacrifices. All the Judges concurred. The mob, wild with distress, and ferocious with despair, were uttering threats against the Court, but to give some appearance of moderation to their proceedings, a deputation was sent to confer with them. The plan was explained, the committee were satisfied, but were unable to explain it to their constituents, the mob, who called loudly on Judge Cobb to appear. He instantly went amongst them alone, and unarmed, and using the ready and clear elocution with which he was gifted, the mob comprehended the plan— were satisfied and dispersed—shouting his praises.

The next term of the Court of Common Pleas was in September. The day arrived; the people were not relieved; their debts were increased, and their means of payment lessened. The spirit of discontent was marked with deeper ferocity, and amongst the malcontents the determination that the Courts should not sit was general.

Although Gen. Cobb was indulgent and humane, yet he never temporized when great principles were at stake. He perceived that a crisis had arrived when the laws must be supported by force, or yielded to anarchy. The executive government of the State had thrown the whole responsibility of defending the laws on the Courts, the Sheriffs, and the Major Generals; and Cobb was obliged to assume a double responsibility. But he was equal to the crisis. He would not believe that crimes involving treason against the commonwealth were the excesses of passionate zeal; the destruction of social order, a redress of grievances, or that rebellion and civil war

12

were the outward evidences of the existence of
liberty!

The tenderness of his nature led to no misgivings.
He was determined to support the court and the
laws, even to the shedding of blood. The militia
were ordered out. Court day arrived. The robe
of the Judge was thrown aside. The military plumes
waved over his head, and the sword of the warrior
flashed bright in the sunbeams! Sounds ominous
and threatening arose from the mob:—'*the blood of
the people—the blood of the people is to be shed,*'—
was the cry for the onset. But when steady at their
posts the citizen soldiers were seen extended in
double lines from the door of the court house,
when the resolute demeanor of the commander was
observed, the tone of defiance sunk to supplica-
tion, and he was entreated to withdraw the soldiers.
'Away with your whining,' was his determined and
memorable reply; 'I will sit this Court if I sit it
in blood—I will sit as a Judge, or I will die as a
General!' In an instant all was quiet. Secret
and silent the mob stole off, and the laws triumphed
—yet the spirit was not quelled.

The Supreme Court commenced a session at
Taunton in October. All the western counties of
the State were in open rebellion, and the spirit of
insurrection pervaded the county of Bristol. A large
body of armed insurgents appeared on Taunton
Green, under the command of David Valentine. A
large portion of the most substantial population of

the county were Quakers, whose services, of course, were not available in such a crisis. With the exception of the militia of one town, it was difficult to rally one entire company in either of the towns to the defence of the government, and General Cobb was compelled to rely on volunteers, and on a full regiment from Bridgewater. He drew up his force before the doors of the court house in which the court was then sitting. The insurgents faced him with the appearance of spirit, and amongst them were two or three revolutionary officers. Cobb's single cannon was charged, and the match was waving. Valentine, the rebel leader, suddenly dismounted, and preceded by music, approached Cobb's line. He met him half way. His last orders from the Executive were peremptory, to defend the court to the last extremity. Drawing a line along the ground with his sword, he said to the rebel leader—"Pass that line and I fire —the blood will be on your own head." Valentine approached the line—paused—turned his back and retired. The laws triumphed once more; the court sat in peace. In the night the insurgents dispersed, and no more mobs assembled in the county of Bristol. The energy of Cobb not only sustained the laws, but prevented the effusion of blood.

General Cobb encountered these perils and rendered himself obnoxious to the resentment of a large body of desperate and factious insurgents to protect the rights of property,—yet he had no property to protect; he had shared the common inheritance of the officers of the revolutionary army, hardship, and suffering, and poverty, and he had more reason to dread the processes of the law against debtors, than any who resisted such processes in arms. He led, as country physician, a harder life to gain a bare subsistance than any day laborer amongst the rebels. He would have prospered by an Agrarian law. But poor as he was, unpopular as was his command, he would have done his duty and defended the courts had his name been borne on half its entries as a defendant debtor, and had its judgments and executions reduced him to beggary.

In 1789, and in three succeeding years, he was elected a representative to the General Court, and each year held the Speaker's chair.

His faculty of arranging, simplifying, and despatching the legislative business was remarkable. He presided with dignity; and in reading, his emphasis, voice and manner imparted an interest to the most ordinary technical document.

In 1792, according to a peculiar mode of choice then in operation, he was elected a representative in the third Congress for the whole State. At Philadelphia he was received with great satisfaction by his old companions in arms. Washington was President, Hamilton Secretary of the Treasury, Knox Secretary of War, Pickering Post Master General, Edmund Randolph the Attorney General, and Jonathan Trumbull the Speaker of the House of Representatives, some of whom had belonged to Washington's military family. Many revolutionary officers were serving in both branches of Congress—a Congress illustrious by the names of Fisher Ames, Madison, Giles, Dexter, King, Strong, Cabot, and many other statesmen of renown.

When the House of Representatives went into Committee of the Whole, General Cobb was usually called to the chair, and presided with the same dignity and efficiency as he had done previously in Massachusetts. He was sometimes impatient under the prosings of dullness, but a flash of genius, no matter in what association it was found, no matter from what party it proceeded, always irradiated his countenance with a triumphant smile.

Having an offer from William Bingham of a land agency in Maine, he thought his fortunes might be bettered, and declined a re-election. His term expired March 3, 1795, and soon afterwards he left Taunton and became an inhabitant of Oldsborough, near the eastern frontier of Maine. He devoted himself to the business of his agency, and to the cultivation and improvement of his farm, for the love of agriculture was with him a passion. In the secluded spot in which fortune had placed him he delighted in the practices of hospitality ; Mr. Bingham, the Viscount Noailles, Lord Ashburton, General Knox, Mr. Laboucheire, and other distinguished persons, were occasionally his guests. The Indians shared the plenty of his kitchen, and many was the weary wayfarer who was cheered and refreshed under his hospitable roof.

He soon received the appointment of Chief Justice of the Court of Common Pleas for the county of Hancock, over which he presided several years, and by his long experience in the courts he became a well informed and judicious lawyer.

In 1802 he was elected a Senator from the Eastern District in Maine, and was immediately called to the chair of the Senate, and officiated as President until 1805. In 1808 he was elected a Councilor, and in 1809 Lieutenant Governor of the State of Massachusetts (Maine was then a Province of Massachusetts). In 1812 he was again elected a Councilor and soon afterwards Major General of the 10th Division of Militia, and with Gen. Heath and Col. Pickering constituted the Board of War for the State. He remained in the Court several years, and after he withdrew from public life, his latter years were passed at Taunton. Being afflicted with a chronic complaint he sought relief at the General Hospital in Boston, and there, on the 17th day of April, 1830, his life was closed, at the age of 82. In his last hours his early associations were in full force.

> " Et dulces moriens reminiscetur Argos."

He chose his grave in Taunton, and there it was made.

It will be perceived that but a few years of the long life of General Cobb were devoted to his original profession. He had not been in practice more than four or five years when the revolution commenced. After the disbanding of the army, his professional pursuits were much interrupted by his civil and military duties, and after his election to Congress

in 1792, he resumed them. His cotemporaries represent him as having been exceedingly skillful in
midwifery, an expert surgeon, and in his general
practice bold, sagacious and judicious—somewhat
inclined to the Brunonian system, but not to its
extravagances. A case or two may illustrate his
practice. A gentleman of considerable note in
Taunton was attacked with dysentery. His constitution was very feeble, and he sunk under the
disorder, hiccough ensued, and his attending physicians gave him up. At the time of the attack Gen.
Cobb was absent ; when he returned he found him
almost in *extremis.* Knowing something of his constitution he ventured to guess that his disorder had
been much aggravated by an acid stomach, and he
ventured on the experiment of counteracting the
acid with alkali, and ordered him to chew and swallow the juice of tender beef steaks, and afterwards
to try brandy. He effected a cure, and the world
wondered. He had cured by a remedy which, according to the notions of the day, was death. On
another occasion he cured a farmer's wife in the
lowest stage of debility, arising from a deranged
stomach, and occasioned, as he said, by drinking sour
cider and eating brown bread—by putting her on a
more generous diet, with a slight infusion of brandy.

His sagacity in discovering those hidden diseases
which often baffle the penetration of the faculty, and
are only ascertained by post mortem examinations, is
represented as having been wonderful. He brought
much comfort to the bed of the sick, and had much

faith in the efficacy of hope. He would not deceive, but was willing to cheer his patient back to health.

As a soldier he was fearless and intrepid : calm and collected in danger—rapid and decisive in judgment, and prompt in execution.

In the Courts, his clear perceptions and strong sense enabled him to detect sophistry, and to remove the impediments with which artifice and legal ingenuity too often contrive to embarrass the progress of science.

As a statesman he was distinguished for his love of order, and his attachment to the constitution. He was never turned aside from an honorable course by any considerations of interest or popularity. He shunned no responsibilities, and regarded only the great and permanent interests of his country. Reared in the old Federal school, his principles were strictly conservative. He was too proud to flatter the people, and too honest to deceive them.

Graceful and dignified when presiding over a public body, he was quick to perceive, and prompt to explain. He despatched the public business with facility, and by his impartial deportment satisfied even his adversaries.

His conversation, always elegant, was sometimes terse and epigrammatic. After the termination of the war, Gen. Washington was lamenting the cheerless prospects of the New Englanders. ‘You will lose,’ said he, ‘your trade with the British colonies —you raise no grain sufficient for your bread—you have no staple export, and your condition will be worse than ever—what will your people do?' 'Sir,' said Cobb, 'we never had any thing but our heads and our hands, and having these left we shall find something to do with them!'

He was impatient of contradiction, and sometimes irritated by the pertinacious assumptions of ignorance, and the mawkish complacencies of self-conceit : incensed by sophistries and falsehoods, and transported by the ardor of his temperament to give way to gusts of passion, and affronted many who were unable to appreciate the real excellence of his moral and mental qualities. The wounds of self-love are difficult to heal, and many imputed what they called rudeness to a domineering and arrogant spirit, when in fact it was no more than a burning zeal for truth, and a consciousness of rectitude.

As time paralyzes the strength and tames the passions—as contemporaries drop away—it is one of the calamities of the aged to depreciate the social comforts and enjoyments, and to institute querulous comparisons between times present and times past. They linger in the world as strangers, imbibing their scanty draughts of pleasure from the fountains of recollection. Not so with General Cobb; he never lingered in the race of life—he kept even with the times. He went into the great world, and extracted all its comforts. He used the true philosophy of life, and multiplied his pleasures by taking a lively interest in the happiness of his friends and neighbors. He rejoiced in their prosperity. He

13

felt none of that miserable and rancorous envy which induces some to regard the thrift of others as so much deduction from their own. He had no narrow views. He delighted to watch the progress of all improvements in science and the arts, and to witness their application to the purposes of life. This disposition induced him to seek the society of the young, and of those in active life, and none enjoyed with keener pleasure the efforts of childhood, when it called up its puny powers to grasp new objects of knowledge, and with a perception and taste almost intuitive, he understood all the delicate peculiarities of the female mind, and made his conversation deeply interesting to women. His social powers were of the first order. The stream of his conversation was no shallow rill. He never magnified trifles, paraded truisms or affected learning. He threw off from the superabundance of his mental riches, maxims which might have instructed sages and statesmen, and fancies which sparkled and blazed and burned with all the fire of a poet; and this power of conversation, (so to speak) was equally adapted to all classes of society. At the table of Washington, his wit and humor, his fund of anecdote, and his power of narration, gave a blander character to the feasts of heroes; and even the high bred cavaliers of Rochambeau's army found that genius and wit and polished manners existed in the wild vallies of the Hudson, as well as in the *salons* of Paris. He never imposed on his companions his own topics, but seizing theirs, he discovered such facility of illustration, such a glowing imagination, such a poetical flow of language, and such varied and universal knowledge, that if he failed to convince, he never failed to charm. This power of pleasing he could exercise alike in the splendid pavilion of the General, and in the humble tent of the Private.

> " For trained to camps he knew the art
> " To win the soldier's hardy heart."

This faculty remained to the last, brightening the evening of life, and well might the apostrophe of Anacreon have been addressed to him:

> " How I love the mellow sage,
> " Smiling through the veil of age,
> " And whene'er the man of years
> " In the dance of joy appears,
> " Age is on his temples hung,
> " But his heart—his heart is young."

On the whole David Cobb was a learned and sagacious physician, a true patriot; a gallant soldier; an accomplished legislator; a tasteful scholar; a delightful companion; a man of universal knowledge, and a liberal christian who loved the whole human race, and was always ready to return good for evil. Educated in the revolutionary school he had a high sense of personal honor, and a distinterested spirit which sought no other reward than the consciousness of virtue.

When he was laid in the quiet place ' where the wicked cease from troubling and the weary are at rest'—no banner waved over his coffin, no martial

dirge sent forth its mingled strain of wail and of triumph, no thunder from the cannon announced that
a companion of Washington had gone to his eternal
rest.   He well knew the heartlessness of public exhi-
bitions of sorrow, and refused to have his grave pro-
faned with the mockery of woe.

His family were numerous, but most of them are
dead ; William was an Ensign in the army of the United States, and after discovering great gallantry and
prowess was killed in the disastrous battle of General St. Clair with the Western Indians.   David was
also killed by the Indians in an affair on the North
West Coast.   Thomas was Clerk of the Courts in the
county of Hancock, and David G. W., Register of
Probate in the county of Bristol.   Two other sons
are supposed to be living in Maine.   One of the
daughters died young and unmarried.   One married
Allen Smith, Esq., another James Hodges, Esq., another Judge Wilde of the Supreme Court of Massachusetts, who was the mother of the late Honorable Caleb Cushing.   His only surviving daughter is
the wife of Col. John Black, of Ellsworth, Maine.

DR. MASON FITCH COGSWELL.   In an introductory lecture delivered before the Medical Class at
Yale College, Nov. 2nd, 1838, by the distinguished
Professor Jonathan Knight, M. D., I have found
the following notice of Dr. Cogswell.

Mason Fitch Cogswell was born in Canterbury,
Connecticut, in the year 1761.   His father, the

Rev. James Cogswell, a native of Saybrook, was the clergyman of Canterbury for many years. From this place he removed to Scotland, a parish of Windham, where he resided until, as we are informed by the Rev. Dr. Strong, in a sermon preached at his funeral, 'being rendered incapable of public ministerial services, through the natural infirmities of age, it became necessary for his comfortable support, to remove him to the family of his son, Dr. Mason Fitch Cogswell, of this place. This was a comfortable retreat to the venerable parent, and here the Lord repaid to him in kind, his filial duty to his own parents in their old age; here he hath been nourished with the most tender affection, which may God reward, until January 2nd, 1807.' His mother, whose maiden name was Fitch, the daughter of Jabez Fitch, Esq., of Canterbury, belonged to a family from which have sprung many men of great eminence and worth. She died when he was quite young; and in consequence of this event he was placed in the family of Gov. Huntington of Norwich. Here he pursued his studies preparatory to entering College. He graduated at Yale College in 1780. As a proof of his talents and assiduity, it may be mentioned that although the youngest member of a class which contained as his competitors, such men as Matthew and Roger Griswold, Jonathan O. Moseley, and others of great respectability, yet he received the appointment of valedictory orator. After leaving College he pursued his professional studies under the direction of his elder

brother, Dr. James Cogswell, who after the close
of the war of the revolution, and I believe before
its commencement, was a respectable practitioner in
the city of New York. At this period there were
no public lectures on medicine, except at Philadelphia; and these were much interrupted by the
events of the war. Dr. James Cogswell was a surgeon in the American army, and his brother was
for several years his assistant. Here he undoubtedly acquired that fondness for surgery, and that
knowledge of its principles and practice which distinguished him through life. While in the army,
he was stationed for a time in Stamford, where he
formed friendships with the best portion of the inhabitants, which were permanent.

In the year 1789, he established himself permanently as a physician and surgeon in the city of
Hartford. In this place there have always been
physicians of deserved reputation and eminence. I
know not, however, that he was immediately preceded by any distinguished surgeon. Whether it
was so or not, he soon took a high rank in this
branch of his profession. Although he had not
those opportunities of acquiring a knowledge of anatomy which most students enjoy, yet he is known
to have pursued the study of anatomy by dissection,
and suffered in consequence of it a severe attack
of Erythema Anatomicum. In this way he obtained
such an acquaintance with surgical anatomy as enabled him to perform with skill every necessary operation; so that I have never heard a want of anatomi-

cal knowledge attributed to him. For the performance of surgical operations he was peculiarly fitted.
In addition to what Chesselden mentions as having
contributed largely to his own success, ' a mind that
was never ruffled or disconcerted, and a hand that
never trembled during any operation,' Dr. Cogswell
possessed in a greater degree than any surgeon
whom I have ever known, that happy dexterity in
the use of instruments which gave him the power of
operating with great accuracy, neatness and rapidity.
I have been told that he amputated a thigh in forty
seconds. He first introduced in the region where
he practised, the most important operations on the
eye. In the performance of them, especially for cataract, he was peculiarly successful. The operation
which he performed was that of extraction.

He was the first person in this country who secured the carotid artery by a ligature. The necessity for this arose during the removal of a schirrous
tumor from the neck, which enveloped the artery.
The ligature came off from the artery on the fourteenth day. The patient lived till the twentieth day,
and then sunk in consequence of a slight hemorrhage from a small vessel near the angle of the jaw,
acting upon a system enfeebled by a long standing
disease. This was in November, 1803. A year or
two before, the artery had been secured under similar
circumstances on the continent of Europe, and by
Mr. Abernethy in London. There is, however, no
reason to believe that Dr. Cogswell was acquainted
with these facts ; and he is fully entitled to the credit

of having originated the operation. At the present day, when operations upon the arteries are so frequent, it is difficult to estimate rightly the boldness and judgment necessary to place a ligature upon so large and important an artery as the carotid. During his whole life he was engaged in performing the various surgical operations which would fall in the way of one who enjoyed the confidence of a widely extended circle of professional friends; and it is well known that patients resorted to him from great distances to avail themselves of the benefit of his kindness and skill.

In one branch of his profession, Obstetrics, he was nearly unrivaled. The delicacy and kindness of his attention to parturient patients in a time of great anxiety and distress, both mental and bodily; his abandonment of many customs formerly prevalent by which the sensitive feelings of females were often wounded, as well as his great professional skill, gained him at once confidence and esteem. It is questionable whether any person ever practised this branch of medicine more skillfully and acceptably, or more extensively in proportion to the population of the place where he lived.

As a physician Dr. Cogswell was extensively employed and much esteemed.

No man whom I have known, enjoyed more entirely the confidence, esteem, and respect of all with whom he was in any way associated, than the subject of this sketch. To account for this great uniformity of kind feelings towards him, we must look to something beyond his mere professional attainments and qualifications.

He was, as all who knew him agree, a kind, benevolent, and noble spirited man. The fruits of these traits of his character were bestowed upon his patients in full measure. Assiduous in his attention to them, mindful of all their wants, full of compassion for their sufferings, especially to those who were both sick and destitute, and from whom he could hope for no reward ; he was the comforter of their distress in sickness, and the sympathizing sharer of their happiness when health with her spirit-stirring joyousness revisited them. It was this obvious sympathy with their feelings, prompting all his efforts to do them every good in his power, which so uniformly made his patients his personal friends. He also possessed strong and kind social feelings. In the domestic circle, and in the society of his friends, he was polite, cheerful, and abounding in pleasant and instructive conversation. In amenity of manners and in gentlemanly deportment he was rarely excelled.

He was an assiduous and successful cultivator of polite literature, especially of poetry. In these pursuits he was the companion and the compeer of Dr. Hopkins, Judge Trumbull, Rev. Dr. Strong, Mr. Richard Alsop, Mr. Theodore Dwight, and others of a kindred spirit.

In music he was a proficient. It is said that while residing in Stamford, he instructed the choir in that place not only in the common psalm tunes, but also in an anthem or other piece of set music for every Sabbath in the year.

14

He was the active friend and supporter of every plan for the relief of the misfortunes and distress of his fellow men. It was a misfortune to him, but the means of great blessing to many others, that one of his daughters, in consequence of sickness in her early childhood, became a deaf mute. This led him to examine what modes had been adopted for the relief of those who were thus afflicted. Upon learning that a successful mode of instructing these unfortunate persons was in operation in France and England, he took measures to ascertain what the method was, and how the benefits of it might be brought within the reach of those similarly situated in this country. The result of his exertions, aided as he was by others of kindred feelings, was the establishment of the Asylum for the Deaf and Dumb in Hartford, one of the noblest institutions for the relief of the unfortunate which this country can boast. That this Asylum owes its existence to the exertions of Dr. Cogswell, in the first instance, is as familiarly known as the institution itself. For his exertions in this cause, the benediction of thousands who cannot speak his praise will rest upon his memory.

He was also the active friend and supporter of the Retreat for the Insane in Hartford, and of the Hospital in this city. He was one of the original members of the Connecticut Medical Society, and was always interested in its proceedings; and was the friend of every measure by which the profession of medicine might be advanced in respectability and usefulness. The feeling which was entertained towards him by his professional brethren may be gathered from the fact that he was successively Secretary, Vice President, and for ten years President, of the State Medical Society.

I may here remark that few men have ever lived in habits of more free and friendly intercourse with the members of their own profession than he did, or enjoyed such intercourse more highly. And although he did not escape the censure of those with whose notions he could not agree, when during the prevalence of a severe epidemic disease the opinions of medical men were much divided, and feelings arose which threatened, and to a certain extent accomplished, the destruction of the harmony which ought to exist among them ; yet here, the amenity of his manners, his gentlemanly deportment, and the uniform mildness of his conduct, disarmed even professional hostility of the weapons of its warfare.

As an instructor Dr. Cogswell was much resorted to by young men for pursuing the study of medicine. For this business he was well qualified. He was himself a scholar, and continued his habits of study during his life. It was his custom to spend several hours in the evening, after the labors of the day were over, and usually after his family had retired, in reading, principally professional books. His library was one of the best in the State. By directing his students to the best authors, by studying with them such subjects as were not well known to him, such as chemistry and botany, by allowing them to witness his practice, and by exciting them to diligence, he probably rendered them more lasting service than if he had devoted more time than he did to oral instruction. He was also careful to instil into their minds correct principles of manners and morals; often warning them against such conduct as would be derogatory to the character of a gentleman and a christian. His wish evidently was to make them good christians and good men.

It was thought highly desirable by those who were engaged in the establishment of the Medical Institution at Yale College, that some gentleman of established reputation and known experience should be placed in the chair of surgery. There was no one in this place or neighborhood who was sufficiently prominent, in these respects, to occupy that situation. Application was made to Dr. Cogswell, who had long been known as one of the most accomplished and skillful surgeons in New England, to lend his assistance in this department. After much hesitation on account of the difficulty which would attend the delivery of a course of lectures here, while residing in Hartford, and his unwillingness to leave permanently a situation so desirable as that which he occupied there, he consented to make such arrangements as would afford the institution the benefit of his learning and experience. When, however, it was soon after ascertained that Dr. Nathan Smith, then Professor of Physic and Surgery in Dartmouth College, would consent to remove here if invited, he willingly relinquished to him a situation which he had reluctantly consented to occupy; so that although regularly appointed a Professor in the Institution, he did not join it in that capacity.

It can hardly be necessary to remark, that sustaining all relations of domestic life, and enjoying as he did, most fully, its pleasures, he was kind, judicious, and affectionate in the performance of its duties. He married in early life the daughter of Col. Austin Ledyard, who was killed at the fort in Groton when it was captured by the British, as it is said, with his own sword, after it was surrendered into the hands of his captors. She is still living. His children, several of whom survive him, may well remember with gratitude his kind care, his judicious instruction, and his ready assistance ; and if he was not careful to accumulate riches to bequeath to them, he left them what is far better, an honorable parentage, and the bright example of a life devoted to the best interests of his fellow men.

He died of pneumonia typhodes, in December, 1830, in the 70th year of his age.

Dr. ALEXANDER COVENTRY of Utica, New York. The following notice of this distinguished physician is from the tenth volume of the American Journal of Medical Science.

Died on the 9th of December, 1831, Alexander Coventry, M. D., late of Utica, New York. Dr. Coventry was son of Capt. George Coventry, who commanded an independent company raised in the then Colony of New York, in the year 1761, and

served in the forces of his Majesty George III. in
the old French war, as it has usually been called.
Dr. Coventry was born at Fair Hill, the seat of his
father, near Hamilton, Scotland, 27th of August,
1766; was educated in the schools of Hamilton and
Glasgow, and studied the profession of medicine
under Drs. Stewart and Cross at the former place.
In 1783–4 he attended the medical lectures at Glasgow; and in the winter of 1784–5, the lectures of
Monro, Cullen, Hope, and Gregory, at Edinburgh.
In 1785 he was admitted a Burgher of the town of
Hamilton. In July of the same year he sailed for
America to attend to some property which had been
left him there by his father. Dr. Coventry first
settled at Hudson, New York, and soon became
actively engaged in agricultural pursuits in conjunction with the practice of his profession. In 1787
he married Elizabeth, daughter of Mr. John Butler,
of Branford, Connecticut, by whom he had eleven
children, ten of whom are now living. Mrs. Coventry died in Deerfield, near Utica, in 1815. The
Doctor left Hudson and settled at Romulus, on the
east side of Seneca Lake, about the year 1790. It
was while residing in this new and then unhealthy
district, that he had an opportunity of studying the
endemic fevers of the country, in all their forms
and grades. He has been heard to say that on one
occasion he had fourteen sick of fever in his own
house. In notes made at the time he observes that
on his return from a journey to Albany, in August,
1792, he found two thirds of the citizens of Geneva

sick, and in his own family two only remained well. In his own person he had repeated attacks of the prevailing fever. On account of the sickness of himself and family, he left the ' Lake country,' and moved to Utica, then ' Fort Schuyler,' in the year 1796, and entered into mercantile business with Mr. John Post. At the time, it was his wish to abandon the practice of medicine, as his attention was directed to other pursuits. But finding, on further experience, the mercantile business uncongenial to his tastes and habits, and yielding to the frequent calls and solicitations of his friends and acquaintances, he relinquished that business to his partner, and purchased a farm on the north side of the Mohawk river, and once more engaged in his favorite pursuits of agriculture and horticulture. From this period until death, his time and attention were divided between his farm, his books, and the practice of his profession. In the year 1800 Dr. Coventry was elected a member of the society for the promotion of agriculture, arts and manufactures. During several successive years he was President of the Medical Society of the county of Oneida. In 1822 he was elected a permanent member of the Medical Society of the State of New York, and in 1823 was elected President of the same body, and re-elected in 1824. During the same year he was appointed by the Regents of the University of New York, one of the Trustees of the Western Medical College at Fairfield. In 1823 he was elected a member of the Albany Lyceum; and in 1826, Corresponding mem-

ber of the Linnæan Society of Paris. On the organization of the Oneida Agricultural Society, he
was appointed Corresponding Secretary, and delivered the first address before that body. From the
period of his emigration to the west to the time of
his death, Dr. C. was an occasional contributor to
the political and agricultural papers of the day. His
principal medical writings are his addresses before the
State Medical Society, on Endemic Fever—a short
article on Yellow Fever, published in the Edinburgh
Medical and Surgical Journal—an article on Goitre,
and one on Dysentery, in the New York Medical and
Physical Journal. Dr. Coventry possessed naturally a
healthy constitution. After his removal from the west
he rarely if ever complained of indisposition, except
from an occasional attack of rheumatism, a few years
before his death. His habits were uniformly correct
and regular ; in his living, plain and frugal—always
temperate in eating and drinking. During the last
few years of his life he devoted himself more regularly and steadily to his profession, the duties of
which in town and country were too arduous, it is
believed at his time of life ; and yet it seemed impossible it should be otherwise, for as a family physician he was eminently distinguished ; and not only
in our own, but in the adjoining counties, he acquired
and maintained to his death a standing no less respectable, as a consulting physician. Hence, his
medical and other friends and acquaintances felt
happy and safe whenever they could secure his skill
and experience. No man of the profession within

our little circle of acquaintance was more devoutly engaged in the glorious work of relieving the ills to which poor human flesh is heir than our venerable, illustrious Coventry during the few last years of his life. He seemed, like the celebrated Dr. Priestley, determined to finish his own work himself, appropriating all his spare time in bringing up and completing his journal, in which during forty years he had noted daily whatever he conceived useful or important in his profession, in politics, in agriculture and in science, besides devoting himself with unwearied assiduity to all calls in the practice of his profession. In his journal are probably to be found his most valuable writings, and here, as in other instances of his daily conduct through life, he has left us a bright example, worthy of imitation even in these days of human perfectibility. Like the soldier who falls in the defence of his country's cause, our lamented friend and compeer in the midst of a successful and most delightful practice, and while absent from his own house, attending a severe and dangerous case of indisposition, in the family of one of his best and most generous patrons, fell the victim of an attack of the ' epidemic catarrh,' or ' influenza ' as it is usually denominated. And it was not until by his skill and unremitted attention to the case in the family of his friend, during several days and nights, he had been enabled to conquer the fearful malady, that he stopped to address sufficient means to his own. For a time these, as in a thousand cases which had yielded to his skillful and judicious man-

15

agement, seemed to give assurance of ultimate success. But it soon became manifest that the mighty destroyer would triumph over human skill and the best directed efforts of the healing art, and that little else remained for his medical attendants than to behold the perfect calmness and philosophical resignation, which characterized him throughout his illness.

As a general reader Dr. Coventry kept pace with the publications of the day, especially in his profession. And amid all the speculations, theories, and systems in medicine advanced in his time, he always reposed on the surer foundations of personal observation and practical experience. Most truly may it be said of him, that he was never the first to abandon an old remedy or plan of treatment to try the new, however sustained by high names and exalted by public applause. His uniform deportment towards his professional brethren, and to the sick committed to his care, obtained for him unrivaled esteem, affection and respect. His judgment was clear, deliberate, and peculiarly discriminating, and few ever fulfilled with more conscientious rectitude the various professional and relative duties and charities of life. Thus we have attempted a very brief outline of the character of our departed friend, not indeed sufficient, we confess, to show forth its true and striking features in all their strength and beauty. The means by which he attained his distinction, and sustained himself at the head of the medical profession in the western district of our State for thirty years, would naturally afford a subject for honest inquiry among the members of the medical profession. We have only to remark, that personal worth and professional merit were his only passports to honor and celebrity. No hireling flatterers or fawning sycophants ever sounded the note of praise in his behalf—no newspaper puffings or exclusive claims were urged in his favor to procure business, or advance his professional standing. His peculiar *forte* was to *retain* business rather than to acquire it. Would that the community generally understood and appreciated the true difference in these two opposite traits of the medical character.

The writer knew the subject of this obituary notice long and well ; perhaps no one knows better than he does, the high and refined sense which Dr. C. entertained of professional etiquette and medical ethics. And it is believed if all were to emulate his example, the unworthy would rarely be enabled to push themselves forward where men of modesty and worth would fear to tread.   J. M. C.

DR. ASA CROSBY was an uncommon man. At the age of 21 he commenced practice in Stafford Co., N. H., and continued in full practice forty-six years, *i. e.*, until the age of 67. He was a distinguished member of the profession, both in physic and surgery ; and in the latter branch he performed some very important and difficult operations. Indeed, for many years he was the principal operator for an extensive district of country. He was one of those self-taught men, whose force of intellect breaks through the most appalling obstacles, and rises unaided, to skill and reputation. Although deprived of a systematic course of professional instruction, having commenced practice before medical schools were established in New England, he furnished himself with a good library, and spent his leisure hours, and even moments, among his books. By his constant industry and exertions he raised himself to a position in the profession so important as to draw around him for some years a number of young men as pupils—between twenty and thirty of whom may be reckoned as educated by him; and what is much to his credit, many of them are now distinguished men.

The medical profession in New Hampshire is not a little indebted to Dr. Crosby, inasmuch as he was one of the few who interested themselves in procuring the charter of the State Medical Society, of which Institution, as well as of a District Society, he was an active and zealous member for thirty years.

This gentleman reared a large and worthy family. Of seventeen children *ten* remain. One of his sons established himself in the profession of the law; two have distinguished themselves as physicians; and another is a much valued professor of Latin and Greek in one of the New England colleges.

Dr. Crosby never brought reproach upon our profession by the avowal of infidel sentiments; so far from this, he was for many years a member of the Church of Christ, and died in the full hope of a better life.

He died at Hanover, N. H., on the 12th of April, 1836, at the age of 70, of rupture of the gall bladder.—*R. D. Mussey, M. D., in the Bost. Med. & Surg. Jour., Vol. 14.*

DR. EZEKIEL DODGE CUSHING. The destroying angel has slain another victim. Dr. Ezekiel Dodge Cushing died at Hanover, Massachusetts, on the 5th of April, 1828, at the age of 38, ere his arrival at the 'noon of life.' Inheriting from a healthy parentage a robust constitution, his early years gave promise of a long life. He was the son of the late Mr. Nathaniel Cushing of Pembroke, graduated at Harvard University in the year 1808, commenced the study of medicine with Dr. Nathan Smith, at Hanover, N. H., extended his medical education by attendance on the hospital and lectures at Philadelphia, and afterwards went to London, where he became a dresser in St. Thomas' Hospital, under Mr. Birch, and simultaneously attended on the lectures of Abernethy and Cooper and Haighton. From London he went to Paris, in the hospitals of which, while the allies occupied that city, he enjoyed the opportunity of witnessing an extensive surgical practice. His education had been practical, and he had acquired to an eminent degree the tact of the profession. He commenced the practice of medicine and surgery in Boston, and but for the surplus of skill beyond the public demand, his success had been brilliant; a great proportion of his cases, and severe cases too, terminated favorably. Some years back he had been in an epileptic state. Since his removal from Boston to Hanover, his practice in difficult cases extended even to towns quite distant. His opinions had given great satisfaction to both the attendant physician and patient. His last sickness, which terminated in a paralytic attack on the muscles of one side of the face and organ of speech, while traveling to visit a patient, was an atrophy connected with an entire prostration of the tone of the stomach. His sickness and death has shrouded in gloom his whole neighborhood. To his family his loss is irreparable. The odor of an honest fame is the only inheritance he has left to his wife and children. His wisdom had been for his neighborhood, and not for himself or family. His discretion had been discovered in good offices to the sick and suffering, and not in the ingathering harvest for his family. As Dr. Cushing cast his bread upon the waters, may his wife and children, after many days, under the blessing of the widow's God, and the father of the fatherless, gather it up.

Dr. Cushing joined the Massachusetts Medical Society in 1819, and died in 1828.—*Shattuck's Annual Dissertation before the Mass. Med. Society*, 1828.

Dr. Edward Cutbush was formerly a highly respected resident of the city of Washington. He was born in Philadelphia in the year 1772 ; he was a pupil of Dr. Benjamin Rush, and commenced his medi-

cal career in the Pennsylvania Hospital, in which he
was physician for seven years. The record of that
institution bespeaks his ability, assiduity and worth.
In the year 1794 he was Surgeon General in Washington's expedition against the insurgents of Pennsylvania. In 1799 he entered the navy as surgeon under Commodore Barry in the frigate United States,
and was chief surgeon of the fleet in the Mediterranean. While in that capacity the Doctor made an
extensive collection of specimens in the arts and
of antiquity. He rose to the head of the profession
in that service, and while discharging the duties of
his office in Washington in 1829, was suddenly ordered by the Secretary of the Navy to sea service, *on
board of a schooner*. The Doctor deeming this order
very derogatory to his pretensions, resigned his commission, after thirty years of faithful service. He
retired to Geneva, New York, where he was placed
in the Chemical chair in the college in that place, and
became Dean of the Medical Faculty therein. Dr.
Cutbush was emphatically an honest man in every
relation of life ; he was devoted to the improvement
of science, and while a resident at Washington was
among the foremost who began the movement that
has resulted in the establishment of a National Institute. He was a prudent and successful physician
and surgeon; his counsel was sought to the very
verge of his life, and he has died regretted and respected by all who knew him.—*J. G. S. in the National Intelligencer.*

Dr. Cutbush died at Geneva in the year 1843, aged

71 years. He was a distinguished writer, and his communications may be found in Coxe's Medical Museum, and several other of the medical periodicals of the day. He was an Honorary Member of the Philadelphia Medical and Chemical Society—of the Linnæan Society of Philadelphia—of the American Medical Society—Corresponding member of the New Orleans Medical Society—Member of the Medical Society of Ontario County, N. Y.—Corresponding member of the Yale Natural History Society—Member of the Natural History Society of Geneva College—Corresponding member of the National Institute at Washington for the promotion of science—elected in 1842—and formerly President of the Columbian Institute at Washington, revived by the National Institute.

DR. WILLIAM POTTS DEWEES. The following memoir of this distinguished physician is from the pen of his former associate in the Medical department of the University of Pennsylvania, Hugh L. Hodge, M. D., Professor of Obstetrics in that University. It was read before the Medical class in that school, Nov. 5th, 1842, and is slightly abridged by the Editor of the American Medical Journal. I can scarcely do justice to the subject, if I curtail a word of his observations.

Dr. William Potts Dewees, the late Professor of Midwifery in the University of Pennsylvania, was one of the most distinguished individuals that have

Wm. P. DEWEES, M.D.

W.C.Sharp's Lith.Boston.

ever graced the annals of our profession in this country; his name is indissolubly associated with the history of our science; he found it struggling in the weakness of infancy, and left it fully established in the strength and privileges of manhood.

Of the parentage and early life of our departed professor, little is known. His great-grandfather, and probably his grandfather, was among the emigrants from Sweden, the original settlers of Delaware Bay and river, and maintained for a series of years a respectable and influential character. His grandmother belonged to the family of Farmer, which appears to have been of Irish descent, their ancestors enjoying much wealth, part of which was invested in the purchase of immense tracts of land in this country. His mother was the daughter of Thomas Potts, a highly respectable English gentleman, whose family first settled and gave name to Pottsgrove (or Pottstown) on the river Schuylkill.

Dr. Dewees was born on the 5th of May, 1768, at Pottsgrove, and being early left fatherless, and with very little property, he had not the advantages of a collegiate education. It is difficult however—not to say impossible—to restrain genius even by the chains of poverty and neglect. Young Dewees improved all the means at his command, and must have made some proficiency in the languages, as his knowledge of Latin and French, in after life, was sufficient for all necessary purposes. He is represented by those best qualified to judge, as docile, industrious, very affectionate, and amiable.

16

He early determined to study medicine, and was for this purpose placed by his father in the establishment of a Dr. Phyle, practicing apothecary, as was very customary at that period, when the proper distinction between the business of the apothecary and of the physician had not been generally made.

Under the superintendence, for two or three years, of Dr. Phyle, he appears to have acquired his knowledge of pharmacy and its collateral sciences. Afterwards he placed himself in the office of Dr. William Smith, to prosecute more especially his professional studies. During his connection with Dr. Smith, and his residence in Philadelphia, in the year 1787, '8 and '9, he attended lectures in the University of Pennsylvania.

During the infancy of medical instruction in this country, the degree of Doctor in Medicine was seldom sought after, and in accordance therefore with the almost universal custom of the day, Dr. Dewees commenced the practice of his profession without receiving a regular diploma from his preceptors, in the summer of 1789. He was then twenty-one years of age, about the medium height, well proportioned, of a florid complexion, brown hair, rather slender make, and remarkably youthful in his appearance, so that great objections were frequently made to employing a physician apparently so young.

He commenced the arduous duties of our profession about fourteen miles north of Philadelphia, at the village of Abington, where he soon engrossed all the valuable practice, notwithstanding the objections made to his youth and inexperience, and the deficiencies of his education. His talents, united with great industry and perseverance, his affectionate and amiable disposition, secured the attachment, and very soon the confidence, of his patients. In this comparatively retired spot, thrown at an early age upon his own resources, with no means of securing patronage but his character and attainments, without pecuniary assistance, Dr. Dewees, by sedulous attention to business, by careful observation of physiological and pathological phenomena, laid the foundation of his future usefulness and celebrity. He would often in after life allude to observations made, or to treatment pursued, by him while a youth at Abington, confirmatory of his future theoretical and practical views. He was soon called to a more extensive field of usefulness.

At this important epoch in the medical history of our city and of the country, he found the confidence of the public was resting upon a Kuhn, a Shippan, a Rush, a Wistar, and a Griffitts. Dr. Rush soon ascertained the talents and abilities of Dewees, and threw his commanding influence in his favor. An intimacy also took place between Physick and Dewees, and as their course was different, the former professing Surgery and the latter Obstetrics, they assisted each other in prosecuting their respective plans for professional advancement.

Independently of any collateral assistance which Dr. Dewees might have received from the friendship of Dr. Rush, he enjoyed one of the finest opportunities that could be possibly presented for a medical man to rise to wealth and fame. At that period the science of Obstetrics was hardly known in America. The physicians who occasionally engaged in its practice had received no instruction, with the exception of a few, who, having visited Europe, brought home a general knowledge of the subject; but who, from prejudices existing against the employment of such practitioners, had few opportunities and fewer inducements to perfect their knowledge. Hence Midwifery existed almost universally as an art; the aged and imbecile nurse was almost universally preferred to the physician. Women were generally the practitioners of midwifery, as few imagined any particular instruction necessary for an attendance on labor; at least any beyond that derivable from prolonged experience. Our science, however, was too essentially connected with the lives and happiness of individuals and families to remain, for a long time, in such obscurity, when knowledge and science on other subjects were elevating the character and developing the resources of the community. As the arts and luxuries of life increased, the danger and difficulties of the parturient process increased also. Experience lamentably demonstrated that the attentions of the nurse, however experienced, were unavailing; yea, that the officious interference of ignorant practitioners in a process so wonderful and so abstruse as that of parturition, was too often productive of the most fatal consequences to the child and its mother, thus destroying the comfort and happiness of families. In such extremities, all notions of false delicacy are thrown to the winds; the cry for help arising from the emergencies of the case is imperative; but alas, who was prepared to respond to the cry? Who to render the necessary assistance? The physician, who, on such emergencies was called, was unprepared to afford relief; his former studies had been imperfect; his experience in midwifery trifling; his observations of severe cases very limited; and you may imagine the embarrassing and horrible condition in which such a practitioner must be placed, when a human being, and that a female in agony, supplicated for relief—when to him all eyes were turned—when on him rested every hope of a despairing husband, or a broken hearted mother, and he felt conscious that he ought to be able, but still could not afford the proper assistance. Such was the condition of our community some fifty years ago—such, we are sorry to affirm, is the state of many communities, in various portions of our country, at the present day—when often, very often, the cry for help bursts from the agonized bosom, and there is no suitable response from the instructed obstetrician.

The opportunity thus providentially occurring, was embraced by the subject of our address. He felt and realized his own deficiences, but was determined to overcome them. To attain the victory—to prepare himself for the elevated station to which he aspired—could only be effected by rendering himself equal to the emergency. He reviewed his observations made during four years at Abington, at the bedside of his patients,—he compared these results with the experience of others; he went still further— he commenced again an examination of the foundations of his science, the fundamental principles of Obstetrics; and on these he built his stable superstructure, which has and will last, to his own credit, and to the reputation of our school, our city, and our country. He made himself familiar with the then modern authorities—the Osbornes and Denmans of England; the Levrets and Baudelocques of France; and hence derived accurate notions of the science and practice of Midwifery.

His investigations, when compared with the results of his own experience, excited a partiality for French, in preference to English obstetrics. He chose Baudelocque for his teacher, and often declared that he was indebted to the most distinguished French obstetrician for all that he knew himself of midwifery. The disciple was worthy of his master.

Thus armed for the conflict with the ignorance and prejudice of the community—with the irregular, the uneducated, or the imperfectly educated practitioners of the art, he was ready for the emergencies that might occur. Such emergencies were not unfrequent; for, unfortunately, difficult cases of delivery were at that period the result not only of natural causes, but very frequently of the bad and officious practice of ignorant pretenders to the art, who made that labor difficult or laborious, which without their interference, would have been natural and comparatively easy. On such occasions Dewees was often consulted; and a large portion of operative midwifery fell into his hands. For him this was every way advantageous; his theoretical knowledge became practical—his dexterity in operating, as well as his tact in the difficult art of diagnosis, was perfected; his reputation was diffused through the community, and his practice, of course, became more extensive and profitable. In a short period, therefore, after his establishment in Philadelphia, under the conjoint influences. of the causes mentioned, but especially by his own worth and decision of character, his success was complete, and he felt that he might safely enlarge his responsibilities and assume new duties, while he added to his comfort and happiness.

About this period he married Miss Martha Rogers, daughter of Dr. Rogers of New England. Not many years after, this lady, still in the bloom of youth and beauty, became the sudden victim of an acute disease—to the destruction, for the time at least, of that domestic comfort and support to which her husband had aspired, and which is so needful for all, especially for a physician, whose mind and heart are so constantly engrossed with the sufferings of his fellow beings, and whose periods of relaxation are so rare and imperfect.

Dr. Dewees soon after this period conceived the idea of rendering himself useful, not only as a practitioner, but also as a teacher of Midwifery; the science and practice of Obstetrics being little understood in our country, for very few necessary attempts had been made to impart even a general knowledge of this most important subject. Dr. William Shippen, one of the founders of the University, has the enviable title of being the first teacher of Anatomy, of Surgery, and of Midwifery, in this country; his Professorship embracing these various subjects. So extensive were the duties incumbent on this Professor, so fundamentally important was the subject of Anatomy, and so urgent were the calls for instruction in the elements of Surgery, that Midwifery was necessarily almost wholly neglected in his course of instruction. A few general directions for the guidance of the practitioner, constituted nearly all the information imparted to the student at the close of the Professor's lectures.

As no one could realize more fully than Dr. Dewees the want of more extensive and efficient instruction on the subject of practical Midwifery, we find that he has the high honor of first attempting a full course of lectures on Obstetrics in America. In a small office he collected a few pupils, and in a familiar manner indoctrinated them with the principles of our science; toiling, year after year, in opposition to the prejudices, not only of the community, but even of the profession, who could not perceive that so much effort was necessary for the facilitating the natural process of parturition.

Thus favorably introduced to the citizens of Philadelphia as a practitioner, and to the professional public as a teacher of the science of Obstetrics, his practice became extensive, and his income greatly enlarged.

He again determined to seek the advantages and pleasures of domestic life, and in the year 1802 became united to his second wife, Miss Mary Lorrain, daughter of a respectable merchant in Philadelphia. In this connection he was greatly blessed; Mrs. Dewees was preserved in health and strength as the partner of his prosperity and adversity, enjoying with him the innumerable favors which Providence in the course of a long life had abundantly bestowed, and sharing with him those painful reverses that occurred in the latter periods of his life. By this marriage Dr. Dewees became the father of eight children, three daughters and five sons, most of whom survive him.

Thus successful in his public exertions, blessed in his domestic relations, the object of attention to a large circle of friends, with whom he reciprocated those social attentions to which the natural warmth of his feelings and the sincerity of his friendships constantly inclined him, Dr. Dewees pursued the steady course to a still more extensive reputation and usefulness.

The practice and science of Midwifery were daily gaining importance in the judgment of an enlightened community. Their immense value in preserving life, in ameliorating suffering, in preventing continued and destructive disease, were more and more recognized. The necessity, positive and imperious, of employing as practitioners only those who were

17

suitably indoctrinated, became acknowledged. The practice of allowing females to officiate was constantly diminishing; and the public attention became more steadily fixed upon a Dewees and a James as the proper representatives of Obstetric science, as those best calculated to give it practical efficiency. It soon became evident that Midwifery would be regarded in its proper light by the Trustees and Professors of the University of Pennsylvania; that the time could not be far distant when it would be detached from its efficient and subordinate connection with the anatomical chair, and be separately taught in this model school of American Medicine.

To be prepared for this event in every respect was now no easy task. Competition had already existed for several years with many distinguished individuals, especially with Dr. Thomas C. James, his cotemporary, and who, in addition to the possession of fine talents, an excellent education, great personal attractions and influence, was also a lecturer on the science of Obstetrics, having commenced his course of instruction with the late Dr. Church in 1801. New competitors were also appearing; and one, although young in the profession, a graduate of 1801, who had just returned from Europe, yet by the brilliancy of his talents, his popular address, and the influence of his former friends in Virginia, and his social connections in this city, obtained an influence as a practitioner, and soon as a teacher in Obstetrics, which threatened to distance all his rivals. I allude to the distinguished Dr. Chapman, Prof. of the Theory and

Pract. Med. in the University, who, on the death of Dr. Church, was associated as a lecturer on Obstetrics with Dr. James, in 1805.

Dr. Dewees immediately determined to strengthen his position in public estimation, by attending to the forms, as he had to the essentials, of the profession. He applied in the spring of 1806 to his Alma Mater for a diploma, that he might be fully entitled to the appellation of Doctor in Medicine, as he had for years been engrossed with the duties and responsibilities of the profession. On this occasion he wrote an elaborate *Thesis* on the means of moderating or relieving pain during the process of parturition, in which he assumed the broad ground that pain was an accidental or morbid symptom of labor—the result of artificial modes of living and treatment, to be moderated or destroyed by medical means. Whatever opinions may be entertained as to this general proposition, there is little discrepancy of sentiment as to the efficacy of the remedy chiefly relied upon by Dr. Dewees, which was copious blood-letting ; nor as to the fact that to him the profession, and through it, females universally are under the highest obligations for the introduction of this measure into efficient practice. The Professor of Anatomy, Dr. Shippen, declared that ' it marked an era in the history of Medicine,' and exclaimed, ' how much misery might I have prevented had I known it forty years ago.'

The anticipated crisis respecting the establishment of Midwifery as a distinct professorship, did not occur until the year 1810; so slow is the progress of truth, so difficult to illuminate the minds of men to their true interests.

For this elevation of Obstetrics to its legitimate station, we are much indebted to the late Professor of Anatomy, Dr. Caspar Wistar, who in January, 1809, soon after he succeeded Dr. Shippen as Professor of Anatomy and Midwifery, urged, in a written communication, the Trustees of the University to have Obstetrics separately taught in the school. Another year was suffered to elapse, and it was not till the 11th of April, 1810, that the resolution passed the Board, constituting Midwifery a distinct Professorship; even then, with the miserable provision that an attendance on its lectures should not be essential to graduation.

The struggle for the new Chair in the University was very warm, and the claims of opposing candidates, and the influence of their respective friends, rendered the event doubtful. The strong claims of Dr. Dewees, his talents, his industry, his attainments, —his dexterity, boldness, decision, and judgment, as a practitioner, his great success in the practice of the art, and as a teacher of its principles—his popularity, supported by the strongest testimonials from many distinguished men in the profession, including Rush and Physick, were met by analogous claims of opposing candidates, Dr. James and Dr. Chapman.

On the 29th of June, 1810, the decision was made by the election of Dr. Thomas C. James to the new Professorship, the first in this country. This disappointment to the long cherished hopes and expectations of Dr. Dewees was certainly great, but involved no loss of reputation, as the most ample testimony was borne as to his qualifications and character, and the public confidence in his skill was entirely unabated. It could only be said that his influence with the Board of Trustees proved to be weaker than that of his rivals.

Dr. Dewees, turning his attention from the teaching to the practice of Obstetrics, devoted himself with renewed energy and success to the active duties of his profession, occasionally allowing himself some relaxation in the pleasures arising from social intercourse, and also from indulging a natural taste for painting and music. For these arts he early manifested a decided inclination ; and although he never allowed himself time to study them in detail, yet for both he entertained the feelings and enthusiasm of an amateur, and was often refreshed by their agency amidst the anxieties of his self-denying and engrossing affection.

So devoted, however, was he to business, that his health, although it had been generally excellent, could not withstand the baneful influences arising from want of sleep, irregular hours, laborious occupation, and continued mental and moral excitement, to which every practitioner of medicine, especially an Obstetrician, is constantly exposed. His breast became delicate, and on several occasions he was threatened with hemorrhage from the lungs.

This dangerous indication of pulmonary affection,

conjoined with a tempting pecuniary investment, induced Dr. Dewees, in 1812, to resign his profession, with all its honors and tempting aspects, and to remove to Phillipsburgh, where he invested the proceeds of a life of toil and self-denial. Disappointment followed the speculation, and a few years sufficed to destroy the property Dr. Dewees had been years in accumulating. His health, however, improved, and all fears of pulmonary disease having vanished, he returned in the fall of the year 1817, to the scene of his former prosperity; again a poor man, as regarded pecuniary matters, with a large family dependent·on him entirely for support, but rich in reputation for talents, industry and success in his profession.

His immediate wants being supplied by the kindness of professional friends, he resumed his private course of instruction to medical students on Midwifery, and the practice of his profession. He soon became connected with Drs. Chapman and Horner in the Medical Institute of Philadelphia, founded originally by Dr. Chapman, about the year 1817, and to its success Dr. Dewees greatly contributed, from the period mentioned until 1832, when age, and other pressing circumstances, induced him to resign.

As a practitioner his success was again complete; his former patients welcomed his return; and his increased reputation, supported now by the observations and experience of a long course of active professional duty, soon enabled him to discharge his pecuniary obligations, and to furnish him with the comforts and luxuries of life.

He now resolved to record, for his own reputation, and for the great benefit of the public, the results of his experience and observations on the nature and treatment of diseases, and especially as regarded his favorite science of Obstetrics; thus obeying the good old fashioned and common sense rule, first to study—then to practice—and finally to teach and write; in opposition to the practice of very many who undertake to publish books before they have an opportunity of verifying their opinions by their practice.

The first publication was a second edition of his inaugural essay. The subsequent experience of practitioners has abundantly corroborated the advice of Dr. Dewees urged in the essay as to the advantages of free bleeding in cases of rigidity; advantages not only of a positive character in favor of relaxation, lessening pain, and hastening the process of parturition, but also of a negative character, perhaps still more valuable in preventing a vast amount of suffering, mental agitation, disease, and also of death. Would that his precepts were still more extensively studied, and more frequently acted on. Would that many, eminent in the profession, would sit at the feet of this Gamaliel, this teacher in medicine, and imbibe some fundamental notions of the importance of medical, and the dangers of surgical, measures in cases of tension and rigidity of the soft parts during the process of labor. We should then, no doubt, hear less of some of the terrible cases in Midwifery than at present.

After this, Dr. Dewees collected his scattered essays, which had been occasionally published in periodicals of the day, and re-published them in a distinct volume. This was in 1823. The character of these essays is generally practical ; indeed, all have a bearing on the opinions and duties of a practitioner, although some are of a theoretical and controversial character. In all of them we find displayed the great good sense, clearness and precision of their author, who seems to improve every subject he touches, and to carry forward the principles and teaching of his predecessors to a still greater degree of perfection. These observations are made, not with any design of endorsing all the opinions of Dr. Dewees—for this cannot be done, as no doubt many of them are untenable, especially those which are merely speculative, and those which are connected with the very imperfect physiology of the day ; but with the important object of characterizing the writings of an individual who has accomplished more for Obstetrics than any man in our country, and who has elevated himself, by the character of his publications, to a station of high authority in the profession. He is our representative to other nations on the science of Obstetrics, and as such is continually quoted by European authorities, such a Ramsbotham, Rigby, Clark, &c., in our profession. This is high distinction, and the more worthy of admiration as attained by mere force of chaacter—by talent, industry, and sedulous attention to business without any assistance from education, wealth, or other accidental influences.

By his essays Dr. Dewees has done much in ameliorating suffering and prolonging life, by inculcating good principles, and insisting on a better practice. For example, in one paper he ably sustains the important idea that labor in the human species, and especially in the upper walks of life, ought not to be so exceedingly painful as it is usually observed ; and that by proper attentions, even under all the disadvantageous influences of civilized life, suffering may be materially lessened.

He also ably and successfully notices Dr. Denman's celebrated aphorisms for the use of the forceps, demonstrating their inconsistency and their dangerous tendencies, especially by restricting too much the use of those invaluable instruments.

He has introduced very advantageously into practice, the more extensive and precise use of the ammoniated tincture of guaiacum in the treatment of some of the varieties of dysmenorrhœa and amenorrhœa. His observations on puerperal convulsions, and particularly on the essential importance in these horrible cases of the free use of the lancet, are invaluable. To him we are indebted for the full establishment of a decided practice in such cases—a practice so efficient, that puerperal convulsions are no longer one of the *opprobria medicorum ;* a death now being about as rare an event as a recovery was formerly.

The views of uterine hemorrhage, of retroversion and inversion of the uterus, and the criticisms upon the

18

directions given by some high authorities upon Obstetrics, are almost equally important, and would alone constitute a most powerful claim to the gratitude of all those interested in the health and lives of females.

After the publication of these essays, Dr. Dewees commenced the preparation of a series of systematic works upon which, after all, his reputation must eventually depend. The reputation acquired by any one as a practitioner of medicine, as a successful teacher or lecturer, is, after all, ephemeral. It lives at the utmost only during the lives of the recipients of favors thus conferred. The wave of another generation carries the names thus acquired, to a silent oblivion. He who would live in the memories and hearts of men; or rather, he who would be useful after his body has been decomposed in the grave, must record results of a life of observation and labor.

The first systematic work of Dr. Dewees is probably his best, upon which he bestowed most thought and labor, viz: his 'System of Midwifery for the use of Students and Practitioners.' Few or no publications had been made on this subject in America, and few of the foreign works circulated to any extent. Dr. Dewees was among the first to diminish this evil by republishing in 1807, Heath's translation of Baudelocque; Dr. Chapman in 1810 published an edition of Mr. Burns' (of Glasgow) Principles of Midwifery; and Dr. Bard, of New York, the President of the College of Physicians and Surgeons, about the same time issued a Compendium of the Theory and Practice of Midwifery, designed rather to diffuse among ignorant midwives and practitioners, a knowledge of the rules for practice, as laid down by the best European authorities, rather than make any attempt to enlarge the boundaries of science. At this juncture Dr. D.s' book opportunely appeared—the first regular systematic work of which our country could boast, although to Dr. Bard the credit belongs of being the first to instruct upon a large scale the physicians of our country in the art of Midwifery.

To an American, therefore, the appearance of Dewees' book on Midwifery is an important epoch in the history of our science, as being the first regular attempt to think for ourselves on Tokology, and to contribute to the onward progress of this important division of medical science. It is more important from the intrinsic value of the work, which, with all its deficiencies, probably constitutes now, at the expiration of twenty years from its original publication, the best practical book in our profession, a book which every one of you as Obstetricians, and especially as American Obstetricians, should undoubtedly obtain, and carefully study. It is founded on the French system of Obstetrics, especially on that of Baudelocque. It takes a stand in advance of Denman, Osborne, Burns, and other English authorities in general use in our country at that period, and even of Baudelocque himself, in throwing aside from his excellent system much that was useless, and, it may be said, imaginative.

That the work is not perfect, is to say that it is a human production ; that it is not embellished by fine writing, and that occasionally it is diffuse, indefinite, and illogical, is the misfortune, not the fault, of the author. On the contrary, these very few defects show the obstacles he had to overcome, and contribute to indicate more fully the talent, the good sense, the great industry and the practical efficiency of our great *American Baudelocque*, whose name is inscribed upon the roll of fame, as one of the first of Obstetric authorities—our representative in the great republic of science on the subject of Obstetrics. Nine editions of the System of Midwifery have appeared, and no doubt a long period will elapse before subsequent authorities will be preferred to one now so eminent at home and abroad.

Having contributed so much for the welfare of mothers, by his work on Midwifery, he has contributed greatly to the suitable management of infants by his most systematic work, " A Treatise on the Physical and Medical Treatment of Children," published in 1825, and which has now passed through seven editions.

As its predecessor, this work is in advance of the doctrines and practice of the day; and for all practical purposes, irrespective of certain pathological views, and scientific details, may still be regarded as unrivalled, notwithstanding the numerous publications on the management of infants and children with which the press has been loaded. To him we are indebted simply for fixing attention on the physical management of children, independently of the high value of the directions; for prior to this period, the profession in this country left the details almost exclusively in the hands of nurses and midwives, with all their tormenting ignorance and officiousness.

In 1826, only one year after the publication of the work on children, appeared an elaborate volume, ' A Treatise on the Diseases of Females,' another standard work in our medical literature. Such a publication was much wanted, and was readily received by the community, as well as by the profession, as high authority. It circulated, as well as its predecessor, very rapidly in every part of our land ; and it became, what it still is, the book for reference in all questions of practice, on the important, delicate, and difficult subjects which it embraces.

On the subject of prolapsus and retroversion of the uterus, it may be remarked, that to no one individual are females so much indebted in our country, as to Dr. Dewees, for fixing professional attention on the prevalence of these complaints, their importance, their distressing character, their proper treatment by means of pessaries, and especially for his improvement in the form of these instruments, and the materials of which they are composed ; recommending the glass or metallic instruments in preference to the perishing materials previously employed, and which from this cause chiefly, were the source of so much irritation as to bring these invaluable assistants into great disrepute.

The last of the systematic works issued by our professor was on the Practice of Medicine, in the year 1830. Encouraged by the success of his for-

mer appeals to the public, as well as professional
attention, and anxious that those individuals who
were remote from medical advice on the frontiers of
our country should have some means at command to
assist in the management of their complaints, Dr.
Dewees was induced to prepare a digest of his experience on the various diseases of the human system, with a view to popular as well as professional
patronage. He in part succeeded, as no one can
deny the excellency of the practice usually inculcated
by Dr. Dewees. Still the book has no pretensions to
a scientific arrangement or treatment of diseases ;
and being prepared hastily, and with reference to
popular use, does not partake largely of the confidence of the profession.

While thus much engaged, during a period of
more than seven years, in making large and valuable
additions to our medical literature, the attention of
Dr. Dewees was in no degree diverted from his
practice. How he accomplished so much is wonderful ; how a man engaged night and day in the general practice of his profession, and especially in the
harassing duty of Obstetrics, could so rapidly and
efficiently labor with his pen, can only be explained
by allowing him a happy combination of physical as
well as mental powers ; as rare as it is desirable.
His mind, indeed, never seemed to be fatigued ;
always on the alert, it would, even after great physical exertion, after the loss of rest and sleep, revert
from one object of thought and anxiety to another,
and at any moment be directed from the anxious

contemplation of a dangerous case of disease or of labor, to the quiet but engrossing business of an author, with its memory, acuteness, judgment, and every other faculty, ready for active exercise.

And the explanation is, that Dr. Dewees well knew the value of moments of time, and could well improve them. He never suffered them to be lost, and could, as he often affirmed, carry on a train of thought or an argument for a few moments, and then after hours of interruption resume the current of his thoughts, and immediately prosecute his writing.

During this portion of the life of Dr. Dewees, various changes by death and otherwise had occurred in the University of Pennsylvania, to which we need not allude at this time, excepting to state, that the health of Dr. Thomas C. James, the Professor of Midwifery, had visibly declined, so that he stood in need of assistance in carrying on the course of lectures. This had been partially rendered as regarded the anatomical portion of the lectures, for some years, by Dr. Homer; but in 1825 it was resolved by the trustees, at the request of Dr. James, that an adjunct should be appointed to the chair, and on the 15th of November, 1825, Dr. Dewees was unanimously elected to this station, during the existence of the then incumbent.

Dr. Dewees, on his entrance into the University, was fifty-seven years of age, in full possession of his mental and corporeal faculties. His figure had spread considerably, so that he could be termed portly; while he maintained a comparatively youthful appearance, from his florid complexion and brown hair, still without the silvery gloss of age. The duties of the professorship gradually devolved more and more upon him as Dr. James declined in health, and were discharged in a manner very acceptable to the students. Of course there was no great display of eloquence or erudition in his lectures, but he was always clear, decided, precise, and minute in his directions, speaking in rather a conversational style, with the promptitude and confidence of a man who had formed his own opinions by his own observations, and illustrating all that he taught by a rich fund of cases and anecdotes, drawn, in a great measure, from what he had himself witnessed. Such a teacher could not be otherwise than interesting, and, from the whole character of his mind, with its endowments natural and acquired, you may readily conclude he must have been exceedingly valuable. His popularity was great, and his usefulness became thus greatly extended; his pupils distributing his fame, as well as his valuable instructions, through the extent of our country.

For several successive years, Dr. Dewees reaped, in every way, the harvest resulting from his long and persevering efforts in the cause of medical and obstetric science. His income from his practice, his books and his professorship, was ample for his present and prospective wants; he was admired, beloved, and trusted in the community in which he moved; he enjoyed an enviable reputation in America and Europe, and was continually receiving testimonials in various ways, of the estimation in which his character and works were held. He had been for a long series of years a member of the American Philosophical Society, and was continually receiving certificates or diplomas from medical and other scientific bodies in the United States, in the Canadas, and in Europe, with the gratifying intelligence that they considered themselves honored by adding his name to the list of their members; while private letters from distinguished physicians confirmed, and rendered still more gratifying, these public manifestations of regard and confidence. In the domestic and social circles, his prosperity was equally great, and his warm heart was continually engaged, as far as more important business would permit, in reciprocating convivial enjoyments with his friends and fellow laborers, within and without the profession; while, notwithstanding the lapse of years, his health and strength continued vigorous and active.

These blessings were continued without interruption until February, 1834, when a comparatively trivial accident, a sprain of his ankle, became the turning point of his prosperity—the commencement of a series of trials which continued to the close of life. Owing, probably, to the confinement to the house, in consequence of this accident, his system became gradually plethoric, and he suffered from the want of his accustomed enjoyment of air and exercise. In the month of April he suddenly became apoplectic, but owing to the timely assistance of his friends Drs. Hays and Chapman, the dangerous

19

symptoms were arrested, but his corporeal faculties were decidedly impaired. Cessation from business, traveling, and recreation, were so far successful, that in the fall of 1834 he was able to return to his practice, and received from the trustees of the University the unanimous appointment of Professor of Midwifery ; Dr. James, from his great infirmities, having resigned this office, which he had the honor to occupy for 24 years.

With some of his former vivacity, Dr. Dewees was enabled to discharge the duties of his professorship during the ensuing winter. The exertion was, however, too great. In the spring his health was more impaired, and, notwithstanding every exertion from his medical friends, and the influence of air and travel, the autumn of 1835 found him weakened in mind and body. He made an attempt to deliver the winter course of lectures, but it was apparent to himself, as well as to others, that it was altogether futile, and on the 10th of November he resigned his Professorship in the University of Pennsylvania.

This mournful event, to his colleagues, to the students assembled to recieve the results of his long tried observations, to the University, and to the public, was not suffered to pass unnoticed. Flattering resolutions, expressive at the same time of their sympathy and regret, were passed respectively by the board of trustees, by the medical faculty, and by the assembled students. The latter were characterized by the warmth of feeling so interesting in young men ; by the expression of their high respect and confidence in his talents and attainments, in his honor and rectitude of purpose ; of their gratitude for the favors received at his hands, and especially for the invaluable services he had rendered them and the medical public by his lectures and his works, his oral and written instructions. Anxious to honor their afflicted teacher, to bear testimony to the sincerity of their declarations, and, at the same time, to evince to posterity the gratitude and affection which his talents, industry and virtue had excited in his pupils, they resolved to present to the retiring Professor a magnificent silver vase, with the following inscription :

' PRESENTED TO WILLIAM P. DEWEES, M. D., late PROFESSOR in the UNIVERSITY of PENNSYLVANIA, by the MEDICAL CLASS OF THAT INSTITUTION, as a testimonial of their respect for his exalted worth and talents. Philadelphia, Nov., 1835. *Sempe honos, nomenque tuum, laudesque manebunt.*'

Thursday, the 25th November, 1835, was the day appointed to make the presentation. The scene was most interesting, and could never be forgotten by those who were witnesses and actors on the mournful occasion. To behold this room, the arena of his former efforts to instruct and edify, crowded to excess by physicians and students, anxious to pay their last respects to one so respected and beloved—to behold the venerable professor, famous in both worlds, for his contributions for the alleviation of human misery, himself the sufferer, unable to sustain himself without assistance, seated in the centre of that beloved circle of students, to whom he was anxious to impart instruction, but to whom he was about to bid a long, a last farewell—to witness the great man, the bold, decided, energetic practitioner, bowed down under the influence of physical feeling, and the overpowering moral sentiments by which his bosom was agitated—to hear the chosen representatives of affectionate pupils proclaim his talents, his virtues, his attainments, and to testify by words and actions their gratitude and affection—to discover that the deserved recipient of all these attentions was so overwhelmed by conflicting feelings, by the remembrance of the past, the solemnities of the present, and the prospects of the future, that words failed to express his gratitude,—that another individual, his long tried friend and colleague, Dr. Chapman, had to pour forth the acknowledgment of his grateful heart, for such sincere and lasting testimonials from his beloved disciples—all constituted a scene so impressive that the voice of eloquence alone could do it justice. It was a scene for the painter, or for the poet. It was one of those delightful manifestations of the best feelings of the human soul, rarely, it is true, to be witnessed, but the more impressive for its rarity in this world, where selfish feelings too generally predominate, and stifle the warm aspirations of a generous and noble nature.

This hour may be considered the last of the professional life of Dr. William P. Dewees. He retired from the scene of his labors to embark for Havana, in the Island of Cuba, in search of health and strength. The experiment was not wholly in vain.

He recovered sufficiently to attend to some of the lighter duties of a practitioner in medicine, which he discharged chiefly at Mobile, in Alabama, where he spent most of the time for more than four years, receiving marks of confidence and attention from his professional brethren of the south—most of them his professional pupils.

In 1840 he left Mobile for Philadelphia, where he arrived, after spending some months in New Orleans, on the 22nd of May, 1840, but he was an altered man ; his physical frame had dwindled away under the influence of disease, and although his mind retained much of its original acuteness, he appeared as the representative of the past, rather than a member of the present, generation.

Our cold weather proved unfavorable to his strength and health, causing congestion of his vital organs, and producing so much distress and suffering that he was anxious to be released from a world in which he felt that he had finished his work. Such, however, was the strength of his constitution, that this solemn event did not occur until the 20th of May, 1841, when his anxious spirit was released from its earthly and suffering tabernacle.

On the news of his death a special meeting was called by the Philadelphia Medical Society, and resolutions passed expressive of their deep regret at the decease of their fellow member and late Vice President—of their high sense of the beneficial influences exerted by his talents, attainments, and professional character—and their desire that I should prepare a memoir of their late admired Professor.

His funeral was attended on the 22nd of May, exactly one year after his return to Philadelphia, by his former colleagues, the Professors in the University, by the members of the Medical Society, by the physicians and students then resident in the city, as well as by many of his former friends and patients who were anxious to pay their respects to the memory of their friend and physician. ' *Sic transit gloria mundi.*'

DR. AARON DEXTER was son of Richard Dexter, and was born in Malden, Massachusetts, in Nov. 1750. He graduated at Harvard College in 1776. For many years he was a highly reputable physician in Boston. He was a Professor of Chemistry in the same college for a series of years.

Dr. Dexter studied the profession of medicine with the late Dr. Samuel Danforth of Boston. At the close of his pupilage he established himself as a physician in Boston towards the close of the revolutionary war. Previous to this, however, he made several voyages to Europe as a medical officer. In one of these voyages he was taken prisoner by the British.

He was elected Erving Professor of Chemistry and Materia Medica in the medical department of Harvard College in 1783. He sustained the arduous and responsible duties of this office until the year 1816, when the late celebrated and lamented Dr. John Gorham was elected Professor *emeritus.* He retained this office until the time of his death, which occurred at Cambridge, rather from the effects of old age than from any apparent disease, on the 28th of February, 1829, at the age of 79.

Dr. Dexter was remarkable for his urbanity and kindness, and was universally respected as a physician and as a citizen. A dissertation on the use of blisters in diseases of the articulations, which was read before the Medical Society in 1809, and published in the second volume of their communications, affords practical evidence of his knowledge of the profession, and his desire to contribute to its usefulness. ' His successful efforts during a long and active life to establish and maintain the literary and charitable institutions of his country, furnish a claim of no ordinary character to the grateful remembrance of his fellow citizens.' *Alden, Family Records, Christian Register.*

DR. GEORGE BARTLETT DOANE. The following notice of this distinguished physician is from the New England Quarterly Journal of Medicine and Surgery for April, 1843. It was written by a friend, Dr. G. C. Shattuck, of Boston, with a request that it might be inserted in that Journal.

George Bartlett Doane, M. D., the subject of this notice, was born in Boston, in the year of our Lord 1793. The family from which he descended had been merchants for several generations. His grandfather, Elisha Doane, of Wellfleet, had accumulated a large fortune in commerce and the fisheries, hav-

ing early entered into the whale fishery. Col. Elisha Doane amassed in that spot 120,000 pounds
sterling.   Thomas Boylston, of Boston, whose be-
quest to his native town secured his name to the
public school-house on Fort Hill, and to the school
for young children at the House of Industry, and
Elisha Doane of Wellfleet, were estimated by their
fellow citizens the two richest men in the province
of Massachusetts Bay.   Isaiah Doane, the eldest son
of Elisha, and the father of George, was educated at
Harvard University, where he received his degree in
1774.   He became a merchant, settled in Boston,
married Hannah Bartlett, of Plymouth, a direct de-
scendant from the Pilgrims, and carried on business
largely as a shipping merchant, until British cruisers
at the commencement of the French revolution swept
his ships from the ocean.   A numerous family of children was the fruit of this marriage, viz., five sons
and five daughters.   George was the youngest of
the sons.   The loss of fortune, followed by the loss
of health, and that again by early death on the
part of the father, imposed on the widowed mother
a care that calls into exercise all the active virtues
so characteristic of the pilgrim race.   The mother,
by example and precept, taught her children self-
denial and activity.   She gathered up the fragments,
put her diminished fortune at nurse, retired to the
country in the neighborhood of a good school, and
there instructed her children in the lessons of practical wisdom.   The widow's God and the father to
the fatherless blessed her bereaved household.   The

unshrinking fortitude of the mother was not unobserved by our young school-boy. He strove by diligence to recommend himself to his beloved parent. In 1808, at fifteen, he was admitted into Harvard University. In the year 1812, at 19, he graduated a reputable scholar, in a class that now reflects honor on its Alma Mater. The severe mental labors of the mother in training unaided her numerous children, had impaired her health. The hope of contributing to the reinstatement of the health of his beloved mother, decided the young graduate in the choice of a profession. In the autumn of 1812 he accordingly entered on the study of medicine, resolved to study as a science what might contribute to gratify his ruling passion, filial piety, which sought the renovation of his mother's decayed strength. Although a succession of paralytic shocks experienced by the mother, interrupted his original purpose of becoming the instrument of her cure, still he untiringly devoted himself to the study of the elements of medicine, and never lost the opportunity to do good at the bedside of the sick. Anatomy and morbid anatomy he studied with unwearied assiduity. His pupilage was filled up with self-denial and continued painful toil. He never flinched from duty while the cry of suffering was heard. Nights has he kept vigil at the bedside of the poor, who had submitted to painful and perilous surgical operations, while the curative process was commencing. The lack of nursing among the sick poor always imposes heavy labor on the physician and the faithful student.

So decided had been his character as a faithful medical student and upright man, that one of the best educated physicians of his times, detailed on duty as a regimental surgeon to the militia detached for duty at South Boston, during an early period in the last war with Great Britain, selected and recommended him for a companion as his assistant surgeon. This tour of duty, though short, was faithfully performed by the young pupil. The officers of the regiment esteemed him as a gentleman and scholar, while the soldiers loved him as a skillful physician and kind friend. The odor of his good name reached the capital, and at the close of the year 1814, while yet in his pupilage, he received a commission as an assistant surgeon in the United States navy. In the spring of 1815 he was ordered to repair to the city of New York and report himself to Commodore Jones, who sent him on board the Macedonian, bound to the Mediterranean. On the voyage he writes, ' Never was life so divested of all rational comfort as this.' After a few days he writes again, ' I read, write, and think as well in any situation, although the apartment I occupy is so far below the surface of the sea, that the rays of the sun never penetrate, thereby being entirely shut out from the light of heaven.'

July 2nd, 1815, he arrived at Gibralter, where he was appointed acting surgeon on board the Constellation until her arrival at Port Mahon. This was the naval station for the American fleet, where a Hospital was founded for the sick, to which Dr. M.

Reynolds had been appointed as the surgeon, and
Dr. Doane as the assistant surgeon. Dr. M. Reynolds had sailed, leaving to Dr. Doane the entire
charge of the establishment for several months. On
the return of Dr. M. Reynolds, Dr. Doane writes
in his journal, ' I have been more than three months
entirely alone, the only responsible person here, and
burdened with every thing, attending personally to
every article of provision, medicine, clothing, pur-
chasing and expending, paying all bills, examining
all accounts, and at the expiration of every month,
making a settlement of every thing, and having also
by night and day the constant care of the sick to
prescribe, and give all the medicine with my own
hand ; yet, from habitual method, there is no confusion, no irregularity. This is a situation which
calls forth and holds in exercise all the energies of
my mind. I have also become engaged in quite an
extensive practice among the poor, and as I attend
them all gratis, between thirty and forty children are
brought to me daily. They express much gratitude,
and it is impossible to attend on the poor and sick
without feeling for them the sincerest compassion.
Here the poor never beg, except of God, and of
him for patience only.' While on the tour of duty
in the Mediterranean, small pox broke out in the
fleet, the cases of which were committed to the
treatment of Dr. Doane on board the frigate United
States, which was selected for quarantine. The sick
were sent to the island of Minorca in this vessel.
He thus describes in his journal his situation : ' I

have learnt to accommodate myself to disappointment
and privation, have entirely discarded from my
thoughts all pleasure, and am now influenced by motives of improvement only.' He proceeds: 'I have
now been in quarantine twenty-one days, with thirty-
eight men and one midshipman sick of small pox;
many of them have had the disease to a most dreadful degree. I have had the good fortune to lose
but three cases. On this island it is fatal to a most
desolating extent. I have seen death and disease in
all their varied forms, but never did I conceive of
any thing so loathsome and disgusting. All disease
here seems nothing compared to it; and as Burke
says, ' all the horrors of sickness before known or
heard of, seem mercy to this noxious havoc.' He
subsequently writes, ' The sick nearly all recovered,
and the term of quarantine has nearly expired. Yet,
although confined to this small island, I am contented
and happy, and find constant occupation with my
sick and my studies.' When Commodore Decatur,
off Cape De Gatt, had crippled and conquered the
Algerine fleet, Dr. Doane was ordered on board the
Meeshanda, the flag ship of the enemy, to take charge
of the wounded. Here his sympathies were well
tried. The barbarous custom of inflicting corporeal
punishment on criminals by the mutilation of their
limbs, had awakened among the Algerines a horror
of surgical operations, as badges of disgrace. These
brave warriors preferred death to dishonor. Dr.
Doane had much to encounter from this prejudice,
as those whose mutilated limbs had been amputated

reluctantly endured the dressings essential to the cure. With the zeal of an apostle he besought their patient endurance of the necessary treatment, and succeeded in disabusing their minds of their unnatural prejudices.

When his kindness and skill had won them back to the love of life, their gratitude was unbounded. They besought him to accompany them to Algiers, where they promised him a life of ease, the great boon of existence in warm climates. Exemption from the necessity to labor, all men covet. In the low latitudes it is the *summum bonum* of human bliss. When the Dey of Algiers had ratified his treaty of peace between the Regency and the United States, dictated at the cannon's mouth by Commodore Decatur, the Algerine fleet was restored. Dr. Doane was then ordered to Carthagena, where he remained until the arrival of the United States ship of the line Independence and her squadron, when he accompanied them in their cruise to Leghorn and Pisa. At the latter place he mentions a valuable Medical Garden, with the following singular inscription on the gate at its entrance : ' Enter with the eyes of Argus, but not with the hands of Briareus.' The diligence, skill, and urbane manners of Dr. Doane had won for him the love and confidence of all observers. He had acquired a competent knowledge of the French, Spanish and Italian languages, to profit by the new scenes to which he had been introduced. His previous classical education had imbued his mind with a curiosity to see what had been said and sung by the

historians and poets of Rome and Greece. His letters and his journal contain graphic descriptions of
the interesting objects, both of nature and art, abounding in those countries, exhibiting great enthusiasm in
the admiration of the sublime and beautiful. He returned from the Mediterranean in 1819, when he resigned his commission. His brother officers under
whose command he had sailed, bear testimony to his
character in the following language : ' Dr. Doane
has been distinguished by his zeal, attention to the duties of his profession, and gentlemanly deportment.'
This is an extract of a letter of Capt. W. M. Crane
to the Secretary of the Navy, recommending him for
promotion as a Surgeon. In another letter he writes,
' his skill, his correct gentlemanly deportment, secured him the respect and regard of his brother officers. He was several months the acting surgeon of
the Naval Hospital at Port Mahon, in Minorca, and
gave great satisfaction in the discharge of his duties.'
This letter is dated Gosport, Oct. 6th, 1820. Capt.
John Shaw writes of him, the letter dated U. States
Ship Independence, Charlestown, Sept. 27th, 1820 :
' His skill, kindness and humanity were manifested in
the arduous duties of an assistant Hospital Surgeon
on a foreign station. The police and general good
condition of the men under his charge, reflected credit on his exertions, and draws from me the expression
of my high approbation of his official character and
service while under my command.' In 1820, Dr.
Doane submitted to an examination for a degree
as Doctor of Medicine, after which he commenced

a practice in Boston, his native city. His well
known good character had secured him the respect
and good wishes of several among the eminent physicians of the town, as shown in a written recommendation, at the head of which stands the name of Samuel
Danforth, the patriarch of the Faculty in Boston at
that time. Dr. Doane was recommended to his neighbors and fellow citizens as a practitioner of medicine
and surgery, and his humanity and skill while in the
navy well declared the origin of the recommendation.
The following is the concluding sentence in the recommendation: ' Diligence, decorum and integrity
have uniformily characterized his manners and habits.'

With such preparation and recommendation, Dr.
Doane did not wait long for opportunity to signalize
himself. Two cases of gun-shot wounds fell under
his treatment, both very severe, but were successfully
treated by the young aspirant after literary fame.
In one case, a young man had attempted suicide by
the discharge of a pistol under his chin, the contents
of which passed up through the roof of his mouth
and shattered the bones of the nose, as they had
passed through that organ. In the other case the
accidental discharge of a rifle had thrown a bullet
into the head through the external angle of the eye,
without leaving any trace of its direction or lodge-
ment. The fortunate treatment of both cases secured the young surgeon reputation for skill in the several neighborhoods of their residence. Still, as the
general surgery of Boston had been engrossed by his
seniors, strong in the confidence of the community,

Dr. Doane turned his attention to a miscellaneous practice, in which he soon gained the confidence of the people. On the 12th of Feb. 1821, Dr. Doane was unanimously elected physician to the Boston Asylum for Indigent Boys. A further expression of the confidence of the community in Dr. Doane's professional character may be found in the records of the Trustees of the Massachusetts General Hospital, by whom he was unanimously chosen one of its consulting surgeons in Feb. 1837. Such were the delicacy of his manners and devotion to his cases, that he early acquired a large Obstetrical practice, and practice among children. More than three thousand cases of Midwifery are recorded on his books, between the commencement of his practice in 1820, and his death in 1842, which is an average of over one hundred and thirty-five per annum through the entire term. During seven years are recorded one thousand and seventy cases, which makes an annual average of more than one hundred and fifty-two cases. During his last three years of practice, more than six hundred cases are on record, which equals nearly four per week. The extent of his other practice taken into the account, it is a large practice in Midwifery, although exceeded by the practice of some of his contemporaries during their most palmy days.

Dr. Doane was never married. His philanthropy was therefore more diffusive than otherwise it might have been. His sisters shared largely in their brother's affections, and participated freely in the fruits of his prosperity. The poor, particularly the sick poor, found in him a friend. His time, his labor and his money, were freely employed in the efforts to alleviate the condition of suffering humanity. His benevolence knew no limits in the effort to aid rising merit, and its onward struggles. So general had been his kindness to all within his reach, that he was universally hailed as a benefactor and philanthropist by his contemporaries. His generous labors literally wore him out and broke him down. He visited patients on the very day preceding the night of his death. It is supposed that an affection of the heart, aggravated by unremitting professional toil, might have caused his sudden death. In a paroxysm of dyspnœa, he had but just time to alarm a beloved sister, in whose arms he quietly breathed out his life. Medical aid had been summoned, but in vain.

Dr. John Eberle, late Professor of the Theory and Practice of Physic, in the Ohio Medical College, and in Jefferson Medical College. The following notice of him, is from the graphic pen of Professor John W. Francis of New York.

John Eberle, M. D. and P. He was born in Hagerstown, Maryland, on the 10th of December, 1787 ; studied the profession of medicine under Dr. Carpenter of Lancaster, and Dr. Clapp, senior, of Philadelphia, and graduated Doctor of Medicine at the University of Pennsylvania in 1809. The subject of his inaugural discourse was Animal Heat. He

21

entered upon the practice of his art, first in Man-
heim, Lancaster county, when, after a few years
he removed to Lancaster city, where, after a short
time, he accepted of a commission as Surgeon to
the Lancaster Militia, and was at the battle at Baltimore in 1814. Soon after this occurrence he removed to Philadelphia, where he received an appointment as Physician of the city for the ' out door poor.'

In 1815 he began in Philadelphia his career as a
public writer, as editor of the Medical Recorder, and
was afterwards associated with Dr. Ducachet in the
continued publication of that periodical Journal.
The year after, the Linnæan Society of that city elected him a member of their body, and in 1822 the
Berlin Medico-Chirurgical Society enrolled his name
in their list of foreign members. In 1825 he was
chosen a member of the Academy of Natural Sciences of the same city.

He was active in promoting the interests of the
Jefferson Medical College, and may be considered
one of its most efficient founders. In this Institution
he was appointed the Professor of the Practice of
Physic in 1825, and in 1830 he was transferred to the
chair of Materia Medica in the same College. He
also lectured on Obstetrics. In the fall of 1831 he
removed with his family to Cincinnati, and was selected as the Professor of Materia Medica in the Ohio
Medical College. In the changes which necessarily
occurred on this occasion, he was called upon to resume the branch he had formerly taught in Jefferson
College, and the practice of medicine again came

within the immediate duty of his professional chair. He continued to discharge this responsible trust until 1837, when he was induced, from many circumstances, once more to change the scene of his labors, and he removed to Lexington, Kentucky. The Professorship of the Practice of Medicine was now tendered to him in the medical department of Transylvania University. He died at Lexington on the second of February, 1838, aged fifty years, one month, and sixteen days.

Besides his literary labors with the Medical Recorder, he is the author of several distinct Treatises, which will long render his name familiar to the medical student. In 1823 he published the first edition of his admirable work on Therapeutics and Materia Medica, in two volumes, octavo, a performance of great merit, and in which he has philosophically considered the nature of remedial agents on the disorders of the human constitution. In this treatise he has also greatly added to the knowledge we previously possessed of the American vegetable kingdom, as derived from the works of Schoef, Barton, and Thacher. This work has already had an extensive sale, and reached a fifth edition. In 1830 appeared his Practice of Physic in two vols. octavo, deservedly a popular work, and several times re-printed. In 1833 he issued his first edition of his Treatise on the Diseases of children. The two former ones have been honored with a German translation.

From the preceding sketch it is evident that the life of Dr. Eberle was closely appropriated to the

advancement of the profession he had selected as the
business of his existence. His knowledge, the result
of great individual effort, often under the most discouraging circumstances, was extensive and various.
To modern science he added a familiar acquaintance
with Hippocratic medicine, and his regard to the
ancients, sometimes led him to estimate somewhat
unduly their merits. That he labored not in vain,
may be inferred from the extensive circulation of his
writings and the estimation in which they are generally held, both by the students of science and by
men of clinical experience.

Dr. Alban Goldsmith, who was for five years a colleague of Dr. Eberle in the Medical College of Ohio,
in a letter to Dr. Francis of New York, thus writes
of his lamented friend: 'In a wide survey of medical men with whom I have had intercourse, I have
rarely encountered one who possessed a larger share
of professional knowledge in the several branches of
healing than Dr. Eberle. To great extent of information he united a kind and courteous demeanor,
and was never obtrusive in enforcing his practical
opinions, except when they were assailed by ignorance and unwarrantable assurance. During the period that we labored together he was a constant and
indefatigable student, taking a wide survey of the
philosophy of medicine. His lectures were always
of a practical nature, and his hospital clinics filled
with the most valuable facts, the result of a careful
observation. His deportment towards the junior
members of the profession was universally kind and

paternal, and he was always ready to offer them aid in their inquiries. He was totally free from all professional envy, and in his intercourse with his colleagues was characterized by the strictest laws of etiquette. Medicines or money were dispensed by him with like liberality, to remove the sufferings or alleviate the calamities of the poor. In short, he was liberal to a fault, and often careless of his own proper interests. He deserves to be recorded as a successful pioneer in that valuable corps who have promoted the diffusion of real science in the great west, and his medical writings, I think, may be justly estimated as having added to the claims which indigenous literature and science have upon the confederation of the American Medical Faculty.'

DR. JOSHUA FISHER, a distinguished patron of Harvard University, was born at Dedham, Massachusetts, in May, 1749, and was graduated at Harvard College, in 1766. After studying medicine he commenced practice ; but on the declaration of hostilities between Great Britain and the United States in 1775, prompted by the spirit of enterprise or patriotism, he embarked as surgeon on board a private armed ship, and was subjected to the perils of this species of warfare. He was captured, escaped into France, entered again into the same service, and after successes and reverses of fortune, returned and established himself in his profession at Beverly, in Massachusetts. As a physician he is represented by his biographer,

Dr. Walter Channing, who wrote a life of him, entitled 'A brief memoir of Joshua Fisher, M. D., late
President of the Massachusetts Medical Society,' as
'being largely gifted with those moral and intellectual
qualities which give honor and usefulness to his profession,' as 'having professed extraordinary powers
of observation and reflection ; as understanding how
to select with wonderful taste from a multitude of
facts, just what was most worthy of consideration,'
and as 'displaying in his practice great independence
and originality.' His reputation was great ; he was
beloved by his patients, and his practice as a consulting physician extended over a very wide circuit. But
'most especially is he remembered for the purity of
his mind and heart, which gave to his intellectual
nature great beauty, power and attractiveness. It
constituted the tone of his mind and was the atmosphere in which it expanded, and by which it was invigorated. Such a mind was admirably fitted for the
study of nature, and few in this country have felt
and acknowledged a deeper interest in Natural History than Dr. F. His strong power of observing,
comparing and remembering, singularly fitted him for
this branch of science, and he devoted himself to it
whenever opportunity served. He was a genuine
lover of nature. He felt its beauty in its truth, and
derived perpetual pleasure from the perception of it.'
At the close of his life, which occurred in March,
1833, at the advanced age of eighty-four, his zeal and
interest in this science was manifested by his be-
queathing ' to the President and Fellows of Harvard

College, the sum of twenty thousand dollars, the income of it to be appropriated to the support of a Professor of Natural History, comprehending the three kingdoms, animal, vegetable, and mineral, or a part of them.' *Quincy's History of Harvard College.*

DR. OLIVER FISKE was son of the Rev. Nathan Fiske of Brookfield, Mass., and was born September 2nd, 1762. Samuel Jennison, Esq., says of him that his early education was superintended by his father, whose productive fame, during most of the revolutionary war, was, from necessity, principally confined to his management. In the summer of 1780 a requisition for recruits was made. The quotas of men had, thus far, been furnished without compulsory process; but levies had been so frequent that none would enlist freely, at a season so busy. The company then commanded by the late Major General John Cutler, was ordered to meet for a draft. Exempted by the courtesy extended to clergymen, from military duty, and never having been enrolled, Dr. Fiske offered himself as a volunteer, with the approbation of his father, who applauded the patriotic spirit, while the personal sacrifice it involved was severely felt. Animated by the example, the requisite number came from the ranks on the parade. The regiment in which they were embodied, was ordered to West Point, and was stationed in the vicinity of that post at the defection of Arnold, and the capture and execution of Andre. On being dismissed he returned

to the farm, and was employed in its cultivation until
the close of the war, in 1783, when he entered Harvard College. At the breaking out of Shay's insurrection he was instrumental in reorganizing the Mar-
tin Mercurian band of the University, in obtaining
an order from Gov. Bowdoin for sixty stand of arms
at Castle William, and was second officer of the
Company. When the Court commenced at Concord,
he was the organ of petition from this corps to march
in support of government, which was properly declined by the authorities of the institution. In the
winter vacation of 1786-7, he took a school at Lincoln, but hearing of the threatened movements of
the malcontents to stop the judicial tribunals at Worcester, he procured a substitute to assume his engagement, exchanged the ferule for appropriate weapons,
and hastened to this place. Finding the enemy dispersed, and the troops on their way to 'Springfield,
he went out to visit his father. On the heights of
Leicester, the report of Gen. Shepherd's artillery diverted him from his course. Uniting himself to a
body of light horsemen, then on their route, he joined Gen. Lincoln's army. When the rebellion was
suppressed he resumed his studies, without censure
for his long absence, and graduated in 1787, after
the usual preparation, under the tuition of Dr. Atherton, of Lancaster. He commenced business in
Worcester in 1790. He was active in forming a
county Medical Association, and in obtaining the establishment of the present district organization of the
Massachusetts Medical Society. Soon after the for-

mation of the last named body in the second medical district, he was elected President, and was elected Counsellor and Censor until he retired from the profession. In Feb. 1803 he was appointed Special Justice of the Court of Common Pleas. During five years succeeding 1809, he was a member of the Executive Council. The commissions of Justice of the Peace, and of the Quorum, and throughout the Commonwealth, were successively received, and the latter has been renewed to the present time. Dr. Fiske was Corresponding Secretary of the Linnæan Society of New England in 1815; of the Worcester Agricultural Society, from 1824; and Counsellor of the American Antiquarian Society. He was Register of Deeds during the triennial term from 1816 to 1821. From this period an increasing defect in the sense of hearing, induced him to retire from busy life, and devote himself to the pursuits of horticulture and agriculture—those employments, in his own graceful language, ' the best substitute to our progenitors for their loss of Paradise, and the best solace to their posterity for the evils they entailed.' The results of that taste and skill in his favorite occupations, early imbibed, ardently cherished, and successfully cultivated, have been freely and frequently communicated to the public in many essays; useful and practical in matter, and singularly elegant in manner. He died at Boston in 1836, aged seventy-four years.

Dr. Fiske was also a member of the American Academy of Arts and Sciences. Bradford, in his New England Biography, says, ' he was a scientific

22

physician, being well acquainted with natural philosophy, chemistry, and physiology, so far as contributed to a correct and successful practice.'

I have understood that he was a popular physician, and had he devoted himself more particularly to his profession, would have continued to share an extensive patronage and employment. When the Spotted Fever suddenly appeared in this vicinity, exciting greater alarm for a time than any other epidemic which had been known in the same region during the last century, excepting the Cholera, he was called to visit cases in several of the towns of Worcester county, and great confidence was manifested in his skill in the treatment of the disease. But the versatility of his mind led him to engage in other pursuits ; in merchandize, in the superintendence, in connection with others, of the construction of the Boston and Worcester Turnpike ; and in political life, so that he was gradually withdrawn from medical practice, a result to which the growing infirmities of deafness also contributed.

He was never unmindful, however, of the dignity of the medical profession. He maintained that a good education was necessary to qualify the practitioner for his duties, and would not willingly have dispensed with any of the required formalities of initiation.

In politics he was a Federalist, and exerted no small influence in party management, and in the frequent contests of the day. He was a ready writer on topics of current interest, terse and epigrammatic in his style, and often humorous. For some time he was the Editor of the ' Massachusetts Spy,' an old and prominent political paper at Worcester.

He was generous and public spirited, ready to engage to the full extent of his ability in the promotion of objects of public utility, and for the relief of private suffering. The circumstances under which he was placed seemed to afford him the means of acquiring wealth, but a want of method and watchfulness in the management of pecuniary affairs, prevented its attainment. In the latter years of his life he found his greatest pleasure in the cultivation of his garden, and in horticultural labors and experiments.

He published an oration delivered at Worcester by him in 1797 ; and the annual Agricultural address before the Worcester County Society in 1823 and 1831, were published ; also an Essay on the epidemic disease called the Spotted Fever, forming a part of the Transactions of the Massachusetts Medical Society. I have seen in manuscript many of his early compositions, both in prose and verse, written while in college and pursuing his studies, at Lancaster, which evinced a cultivated taste, but have seldom recognized many of them in print.

He married Sarah, only daughter of Andrew Duncan, a native of Glasgow, who, before the revolution, established himself at Worcester as a merchant. Robert T. P. Fiske, M. D., of Hingham, is his son.

Dr. John Frink, Senior, was an eminent practitioner of medicine in Rutland, in the county of Worcester, and State of Massachusetts. He was one of the founders of the Massachusetts Medical Society, and he was also one of the most distinguished physicians in the county of Worcester. He studied the profession of medicine with Dr. Goffe, of Marlborough. He had two daughters, one of whom married Dr. Russell, of Paxton, the other Professor Adams, late of Dartmouth College. He had a son who served in the revolutionary army, and received a pension, and another son, Dr. John Frink, who succeeded his father in the practice in Rutland, and who was respectable. This son died in Bristol, R. Island, in the year 1838. Dr. Frink died at Rutland in 1807.

In dress Dr. Frink was said to be particularly neat. His manners were extremely urbane and affable. He was, also, very facetious. The late Dr. Stone of Springfield, whose biography will be found in another place, has related to me, in former days, some anecdotes illustrative of this position, but they have mostly escaped my memory. Dr. Stone studied the profession of medicine with Dr. Frink. In one of his visits to his patients, Dr. Stone accompanied him. Upon examining the patient he was found not to be very sick, but he was anxious to see several other physicians, some of whom were empirics. Upon their leaving the house Dr. Frink observed to Dr. Stone, 'Johnny' (a familiar mode of expression with him,) 'Johnny, that man has the running fever.' The running fever, sir ? I do not recollect to have read any thing about such a fever. 'Why, yes,' says Dr. Frink, 'he has the running fever. He is for running after every physician within the circle of his acquaintance.' He is said, also, to have had somewhat peculiar views in relation to consultation. 'Two physicians,' he would observe, 'were enough in all conscience, but three were enough to kill the Devil.' He was hardly willing to allow of the rapid improvement of medicine. On one occasion, within little more than half a century, while some one was extolling the writings of Cullen, he with a great deal of warmth repelled the defence, and observed with great emphasis that 'the works of Bœrhaave would stand the test of ages.' What would he not have said had he lived at the present time, when the writings of Cullen, of Brown, of Darwin, and innumerable others, are cast into the shade ?

Through the politeness of Dr. Woodward of Worcester, I have been favored with the following notice of Dr. Frink, in an extract of a letter from the Rev. Josiah Clarke, of Rutland, to the Rev. Geo. Allen of Worcester.

Dr. John Frink, junior, was the son of Dr. John Frink, whose biography I have just given, who was the son of the Rev. Thomas Frink, the first ordained minister of Rutland. Dr. John Frink, senior, was born in Rutland, Sept. 7, 1731. He not only ranked high as a physician, but as a patriotic and trustworthy citizen. He was a justice of the peace, when it was considered some mark of distinction to be one. He was also a member of the Convention that formed the Constitution of Massachusetts, and the first President of the Worcester County Medical Society. And I have been informed that but few physicians had more extensive practice.

The late Dr. JOHN FRINK, Jr., was born in Rutland, in 1762. He spent most of his days in his native place, but I believe he passed a few years in Charleston, S. C., with his uncle Samuel, a respectable clergyman of that city. He was a Surgeon in the army at the time of Shays' insurrection, and I have the impression, though I am not certain, that he was a few months a Surgeon or Surgeon's Mate in the revolution. His brother Samuel is a revolutionary pensioner, and is living either in Paxton or Leicester.

The late Dr. John Frink's education was respectable, though not liberal. He had in early and middle life an extensive practice, and was esteemed as a safe and skillful physician. He emphatically, in manners and practice, belonged to the old school. He was strongly tinctured with aristocratic notions and family pride, and if he had the power, he had not the will, to accommodate himself to modern manners or practice.

Dr. Frink, though a man of accomplished manners, and of a refined mind, could not be said to be a scientific man. He was better as a practitioner than as a theorist. He belonged to that class of men who exercise correct judgment without being able to give a reason for it. He seemed to me to acquire his skill and reputation more from experience, or from long practice with his father, than from mental discipline or investigation. He possessed, however, many excellent traits of character. His moral discernment was quick and delicate. No one could sooner or more correctly discover beauties or blemishes in the conduct or writings of others. He was a constant reader and admirer of English literature. At the head of his family he appeared to great advantage, and his house was for a long time a favorite place of resort for people of taste and refinement, and no pains were spared to make the guests sociable and happy. Dr. Frink might with great propriety be called a christian gentleman. After his wife died in 1834, the Doctor passed part of his time with his son in New York. In 1837 he went to Bristol, R. I., to spend a few months with his younger son, who was a member of the Bristol Wm. Penn sect in religion, and died there July 18th, 1838.

Dr. Joseph Glover, late of Charleston, South Carolina. A committee composed of John Bellinger, M. D., chairman, J. C. Whitridge, M. D., and T. G. Porcher, M. D., were appointed by the Medical Society of South Carolina, in the year 1840, to prepare an account of the more important facts which occurred in the practice, and the principal operations performed by Joseph Glover, M. D., one of their Fellows, with a biographical sketch of his career. The following facts are abridged from their report.

The committee who were appointed to report upon that part of Dr. Glover's biography which relates to his connection with this Society, and to bring to your notice such cases which occurred in his practice as might interest the profession generally, beg leave to state, that, having examined the Records of the Society, Dr. Glover's Note Book, and other sources of information, they have found abundant materials for their purpose. In using these materials they have endeavored to be concise.

The committee have been gratified in discovering that, from the commencement of Dr. Glover's career, success and distinction waited on his efforts. As a candidate for the medical Diploma of the University of Pennsylvania, he submitted to the Provost and Faculty a Thesis on Digestion, which was published among Dr. Caldwell's *Selected Theses.* It is entitled to a full share of the encomium with which the editor introduces the *second volume* of that collection to the Medical public ; *i. e.* that those essays, ' considered as separate specimens of intellect and investigation, do great credit to the individual writers ; and taken together, constitute a monument peculiarly honorable to the Medical School of Philadelphia.' He graduated in 1800, and in September of that year was elected a member of this Association.

One of the objects contemplated by the founders of the Medical Society of this city was a Dispensary —an institution for furnishing medicines and medical attendance to the poor. A plan of such a charity was drafted cotemporaneously with the Constitution of the Association, an appropriate address to the citizens was prepared and published, and an anxious effort made to accomplish their benevolent designs. Notwithstanding the failure of this attempt—for it did fail—the society renewed their exertions in the year 1801 ; a committee, of which Dr. Glover was a member, was appointed to organize a plan of a Dispensary. A report from them was presented and circulated among the members, and having been discussed and amended, was transmitted, with a suitable explanation, to the city council ; which body, in consequence of the strong recommendations of the Medical Society, enacted an ordinance founding a Dispensary, and authorizing the Society to nominate physicians and surgeons to the same. Dr. Glover was one of the number who offered their services gratuitously to the poor ; and in 1805 received in common with his brother practitioners a vote of thanks from the trustees ' for their diligent, skillful and humane attention,' rendered ' without any pecuniary compensation.'

The next important item of public business with which Dr. Glover was concerned, was a preparation of a Report upon the causes of our ' Endemial Causus,' or Yellow Fever. A considerable portion of this report is upon the subject of burial grounds without the city, and upon removing offals and other filth from the streets, stores, wharves, cellars, &c., which was considered to be very complete, and it is even now often referred to.

23

Among the suggestions made to the city council by the Medical Society in 1795, was that trees should be planted before the houses of citizens; and in Dr. Glover's Report in 1808, the advantages to health of a luxuriant growth of trees were pointed out; and the chemical changes produced in the atmosphere by animal and vegetable respirations explained.

Eminent as several of the medical faculty of this city have been as physicians, it is believed that of those who entered the profession previous to Dr. Glover, no one had devoted much attention to Surgery; that brilliant department of our science was comparatively neglected. He commenced practice, therefore, at a juncture favorable for rapid success. Frequent opportunities occurred for the exhibition of his judgment, boldness, and address; and in a few years his reputation as a surgeon was established. One of the first capital operations he performed, was the rare one of excising part of the spleen. The patient, a negro, belonging to Major Pinkney, was stabbed with a knife on the 12th of August, 1801, at Moultrieville. The weapon penetrated obliquely the hypochondriac region, making a wound of four or five inches in length; the cartilage of one or two of the false ribs was divided; and some of the omentum, together with a considerable portion of the spleen, protruded. Surgical assistance could not be obtained—the next morning he was brought to the city, and at 11 o'clock, A. M., was visited by Drs.

Matthew Irvine and Joseph Glover. He had lost much blood. The protruded parts presented so gangrenous an aspect that their removal was decided on. A small piece of the omentum, and a large part of the spleen, were cut away with the scalpel ; a branch of the splenic artery was secured with a needle and ligature ; the remaining parts having been properly cleaned were returned into their abdominal cavity. The wound was closed with interrupted sutures, which were secured by the necessary plasters and bandages. The ligatures separated early ; and the whole process of healing was as rapid as that of a wound in any part of the flesh similarly neglected at first would have been. In some of its circumstances this case resembles the one reported by Cheselden in vol. xi. of the Philosophical Transactions, which, strange to say, has escaped the notice of the very acute and industrious Hennen, who cites the only three other instances, so far as our research extends, in which the removal of the spleen or a part of it has been accomplished by British surgeons.

Among the earliest of Dr. Glover's cases, were operations upon the eye. For a number of years he almost monopolized the practice of this branch of surgery ; and so considerable was his reputation as an Oculist, that patients from the interior of our own, and from the neighboring states, frequently resorted to this city, for the advantage of being treated by him. For cataracts, he operated either by extracting, or by depressing the lens. Many of his patients were ' elderly' persons, and he ascertained and has recorded the ages of a few old persons upon whom he operated with great success. As it is uncertain at what age operations for cataract may not be undergone, with a fair prospect of relief, we mention the ages of three of these, ' very elderly' individuals, *i. e.* 65, 70, and 83 years.

The next important operation he performed was lithotomy. Calculous diseases are so rare in this locality that to have cut for stone in the bladder constitutes an era in the professional career of any of our surgeons. As late as 1808, only three operations of this kind could ' be distinctly and certainly recollected as having been performed' in Charleston. Two of these were *done* by Dr. Turner, of Connecticut, (tradition relates that this distinguished operator visited our city by invitation for the purpose ;) the third was by Dr. Glover, and all were successful. Since that date, six similar and likewise fortunate operations have been performed ; of these two cases came from abroad. .So that up to the present time, (December, 1840) only seven operations for stone in the bladder have been performed upon persons who were natives, or who had been for many years residents of Charleston.

Excision of the *prolapsed* or *inverted uterus*, although reprobated by Ruysch, has within the present half century been in repeated instances safely performed. The committee regret that Dr. Glover's interesting case has been so loosely reported, as to allow of a doubt whether the tumor excised was a polypus or the uterus itself ; of the causes of deficiency in the publication they do not feel at liberty to remark. In addition to the history contained in the 4th volume of the American Medical and Philosophical Register, they have been furnished with notes of the case, taken at the time by Dr. Glover himself. From these it is clear, that all who examined the tumor, both before and after its removal, were convinced of its nature ; and the expression of Dr. Baron, as significant of the opinions of all, is preserved : ' if this is not an inverted uterus, I have never seen one.' Of Dr. B.'s competency to judge the committee deem it superfluous to argue. Dr. Glover also relates, that in 1834 he had visited his former patient, Mrs. H., whom he found in good health, and that he was assured that she had never menstruated since this operation.

The committee then gives the detail of the operation, which is too long to insert here.

The next operation which we will notice is one towards which the hopes of the profession are at the present time anxiously directed ; we allude to puncturing the head for the evacuation of water. This has shared the fate commom to all important procedures of surgical practice, having been by some strongly condemned, and by others warmly advocated. As it is now in high repute, and as we conceive that they, by whom in modorn times this operation has been performed, have been unjustly slighted by the manner in which Dr. Conquest's cases have been celebrated by a portion of the English medical press, we shall demonstrate that puncturing the head has been repeatedly resorted to and practiced in the last half century, as a remedy for chronic hydrocephalus. The committee then go on to cite numerous English and American authorities in proof of the truth of the position laid down. After quoting numerous authorities, they observe : as puncturing the ventricles had been heretofore regarded as ' impossible,' or as ' not to be attempted,' the committee are disposed to ascribe to Dr. Charles Alfred Lee, of New York, the credit of having first distinctly advised a resort to the puncture, even of the ventricles.' The committee must not dismiss this subject without a distinct avowal of what is due to the doctor ; that his communication is written ' in a modest and philosophical tone (blemished, however, by a paradoxical compliment intended for some of his friends) and that although silent respecting the prior operations of others, he himself has advanced no preposterous claims to originality.

The history of Dr. Glover's case was published in a pamphlet form by the Medical Society of South Carolina in July, 1818. It was reported in the New York Medical and Physical Journal of the same year. The case was copied into the *Philad. Journal of Med. and Phys. Sciences* for 1821 ; it is also noticed in the *Ed. Med. and Surg. Jour.* for 1828, in the review of the essay of Oppenheim, by whom it is cited ; it has been quoted at considerable length by Brechtenau in his article on Compression in the cure of Dropsy, in the *Arch. Gen.* for 1832, and is mentioned by Copland in his *Dict. of Pract. Medicine*, now in course of publication.

Although we claim for Dr. Glover the credit of having contributed to revive an operation which had been neglected by British and American surgeons for forty years, (no instance of its performance having been published in the interval between his in 1818 and Dr. Remmett's in 1778) we desire to be understood as having no faith in its supposed curative influence over hydrocephalus. Our settled opinion is that the past experience of the profession will undergo no change in consequence of Dr. Conquest's *ten* cases, which 'were living when last heard from.'

One other of Dr. Glover's cases deserves to be remembered; it is that which he related in the oration delivered in 1809, of a patient whom he treated successfully for ascites, principally by tapping. He regarded paracentesis not merely as a palliative, but as a curative means, and advocated its early and repeated performance. In the instance to which we refer, it was resorted to *fifteen* times.

The committee refrain from enumerating the more common operations performed by Dr. Glover, as, although numerous, they were not attended by circumstances sufficiently curious to entitle them to particular notice. They conclude their Report by expressing the belief that at home he will long be remembered for his zealous promotion of the objects of our association, and for his boldness, dexterity, and success as a surgeon; whilst abroad his fame will rest upon his having fearlessly undertaken, and having skillfully accomplished, operations, for the performance of which the records of medicine furnish so few precedents.

Dr. John D. Godman. This distinguished physician died on the 17th of April, 1830. He died a victim to pulmonary consumption, brought on by intense application to the pursuit of science, and from great exertions in the discharge of professional duties, too severe for the strength of his personal frame, in the thirty-fourth year of his age.

The following just tribute to his memory is from a 'Memoir of Dr. Godman, being an Introductory Lecture, delivered Nov. 1, 1830,' to the Class in Columbian College. By Thomas Sewall, M. D., Professor.

'There are occasions, gentlemen, when it is proper, when it is profitable, to pause in the career of life, not only to mark the progress of things, but to observe the character of men, and more especially of men distinguished for eminent success, or signal failure, that we may imitate the examples of the one, and shun the misfortunes of the other. The present is such an occasion; and if properly improved, cannot fail to instruct as well as to gratify.

There has recently appeared among us a man so remarkable for the character of his mind, and the qualities of his heart—one whose life, though short, was attended with such brilliant displays of genius, with such distinguished success in the study of our profession and the kindred sciences, that to pass him by without tracing the history of his career, and placing before you the prominent traits of his character, as exhibited in the important events of his life, would alike be an act of injustice to the memory of eminent worth, and deprive you of one of the noblest examples of the age.

I refer to Professor Godman, whose death has been announced since we last assembled within these walls.

This remarkable man was born not far from us, in a place already renowned for having given birth to an unusual proportion of eminent men, the city of Annapolis, the metropolis of the ancient State of Maryland.

But few of the incidents of Dr. G.'s childhood and youth have come to my knowledge. I have learned, however, that he was early deprived of the fostering care which flows from parental solicitude and affection. His mother died before he was a year old, and his father did not survive long. On the death of his mother he was placed under the care of an aunt, then residing at Wilmington, in the State of Delaware; a lady who, for the superiority of her intellect and education, as well as the sweetness of her disposition, and her elevated piety, was eminently qualified to unfold, impress and direct the youthful mind. Under such culture he received the first rudiments of his education and his earliest moral impressions. His alphabet was taught him upon the knee of his grand-

24

mother, and before he was two years old he was able to read in the Psalms.

At the age of four his aunt removed from Delaware to Chestertown, upon the eastern shore of Maryland, and here she first placed the interesting orphan at school. He had already become the idol of the family, but now he manifested such a precocity of intellect, such a fondness for books, and an aptitude to learn, and withal evinced so much sensibility, frankness, and sweetness of disposition, that he gained the affection and excited the admiration of all. His reverence for truth was such, from infancy, that he was never known to equivocate. At the age of six his aunt died, and he was left without any suitable protector or guide, exposed to the adversities of fortune, and the snares of an unfriendly world. It appears, however, that the moral and religious impressions which had already been made upon his mind, though obscured for a time, were never wholly obliterated. During his last illness he was often heard to speak in raptures of his aunt, and say, ' if ever I have been led to do any good, it has been through the influence of her example, instruction and prayers.' His father had lost the greater part of his estate before his death, and that which remained never came into the hands of his children. Young Godman, therefore, was early taught to rely upon his own talents and industry. In this situation he was indented an apprentice to a printer in the city of Baltimore ; but the occupation was not congenial to his taste ; and after a few years he left the business in disgust, and at the same time entered as a sailor on board the Flotilla, which was then, in the fall of 1814, stationed in the Chesapeake Bay. At the close of the war, having arrived at the age of fifteen, he was permitted to pursue the inclination of his own mind, and he immediately commenced the study of medicine. He first placed himself under the instruction of Dr. Luckey, of Elizabethtown, in Pennsylvania, but soon removed to Baltimore, and entered the office of Dr. Davidge, at that time Professor of Anatomy in the University of Maryland.

Here he pursued his studies with such diligence and zeal as to furnish, even at that early period, strong indications of future eminence. So indefatigable was he in the acquisition of knowledge, that he left no opportunity of advancement unimproved, and notwithstanding the deficiencies of his preparatory education, he pressed forward with an energy and perseverance that enabled him not only to rival, but to surpass, all his fellows.

As an evidence of the distinguished attainments he had made, and of the confidence reposed in his abilities, he was called to the chair of Anatomy in the University some time before he graduated, to supply the place of his preceptor, who was taken from the lectures in consequence of the fracture of a lower extremity. This situation he filled for several weeks with so much propriety, he lectured with so much enthusiasm and eloquence, his illustrations were so clear and happy, as to gain universal applause ; and at the time he was examined for his degree, the superiority of his mind as well as the extent and accuracy of his knowledge were so apparent, that he was marked by the professors of the University as one destined at some future period to confer high honor upon the profession. Upon this occasion a prize medal was awarded him for the best Latin thesis.

After he graduated he settled at New Holland, in Pennsylvania, but soon left this situation and repaired to a small village in Anne, Arundel County, in his native State, and established himself as a practitioner of medicine. Here he entered on the active duties of his profession with the same energy and diligence which had distinguished him while a pupil, devoting all the hours he could spare to professional and other studies. It was at this time that he commenced the study of natural history, a science in which he became so distinguished an adept, and for which he ever after evinced so strong a passion. But the place was too limited for the exercise of his powers; and not finding all those advantages which he wished, for the cultivation of his favorite pursuits, he removed to Baltimore, where he could enjoy more ample opportunities for the study of Anatomy, which he justly regarded as the foundation of medical science.

About this time he formed a connection by marriage; an event which contributed equally to his domestic happiness and literary advancement. Soon after his marriage he removed to Philadelphia, but had scarcely settled in that city when he received a

pressing invitation to accept the professorship of
Anatomy in the Medical College of Ohio, an institution then recently established. During his western
tour, he encountered difficulties which would have
broken down a spirit less energetic than his own;
but he bore up under his accumulated labors and
privations with unshaken firmness and steady perseverance. He however remained but one year, and
returned to Philadelphia; and here commenced that
career of research and discovery which had laid the
foundation for his future eminence.

More ambitious of fame, and more eager for the
acquisition of knowledge, than the accumulation of
wealth, Dr. Godman, on settling at Philadelphia, rather retired from the field of practice, that he might
employ all his time, and exert all his powers, in scientific pursuits. He there found himself at once removed from the pitiful rivalries and jealousies of the
profession, and placed in a situation in which he
could enjoy the friendship, without alarming the fears,
of his brethren.

His main object was to make himself a thorough
anatomist, and to qualify himself for teaching the
science. To this end he opened a room, under the
patronage of the University, for giving private demonstrations; and the first winter he drew around
him a class of seventy students. He now found himself occupying a field which furnished ample scope
for the exertion of all his powers, as well as for the
gratification of his highest ambition; and it was
while engaged in the discharge of the duties of this

station that the foundation was laid of that fatal disease of which he died; for so eager was he to acquire knowledge himself, as well as to impart it to
those around him, that he would not only expose himself to the foul atmosphere of the dissecting room
during the whole day, but often subject himself to the
severest toil for a considerable part of the night; and
the moments which were spared from his anatomical
labors, instead of being spent in relaxation, or in exercise in the open air for the benefit of his health,
were employed in composing papers for the medical
journals, in copying the results of his anatomical and
physiological investigations, in preparing parts of his
natural history, or in carrying on other literary and
scientific studies. It is impossible that a constitution
naturally delicate, could long remain unimpaired under such strenuous and unremitting exertion.

After Dr. Godman had prosecuted his Anatomical
studies in Philadelphia, for four or five years, his
reputation as an Anatomist became so generally
known, his fame so widely extended, that the eyes of
the profession were directed to him from every part
of the country; and in 1826, he was called to fill the
chair of Anatomy in Rutgers' Medical College, established in the city of New York. There could
scarcely have been a stronger testimony of the high
estimation in which he was held, or of his reputation
as a teacher of Anatomy, than in his appointment to
this station; an institution around which several of
the most eminent professors of the country had
already been rallied, and which was called into ex-

istence under circumstances of rivalry that demanded the highest qualifications in its instructors. This institution, as well as every other in which he had been placed, he sustained with a popularity almost unparalleled. He never exhibited in public but he gathered around him an admiring audience, who hung with delight upon his lips. But the duties of the chair, together with his other scientific pursuits, were too arduous, and the climate too rigorous, for a constitution already subdued by labor, and broken by disease ; and before he had completed his second course of lectures, he was compelled to retire from the school, and seek a residence in a milder climate.

He repaired with his family to one of the West India islands, and remained till the approach of summer, when he returned and settled in Germantown. In this place, and in Philadelphia, he spent the residue of his life, mainly by the strong solicitations of Drs. Mott, Francis and Hosack.

From the time Dr. Godman left New York his disease advanced with such a steady pace as to leave but little hope, either to himself or his friends, of his final recovery. He, however, continued almost to the last week of his life to toil in his literary and scientific employments ; and this too, with all that ardor and enthusiasm which distinguished the more youthful part of his career.

But for what purpose did he thus toil ? Not for the acquisition of wealth, for this he could not enjoy ; not for posthumous fame, for this he did not desire. It was, as he affectingly tells us, for the more noble purpose, the support of his family, and the good of his fellow creatures.

The productions of Dr. Godman's pen, and the fruits of his labors, are too numerous to be specified. Among them will be found 'Anatomical Investigations, comprising a description of various Fasciæ of the human body'—'An account of some irregularities of structure and morbid Anatomy'—'Contributions to Physiological and Pathological Anatomy'—'A system of Natural History of American Quadrupeds'—'An edition of Bell's Anatomy with Notes'—'Rambles of a Naturalist'—several articles on Natural History for the American Encyclopedia—beside numerous papers which have appeared in the periodical journals of the day. At one time he was the principal editor of the 'Philadelphia Journal of the Medical Sciences.' Some time before his death he published a volume of addresses which he had delivered on different public occasions.

Most of these admired productions have been before the public for a considerable time; and have been received with high approbation, and several of them favorably noticed, and even republished in foreign countries.

Those of his works which are purely medical have been read with great interest by the profession, and contain much new and valuable information. His investigation of the fasciæ of the human body, and his description of the intricate parts of the animal structure, while they disclose some important discoveries which he made, exhibit the whole subject in

a manner so plain and simple as to divest it of its
obscurity and bring it to the comprehension of the
youngest student;—a subject which, till his researches had been made known, was but little understood,
even by the best anatomists. His contributions, also,
to the physiological and pathological anatomy, though
but the scattered fragments of a great work which
he had designed, contained discoveries and observations which will be read with the deepest interest
by the inquirer after truth. Of his works not immediately connected with the profession, his Natural
History of the American Quadrupeds is the most
elaborate, and is published in three volumes. This
production will long remain a splendid monument of
the genius and industry of its author, and be regarded as a model of composition for works of this description. It should have a place upon every table
in the family, and be put into the hands of all the
youths of our country. Among the latest productions of his pen are his essays entitled Rambles of a
Naturalist, which were written in the intervals of
extreme pain and debility. For strong, lively, and
accurate descriptions, they have scarcely been surpassed. He always came to his subject as an investigator of facts—one who had nothing to learn, but
every thing to discover ; and like the celebrated Buf-
fon, never availed himself of the labor of others till
he had exhausted his own resources. It was this
spirit which enabled him to discover so many new
truths, and which gave to all his works the stamp
of originality. The value which he placed on origi-

25

nal observations, as well as the zeal with which he sought information from this source, may be learned from a single fact, ' that in investigating the habits of a common shrew mole, he walked many hundred miles.'

The volume of his public addresses has been greatly admired for the pure and elevated sentiments they contain, as well as for their high wrought eloquence, in which respect they rank among the finest compositions in our language.

But his public works constituted but a part of the labors of his pen ; and many things which he sent forth were only fragments of a great system, or the commencement of future researches. He had formed vast plans for prosecuting new investigations in various departments of science, which he did not live to accomplish.

Though he wrote with great rapidity, and sometimes without much care, yet all his works bear the impress of a mind naturally vigorous, bold and original, and much disposed to draw from its own resources ; and most of them are written in a style of great elegance and beauty.

Dr. Godman's intellectual character was very extraordinary. He possessed naturally all the characteristic features of a mind of the highest order. Naturally bold, ardent and enterprising, he never stopped to calculate consequences so far as they regarded himself; but rushed forward with impetuosity to perform whatever he undertook. Great and lofty intellectual purposes seemed to be the natural element in which he lived. His perception was quick and accurate, his memory exceedingly retentive, and he possessed an uncommon facility of abstracting his attention from surrounding objects, and of concentrating all his powers upon the subject of his pursuits. It was this latter trait of mind, no doubt, which gave such effect to all his efforts: while he was indebted to the power of his memory for the remarkable facility he possessed of acquiring languages; for although his early education had been exceedingly limited, he had acquired such a knowledge of the Latin, Greek, French, German, Danish, Spanish and Italian languages, as to read and translate them with elegance. His quick and discriminating powers of observation naturally inclined him to notice the habits and economy of animals, and gave him taste for the study of natural history.

But the most striking character of his mind was undoubtedly philosophical imagination. It was this trait which conferred upon him such powers of description and illustration, and imparted freshness and splendor to every thing he touched. All his conceptions were strong, clear, and original, and he possessed the power of holding before him whatever object engaged his attention, till all its parts and relations were brought to view. By those who have listened to his extemporaneous discourses, it is said that while he was speaking, a thousand images seemed to cluster around the subject, and that he had just time to select such as imparted beauty, or furnished the happiest illustration of the object he wished to explain. Yet, while he possessed all this richness and fertility of mind, taste and judgment ever controlled its operations.

He was a laborious and untiring student, and possessed in a high degree the requisites of all true intellectual greatness,—the habit of patient investigation, long continued attention, and a singular love of labor. ' How often,' says one to whom he unbosomed the secrets of his heart, ' have I entreated him, while poring half the night over his books and papers, which were to yield him nothing but empty honors—how often have I begged him to consider his health; but his ambition and thirst for knowledge were such, that, having commenced an investigation, or a language, no difficulty could stop him ; and what he had no time to accomplish in the day he would do at night, instead of enjoying that rest of which he stood so much in need.'

It has been truly and happily said by one who knew him intimately, that his eagerness in the pursuit of knowledge seemed like the impulse of gnawing hunger and an unquenchable thirst, which neither adversity nor disease could allay. Variety of occupations was the only relaxation which he sought for or desire.d

He composed wirh rapidity, but not without a high degree of intellectual excitement, and the most abstracted attention. Under such an influence some of his best essays were sent to the press as they first came from his pen, without the smallest correction.

Considering the defects of his early education, his

acquisitions, for his years, were astonishingly great. Indeed, there were but few subjects of general literature with which he was not, more or less, acquainted.

But it was his accurate knowledge of Anatomy and Physiology, and his uncommon power of teaching these branches of medicine, which gave him his strongest claims to our. regard as a man of science ; and had his life and health been prolonged so as to have directed the whole energy of his mind to the cultivation of this department of our profession, we have reason to believe that he would have laid open new sources of knowledge, discovered new laws, and reduced to order those scattered materials already known, and that the whole study would thus have been simplified and enriched by his labors.

His method of teaching Anatomy was entirely analytical ; and, in this respect, peculiar : that he performed all his dissections in the presence of his class, demonstrating th ediffrent part of the animal structure in succession, as they were unfolded by the knife. But this method, however well suited to a private class in a dissecting room, causes too much confusion and delay to be practiced with success while lecturing by one less dexterous and skillful than its author himself.

Dr. Godman in his manners was plain, simple and unostentatious ; yet he possessed that warmth and affability which rendered him accessible to all, and the delight of the social circle.

His feelings in every thing were ardent and decided. He was devotedly attached to his friends; towards his enemies he was impatient, and felt keenly their revilings. In his conversation he was fluent, and though unstudied, often brilliant, and always full of point and power.

When we consider the circumstances under which Dr. Godman made his way to the profession, and afterwards prosecuted his studies, the multiplicity of objects which he carried forward, and the honor he conferred on every department of science which he touched; when we consider the power of his intellect, the versatility of his genius, and the intensity of his application, we cannot but regard him as altogether an extraordinary personage,—such an one as has seldom been permitted to dwell among men, to share their sympathies, and mingle in their elevated pursuits.

In view of his intellectual character, I cannot withhold the just and elegant tribute which fell from the pen of that distinguished scholar and gentleman, Robert Walsh, Esq., at the time of Dr. Godman's decease; one who, above most others, knew his worth.

' The tributes,' says he, ' which have been paid in the newspapers to the late Dr. Godman, were especially due to the memory of a man so variously gifted by nature, and so nobly distinguished by industry and zeal in the acquisition and advancement of science. He did not enjoy early opportunities of self improvement, but he cultivated his talents as he approached manhood, with a degree of ardor and success which supplied all deficiencies ; and he finally became one of the most accomplished general scholars and linguists, acute and erudite naturalists, ready, pleasing, and instructive lecturers and writers of his country and era. The principal subject of his study was Anatomy, in its main branches, in which he excelled in every respect. His attention was much directed also to Physiology, Pathology, and Natural History, with an aptitude and efficiency abundantly proved by the merits of his published works, which we need not enumerate.

We do not recollect to have known any individual who inspired us with more respect for his intellect and heart than Dr. Godman ; to whom knowledge and discovery appeared more abstractedly precious ; whose eye shed more of the lustre of generous and enlightened enthusiasm ; whose heart retained more vivid and sympathetic feelings amid professional labor and responsibility, always severe and urgent.

Considering the decline of his health, for a long period, and the pressure of adverse circumstances, which he too frequently experienced, he performed prodigies as a student, an author, and a teacher ; he prosecuted extensive and diversified researches ; composed superior disquisitions and reviews, and large and valuable volumes ; and in the great number of topics which he handled simultaneously, or in immediate succession, he touched none without doing himself credit, and producing some new development of light, or happy forms of expression.

He lingered for years under consumption of the lungs; understood fully the incurableness of his melancholy state, spoke and acted with an unfeigned and beautiful resignation; toiled at his desk till the last day of his thirty-fourth year, still glowing with the love of science and the domestic affections. The reputation, the writings, and family, of this victim of the most exalted ambition and refined propensities, should be greatly and widely cherished.'

But there remains another view to be taken of Dr. Godman, to which I have made no allusion; I refer to his moral and religious character.

Dr. Sewall then goes on and occupies twelve pages in describing the religious views of this eminent young physician, who was thus cut off in the midst of his usefulness. My limits will not allow me to transcribe it. Suffice it to say, that in early life he embraced the philosophical and religious opinions of the French Naturalists of the last century, many of whom were deists and atheists. An incident which occurred at the dying bed of a medical student, induced him to search the scriptures, by doing which he became thoroughly convinced of the truth of Christianity. Ever after this he adhered to the tenets of the orthodox portion of the christian world. He promulgated and dwelt upon these doctrines with as much zeal, and with as great an alacrity and fervor, as he devoted to the sciences which he so ardently loved. He died in the fullest assurance that he should become a participator of the joys of the blessed in the regions of the happy, where the just are made perfect. And who can doubt that his hopes are fully realized?

DR. JOSIAH GOODHUE. The following notice of this distinguished physician is from an address which I delivered by request before the Medical class in the Berkshire Medical Institution, of which the deceased was President, Nov. 20th, 1829.

Permit me, Gentlemen of the Faculty, and of the Class, to make a few remarks upon a subject of deep and solemn interest to our institution. I refer to the lamented death of our distinguished and venerable President, Dr. Josiah Goodhue, who expired on the 9th of September, 1829, soon after the commencement of our present course of Lectures. On this occasion, I presume it will not be deemed impertinent for a younger brother to weep upon his tomb, and humbly speak his praise.

Gentlemen, within one short year the medical profession in America has sustained a loss which many succeeding years cannot repair. Before the year 1828 had run its round we were called to mourn the loss of Dr. Wright Post, of New York, one of the most eminent Surgeons our country has ever seen. His eulogy has been spoken by his worthy colleague in Rutgers College, Dr. Mott. Warmly as I was attached to Dr. Post, any farther observations from me

26

commenced its revolution, than I, too, was called to
meet the severest domestic calamity of my life, in
the death of my dearly beloved father, whom I must
be permitted to say, was one of our most eminent
physicians. I have already published his biography
in the Med. Communications of the Mass. Med. Society, vol. 4, part 6, 1829. See also a notice of him
in another part of this work. Yet on the subject of
his decease, and on this occasion,

> ' 'Tis meet that I should mourn,
> Flow forth afresh my tears.'

We had no sooner consigned the remains of my
dearly beloved parent to the cold and dreary mansions of the tomb, than the melancholy intelligence
of the death of Dr. Nathan Smith, New England's
pride and ornament in the profession of medicine,
reached our ears. His life and character are too
well known to need any encomium from me in this
place. His cotemporaries and posterity will do
ample justice to his memory. Soon followed the
distinguished and venerable Dr. Holyoke, whose life
was prolonged to more than one hundred years, the
learned Dr. Gorham, and the eminent Dr. Coffin.
While yet their funeral knell was sounding in our
ears, the melancholy news of the death of Dr. Burbank, our former worthy colleague in this institution,
was announced. Next followed Dr. Davidge, Professor of Anatomy in the University of Maryland.
Last, though not least, our venerable and worthy
President, Dr. Josiah Goodhue, has been called to

taste the bitter cup of death, and the clod of the valley now rests upon his bosom.

Thus in the space of about nine months, nine of the most distinguished physicians in the United States have bowed beneath the all-conquering sword of death. Five of them had been Professors in our most celebrated Medical Colleges, and all of them held high and eminent stations in the profession of medicine. Many of them died in the midst of their usefulness.

To exhibit the character of Dr. Goodhue it is necessary to give a brief sketch of his life. He was son of the Rev. Josiah Goodhue, and was born at Dunstable, Middlesex county, Massachusetts, January 17th, 1759. He early devoted himself to study, and entered Harvard University about the commencement of our revolutionary struggle. Owing to the disturbances of the revolution, the doors of the University were closed, and collegiate exercises suspended. He returned home, and owing to a white swelling upon one of his knees, he was sent to Dr. Kittredge of Fakesbury, for advice. He placed himself under his care a few weeks, and afterwards commenced the study of Physic and Surgery with him, and continued with him two years, the customary period of medical pupilage at that time. He then returned to Putney, in Vermont, where his parents then resided, and commenced the practice of his profession, under many discouragements, at about the age of twenty years. The fame of Dr. Kittredge as a bonesetter and surgical operator was extensively known, as has been

that of their name in New England for a series of
years, and it enabled our novitiate soon to receive
the confidence of the public ; and a successful operation, of minor importance, in one of the neighboring
towns, soon introduced him into business.

It was now, as we may say, that Dr. Goodhue began to lay the foundation of his future usefulness.
The standard of medical education at this time, in
the country, was extremely low.   While with Dr.
Kittredge he had not the advantage and privilege of
resorting to many books.   Dr. Kittredge was a man
of strong powers of mind, but his faculties were uncultivated, and he depended more upon his own resources than the opinion of professional writers.   His
medical library, I am told, did not consist of more
than half a dozen volumes.   Great, then, must have
been the embarrassments of Dr. Goodhue at the
commencement of his practice, from his want of theoretical knowledge.   He was determined to overcome this deficiency, by procuring and thoroughly
studying all the latest and best professional authorities
which could be obtained in our country ; and this
course he adopted and pursued to the close of his
valuable life.   And this course, gentlemen, is the only
one by which you can become in any way useful or
eminent in your profession.   To me it is a subject of
wonder and astonishment, how so many of our physicians succeed in obtaining business who commence
the practice of their profession with ten or a dozen
volumes, and scarcely ever increase their libraries
during the course of their lives.   It appears to me

their reputation with the multitude must be sustained by a kind of empiricism. I can hardly conceive how a practitioner of medicine, however well qualified he might be at the commencement of his practice, can keep pace with the great and important improvements in our profession, without a knowledge of which he ought not to attempt to practice it, unless he procures and studies at least ten or a dozen volumes of the latest and best authorities every year of his life. Even were the science of medicine stationary as mathematics, there would not be much less necessity of resorting frequently to books. The human mind is so constituted, and the memory is so treacherous and evanescent, that unless we are constantly stimulating them by application to books, we are apt to lose what we have once acquired. Dr. Rush observes: ' It is no uncommon thing to find an old physician (from his neglect of books) more ignorant than he was when he commenced the practice of his profession.'

It was by great industry that Dr. Goodhue was soon enabled to obtain an extensive patronage, and his practice extended widely in Vermont, New Hampshire, and even in Massachusetts. The first capital operation he ever performed, which was that of amputating a leg, he performed without ever having seen it done before, and he was guided only by his books; and this was the case with most of his succeeding operations. How different were his facilities for procuring information from what young physi-

cians of the present day possess. Now our lecture
rooms are open, and every operation which it is ever
necessary to perform upon the human body, is shown
the student upon the subject, and every step of the
operation is pointed out and made familiar to him.
Yet industry and application like his knew no bounds.
Whatever he willed to do, that he performed. Like
Franklin he resolved to be eminent and useful, and
like Franklin he conquered. Now it was that students flocked to him from various parts of the country, many of whom in the course of their practice
became useful and eminent physicians. Among his
early pupils we must not forget the name of Dr.
Nathan Smith, almost the father of surgery in the
interior of New England, and founder of the Medical Institution connected with Dartmouth College,
in New Hampshire, one of the oldest and most respectable in our country.

In the year 1800, in consequence of his high attainments and respectable standing in the profession,
the Faculty of Dartmouth College conferred upon
him the highest medical honor which can be granted
to any physician, viz., the honorary degree of Doctor
of Medicine.

So exclusively were his time and attention devoted to his profession that he never coveted or accepted any important office in state or town. He was
once elected a Representative in the State Legislature, and attended as a member of that assembly one
session. For a great number of years he was elect-

ed President of the Windham County Medical Society of the State of Vermont, called the Vermont Second Medical Society.

In the year 1803, in order to extend his sphere of
usefulness, he removed from Putney to Chester in
Vermont, where he remained, enjoying the unlimited
confidence of his patrons and of his professional
brethren, till the year 1816, when, beginning to feel
the infirmities of age, from excessive professional
duty, and in some measure to curtail his business,
and practice in a more level country, he sought the
pleasant valley of the Connecticut, and located himself at Hadley, in Massachusetts. Here, too, his fame
extended itself, and he was soon engaged in extensive and lucrative practice, enjoying also here the
entire approbation of his patrons and his brother
physicians. He continued his practice until declining
health rendered it necessary for him entirely to relinquish it. I have often met him in consultation, and
shall not soon forget the pleasure and instruction it
afforded me.

In the year 1823, he was appointed by the Trustees, President of the Berkshire Medical Institution;
and with what fidelity and zeal he executed the duties
of his office, this board and faculty can answer. Nothing but declining health and a painful disorder,
which rendered travelling irksome, prevented his annually attending, addressing the graduates, and conferring the degrees. To show how much he was
attached to the interests of this school, suffer me to

extract his concluding remarks from the address already quoted.

'Forty-five years of laborious practice in my profession have whitened my head, and brought on the evening of my life. It has, for many years, been my delight to see young men, well stored with medical knowledge, coming forward in the world; and it has always given me much pleasure to be, in any measure, instrumental in promoting their usefulness. And while I have the honor to preside in this Institution, it shall be the business of my declining years to promote its interests in every way in my power.'

A year or two before his decease, he requested that he might be continued the President of this Institution so long as he lived, whether he should be able to meet us any more or not; a request which was most readily granted.

Dr. Goodhue was strongly impressed with the importance of the value of time. His industrious habits led him to be extremely punctual in his attendance upon the sick, and that he might not encroach upon the time of his brethren in consultation, he was strenuous in urging them to be punctual at the appointed hour. He once told me that in nearly fifty years practice he had never varied half an hour from the time he engaged in consultations. He was as punctual in paying a debt as he was in his consultations.

Few men in the country ever had a more extensive practice in operative Surgery. I am sorry I am not able to procure a list of all his capital operations, I believe he kept such an account. In one of my consultations with him he told me that he had trepanned upwards of forty times, and operated for strangulated hernia more than forty times. His operations in the other branches of a capital nature were equally extensive. Except the delicate operations on the eye, and lithotomy, he performed almost every other operation. He has stated, that so far as he knew, *he was the first to amputate at the shoulder joint, of any man in New England.* In deciding upon a capital operation, he always leaned to the side of prudence and caution.

His success as a practitioner of medicine was certainly very great; but with great modesty and equal truth, he was in the habit of attributing this to his untiring attention to his patients. Nothing is more gratifying than such attentions, nothing endears a physician so much to his friends, and nothing gives him so great an opportunity to improve himself in the symptoms of disease, and the successful operation of remedies. From this very circumstance, no class of men, not even clergymen, enjoy so much the confidence and esteem of their fellow men, and are so much beloved as faithful physicians. I am not acquainted with any peculiarities in his practice, either in medicine or surgery. From his constant habit of procuring and studying the latest and best professional writers, I am satisfied he kept up with the improvements in our profession, and that he so far adopted the system of the moderns as they appeared

27

to be in accordance with his judgment. But he was never hasty in adopting the theory of any one, because it was the fashion ; for medicine has its fashions as well as other things. He has mentioned that in the course of his practice the fashion of bleeding and reducing, and its opposite, the stimulant plan, had been in and out of fashion at least five times. He believed, as many of us believe and practice, that the middle course is the safest. He never could subscribe to the doctrine that every pain the patient felt was an inflammation, and that consequently the lancet or leeching must be resorted to. This doctrine, in my opinion, is now exerting a most pernicious influence upon the practice of too many of our physicians, particularly in chronic diseases.

The lancet is the besom which is sweeping our country with fearful devastation. Acute diseases are made chronic by it, and chronic diseases are running into dropsies and incurable debility. When I see the wide spread havoc which is made with this little instrument, I am almost induced to adopt the practice of that eminent physician, Dr. Danforth, and never bleed in any case. Let no one suppose from the above observations that I approve of extremes in either case ; it is the *abuse*, and not the judicious use, of the lancet to which we object.

I am sorry to say that Dr. Goodhue has not favored the world with many of the productions of his pen. It is much to be regretted that so many men of eminence and extensive practice should withhold from the public the result of their experience and

observations. These would be invaluable legacies to
their successors. He once published in one of our
medical journals a case of broken skull, where a portion of the brain escaped, and the child recovered.
He likewise published a paper in the *Medical Recorder*, containing an account of his method of reducing
and retaining in place a fractured thigh. His Inaugural Address to the graduates of this Institution was
published, and it evinces much talent in him as a
writer, and does great credit to his head and heart.

Dr. Goodhue was extremely temperate in his manner of living. He retired early at night, and rose
early in the morning : in consequence of which, with
a feeble constitution, he was enabled to attain the
good old age of '*three score years and ten.*' For
many years he entirely abstained from the use of spirituous liquors, adding another to the list of physicians who have lent their names and example to the
suppression of that vice which has been so great an
opprobium to the medical profession. At the time
of its early adoption, he subscribed the constitution
of the temperance society of the town where he resided. A long time since he abandoned the use of
tobacco, to which in former years he was immoderate-
ly attached. He substituted for it a crust of bread,
which he always carried in his pocket. Previous to
performing a surgical operation he was in the habit
of putting a lump of sugar into his mouth to excite
and moisten the salivary glands.

He married early in life, and reared a family of
eight highly respectable children, four sons and four

daughters, five of whom survive to mourn his irreparable loss. Two of his sons studied the profession of medicine. One of them died in Alabama, where he was engaged in extensive practice, about three years since. The other graduated at the Medical School in New Haven, this fall, after having attended a course of lectures in this Institution, and is now establishing himself as a practitioner of medicine and surgery in Upper Canada. His oldest surviving daughter married Dr. Twitchell, of Keene, who is one of the most distinguished surgeons in New Hampshire.

In his manner, Dr. Goodhue was a pattern of urbanity and gentility. In his appearance and dress he was perfectly neat. He commanded the respect and esteem of all who knew him. In his deportment he was affable and polite to his equals and inferiors; his conversational talents were of such an order as ever to attract attention, and he was always listened to with great interest and respect.

He was always a moral and religious man. Early in life he connected himself with the church in Putney, and in the latter part of it he devoted an unusual share of his attention to the study of the Bible and of theological works, with which his library abounded. Whatever might have been his religious views, it cannot be doubted that he sought the truth with an earnest desire to obtain it, and we hope he is now enjoying the rewards of the blessed in the bosom of his Father and his God.

Dr. Twitchell, at whose house he expired, has favored me with the following account of his closing scene: ' Dr. Goodhue's last sickness was a disease of the urinary organ, or rather of the prostate gland. He had occasionally been afflicted with pains in those parts for fifteen years. He gradually wore down with the pain usually attending such complaints. A few of the last weeks of his life he had to resort to the use of the catheter as often as once in three hours. He retained his senses perfectly to the last. A few moments before he expired, he requested a prayer to be read, which he composed some little time before, for the occasion ; after which he called upon all of us present to bear witness that he died without fear, and full in the faith he had long professed.'

Such, gentlemen of the Faculty and of the Class, is a brief and very imperfect sketch of our venerable friend and illustrious President. May his example stimulate us to increased exertion and untiring industry in the pursuits of that professional knowledge which he so long cultivated with so much reputation, and with such ardent zeal, for the melioration of the condition of his fellow beings.

DR. RALPH GOWDEY. Dr. J. A. Allen of Middlebury, Vt., in the Boston Medical and Sur. Jour. of July, 1840, in his memoir of Dr. Gowdey, says, ' Society is seldom called to mourn the death of an individual whose loss will be more felt than that of him who is the subject of this memoir. As a man, a physician and a friend, Dr. Gowdey was most esteemed by those by whom he was best known.

At an early age he received the literary honors of Middlebury College. Soon after the completion of his collegiate course he removed to the State of Georgia, where he engaged for several years as an instructor. The climate, however, having ultimately an unfavorable effect upon his health, he returned to Vermont, and shortly after commenced the study of medicine. In the year 1825 he received the degree of Doctor of Medicine. Soon after this he commenced the study of Physic in Rutland, Vermont, where he continued to the close of 1828, when he removed to Middlebury, his native place. From this time till his death, he steadily gained the confidence of the community as an *honest man* and *a good physician.*

As a scholar Dr. Gowdey ranked high. His mind was well cultivated and properly balanced. In his deportment he was gentlemanly, unassuming and unostentatious. He read much, reflected much, and remembered what he read. In ordinary conversation he was affable, intelligent and interesting, so that a person could rarely be in his society for any considerable time without becoming interested and delighted. For public speaking and debate he had no relish.

At an early period of his professional course, he may have been influenced to a considerable degree by certain specious and promising theories, ardently advocated at some of our medical schools, but his natural and discriminating mind, aided by experience and observation, enabled him to discern fallacies. This circumstance, in lieu of giving him a disgust and a disrelish for medical literature, as it has often done others, served to give an augmented impulse to his energies. He was led the more carefully to examine authorities, and ponder them in his own mind more thoroughly. And hence, his professional opinions were based upon sound *pathological principles.* Being thus formed, they were entitled to respect and attention. He was strictly a pathological, not a routine, practitioner.

He was well acquainted with modern pathology, and with the general circle of the medical sciences. And if the inscrutable hand of Providence had not prevented, he would unquestionably have given full assurance that his recent appointment to the *important Professorship* in the Vermont Academy of Medicine had been judiciously made. He possessed more than ordinary taste for the study of intellectual philosophy. To this science he devoted considerable attention, and upon this subject he has left several essays unpublished. The direct tendency which phrenology has to explain the history of the mind, led him to cultivate this science also with much interest. Upon this subject a considerable number of papers have been published, generally known to have been his productions.

In his intercourse with his medical brethren he was frank and honorable. This secured for him the universal respect of the profession. The estimation in which he was holden by the public was evinced by his twice being elected a member of the General Assembly of the State without any solicitation or management of his own. On this occasion he was elected because he was the least objectionable and most popular. Office he sought not, but office sought him. As a legislator he more than equalled the expectations of his constituents. His qualifications for a statesman are clearly shown by the journals of the sessions. No exceptions ought to be taken, and it is certainly no disparagement to any one to say, that some of the most important papers of each session were from his pen. Especially may be noticed the report of the committee on the *public lands;* and also that of the committee in relation to the *geological survey of the State.* This latter, in a particular manner, is drawn up with much ability, and is distinguished for being a plain and practical document, which will undoubtedly receive ultimately the sanction of the Legislature, and be carried into effect.

Some years since, Dr. Gowdey became a hopeful convert of Christianity, and made a public profession of his faith by uniting with the Congregational church. It is said, of the great and solemn realities of religion he never doubted. As a Christian, he was uniform and consistent. With him the practical exhibition of the cross was an every day concern. This secured for him an uncommon degree of calmness and equanimity. His confident assurance of the goodness and mercy of God sustained him, when, some time since, a beloved wife and dear child were taken from him by death. On these occasions he experienced severe trials. Speaking, a little while afterwards, to a friend on the circumstances of the profession, he remarked : ' I believe the trials and sufferings of a physician, on these events, are greater than those of any other profession. On all occasions when we are unable to afford relief, or mitigate the sufferings of the sick and dying, a wound must be given to our sympathies and sensibilities ; but when the object of our anxieties and solicitude is a *wife* and child, the distress is doubly augmented.' ' When,' continued he, ' my dying wife reached her trembling hand, and directed her anxious eye, towards me for help, and I was unable to afford any, my feelings can better be imagined than described. None but those who have been similarly situated can have any idea of the anguish which must thus rend the heart of a humane physician.'

One of the essential traits of character which he required his pupils to possess was to be humane, to sympathize with the afflicted. This trait of character the subject of this memoir possessed in an eminent degree. In him it was not the rash, impetuous emotions of a burst of sympathy, but it was a native inherent principle, cultivated by science and reason, and controlled by religion. These influences rendered him calm and composed through a trying, painful and protracted illness. And these rendered his last moments serene and unmoved. When in the full view of immediate death, he was addressed by a warm hearted visitant, in the pure language of com-

28

passion and sympathy, ' Doctor, I am sorry to see you in such trouble,' he calmly replied, ' *I am not in trouble, I am happy.*' These were his last words. He has left a widowed mother, an only sister, and a daughter, yet too young to appreciate her father's excellencies, and the irreparable loss she has sustained. To his friends, and it is believed he had no enemies, it is a pleasing consideration, that his sun, setting at noon-day, should have descended in such glorious triumph. Death to him had lost its sting. The grave obtained no victory. He died on the 13th of June, 1840, in the 38th year of his age.

Doctor Lyman Hall, one of the signers of the Declaration of Independence, was a native of Connecticut, where he was born about the year 1731. After receiving a collegiate education, and having acquired a competent knowledge of the theory and practice of medicine, he removed in 1752 to South Carolina. He was induced, however, during the same year to remove to Georgia, where he established himself in Sunbury, in the district of Medway. In this place he continued attending to the duties of his profession until the commencement of the revolutionary contest.

On the arrival of this important crisis in the history of the colonies, the patriotism of Dr. Hall became greatly excited, to the interests and dangers of his country. He perceived that the approaching storm must necessarily be severe; but, with the kindred spirits of the north, he was determined to meet it with patriotic firmness and resolution. Having accepted of a situation in the parish of St. Johns, which was a frontier settlement, both his person and property were exposed to great danger from his proximity to the Creek Indians and to the royal province of Florida.

The parish of St. Johns, at an early period of the contest, entered with great spirit into the general opposition of the country against Great Britain, while a majority of the inhabitants of Georgia entertained different sentiments. So widely different were the views and feelings of the people of this parish from those of the inhabitants of the province generally, that an almost entire separation took place between them.

In July, 1774, the friends of liberty held a general meeting at Savannah, where Dr. Hall appeared as a representative of the parish of St. Johns. The measures, however, adopted at that time, fell far short of the wishes both of this patriot and his constituents. In January, 1775, another meeting was held at Savannah, at which it was agreed to petition the king for a redress of grievances, and for relief from the arbitrary acts of the British ministry.

The parish of St. Johns, dissatisfied with the temporizing policy of the Savannah convention, in the following month made application to the Committee of Correspondence in Charleston, South Carolina, to form an alliance with them, by which their trade and commerce should be conducted on the principles of the non-importing association. The patriotic views

and feelings of this independent people were highly
applauded by the committee, but they found themselves under the necessity, by the rules of the continental association, of declining the alliance.

Upon receiving this denial the inhabitants of St.
Johns agreed to pursue such independent measures
as the patriotic principles they had adopted should
appear to justify. Accordingly, they resolved not to
purchase slaves imported into Savannah, nor to hold
commercial intercourse with that city, nor with the
surrounding parishes, unless for the necessaries of
life, and these to be purchased by direction of a committee. Having taken this independent stand, they
next proceeded to choose a representative to Congress,
and on counting the votes Doctor Hall was unanimously elected.

In the following May, Doctor Hall appeared in the
hall of Congress, and by that body was unanimously
admitted to a seat. But as he represented not the
colony of Georgia, but only a parish of the colony,
it was at the same time resolved to reserve the question as to his right to vote, for the further deliberation
of the Congress.

The above question at length coming before the
House on the occasion of Congress taking the opinions of its members by colonies, Dr. Hall expressed
his willingness to give his vote only in those cases in
which the sentiments of Congress were not taken by
the colonies.

Fortunately for the cause of liberty, on the 15th
of July, 1775, the convention of Georgia acceded

to the general confederacy, and proceeded to the appointment of five delegates to Congress, three of whom attended at the adjourned meeting of that body September 13, 1775.

Among the delegates thus appointed, Dr. Hall was one. To this station he was annually re-elected until 1780, at the close of which year he finally retired from the national legislature.

At length Georgia fell temporarily into the power of the British. On this event Dr. Hall removed his family to the north, and suffered the confiscation of all his property by the British government established in the State. In 1782 he returned to Georgia, and in the following year was elected to the chief magistracy of the State, or to the office of Governor.

After enjoying this office for a time he retired from the cares of public life, and about the sixtieth year of his age died at his residence in the county of Burke, whither he had removed.

Dr. Hall in his person was tall and well proportioned. In his manners he was easy, and in his deportment dignified and courteous. He was by nature characterized for a warm and enthusiastic disposition, which, however, was under the guidance of a sound discretion. His mind was active and discriminating. Ardent in his own feelings, he possessed the power of exciting others to action; and though in Congress he acted not so conspicuous a part as many others, yet his example and his exertions, especially in connection with those of the inhabitants of the circumscribed parish of St. Johns,

powerfully contributed to the final accession of the
whole colony of Georgia to the confederacy; thus
presenting in array against the mother country this
whole number of her American colonies. *Lives of
the Signers to the Declaration of Independence.*

DR. WILLIAM HAMILTON. I take great pleasure
in inviting the attention of this Society to the merits
of this enterprising physician, who was cut off in the
midst of his usefulness at an early age. Few men in
our country exhibited a greater promise of future
usefulness. He was rising into eminence, not in that
rapid manner which is evinced by many young physicians who are lauded to the skies in the first two
or three years of their professional career, and afterwards as rapidly sink in public estimation. Such
fame is almost always ephemeral. I consider it unfortunate for any young physician to enter at once,
at the commencement of his professional life, into a
large run of business. It does not give him sufficient
time to investigate the important cases which may
fall under his notice, and it often leads him into a
loose and careless method of practice. He has not
time to avail himself of the experience of the wisest
men in the profession, through the medium of their
writings; and he often substitutes his own experience
for theirs. I have hardly ever known such a physician ultimately to succeed as a useful and talented
practitioner. When I hear a young man boasting
of having charged one hundred and fifty or two hun-

dred dollars a month, I immediately distrust him, and think he is doing it for effect. A modest, unassuming young man will not praise himself in this way, but will leave it for others to do it, if he deserves it. Dr. Hamilton rose upon his own merits, and was slowly, but surely, securing the confidence of the public where he practised, and the applause of his professional brethren.

He was son of Capt. Robert Hamilton, a meritorious officer in the war of the Revolution. His mother is still living (1842) and in vigorous health, at the age of 95 or 96 years. About ten years ago she had the misfortune to fall and break the neck of the thigh bone, and she has not been able to walk a step since. He was born at Conway, Mass., in the year 1772. In early life, I understand, he had a lameness of one of his legs, and that in consequence he devoted his attention to books. After preparing himself for the study of medicine, he entered the office of the elder Dr. Cutler, of Amherst, who was a Fellow of this Society. He remained there awhile, and then completed his medical pupilage in the office of Dr. William Kittredge, who then resided in Conway. He then commenced the practice of his profession in his native town, where he continued in the discharge of his professional duties, to the universal satisfaction of his employers, till the time of his death, which happened in the year 1810, at the age of thirty-eight years.

He was always fond of study, and was a reading and reflecting man. He educated several medical students, most of whom proved to be highly respectable practitioners. In civil life, he enjoyed the confidence of his townsmen, in an eminent degree, and in the brawls and discords which sometimes occur among neighbors, he was often called upon to heal the disturbances of the mind, as well as of the body. On one memorable occasion, in the height of political excitement, during the embargo, about the year 1808, when the public mind was almost ripe for civil war, by his influence and exertion, he probably saved the effusion of much blood, in a contest which must inevitably have ensued between some of his fellow citizens and those of a neighboring town. This is not the place to enter into a detail of that event. Suffice it to say, that were it not for his exertions a riot must have followed, many lives would have been lost, and the miseries which must have ensued would have been incalculable. His memory will ever be dear to his fellow townsmen, and to those who were acquainted with him. *My Address before the Mass. Med. Society, May*, 1842.

DR. ANDREW HARRIS. For a number of years Dr. Harris has been considered, with justice, as the most distinguished Surgeon in the eastern section of Connecticut. He performed most of the important operations in that part of the State from the Massachusetts line to the sea shore, as well as a considerable number in the adjoining towns of Rhode Island. His decease has left a chasm, which will take a long time to fill with any one who can share the same portion of the approbation and confidence of the public.

He was a native of Rhode Island, and was born about five miles from Providence, upon a farm which had descended to his father, from the Harris, who was one of the first settlers, and one of the principal men who co-operated with Roger Williams. His academical education he received, or rather completed, at Plainfield, where there was at that day, perhaps, the most flourishing Academy in Connecticut. His private medical studies were pursued under the tuition of Dr. Joseph Palmer, who was his brother-in-law, at Ashford. Thence he attended a course of lectures at Dartmouth College, and was a favorite pupil of Professor Nathan Smith. Here he formed his taste for Anatomy and Surgery. He finally completed his preparatory studies by attending a course at Phidadelphia, where he became familiar with dissection and operative surgery. (It is believed he received the degree of Doctor of Medicine at this institution. S. W. W.) Having a strong attachment to his profession, being uncommonly studious and industrious, and possessing naturally a mechanical skill and dexterity, few candidates for public patronage came forward under such favorable circumstances. By those who knew him, much was expected from him, and his success was such as to gratify these high expectations. Without attempting here to specify the several branches in which he was eminent, it is yet proper to mention one particular,

29

in which his success, from some consideration or other, was pre-eminent. He very frequently extirpated scirrous or cancerous tumors, and, contrary to the experience of many able surgeons, the instances of relapse were very few. The same may justly be said of another of his operations. He was in the habit of tying varicose veins, without any of those unpleasant results, of which many practitioners complain. He had no hesitation, therefore, in operating in either of those diseases, provided the system in general remained tolerably sound, and his usual success demonstrated the soundness of his judgment.

His intercourse with his professional brethren was always attended with frankness and candor. It is rare, if ever, we find a professional man of his eminence, who was so little disturbed by the jealousy or envy of others. He appeared to be on the best terms with every physician in his vicinity. In consultations his opinions were considered as of the highest authority ; but they were delivered with so much modesty, that they never gave offence, even when there might be a difference in judgment. He lived upon a farm of considerable size, which was cultivated under his inspection, and when circumstances would admit, with his own labor. As has been said, he had a mechanical turn. This he improved, and curious and useful inventions and works were to be seen upon his premises, made by his own hands.

He was peculiarly happy in his family, and his

house was the seat of hospitality and benevolence. His residence was distinguished for cultivation and taste, and a degree of elegance not very common in country mansions.

The ardent and active friend of social order, and of the substantial institutions of society, he was distinguished for his exertions—not ultra, but rational—in the cause of temperance, and he was one of the main pillars in the ecclesiastical communities to which he belonged. He bore with calmness, patience, and resignation, his last protracted illness, which was a pulmonary affection, evidently occasioned by his excessive professional labors, in connection with his other various and arduous employments. He was much engaged in the latter part of his life in the study of the Scriptures, and found in them support and consolation.

The Doctor has left a widow and three children, (all daughters,) with a sympathizing community, to lament their irreparable loss. He died at Canterbury, Conn., the last week in May, 1840, in the 53d year of his age.   T. M.

Bost. Med. and Surg. Jour. vol. 22.

Doct. J. Hart. The following notice of Dr. John Hart was written at the request of Dr. Nichols, for his dissertation before the Massachusetts Medical Society at their annual meeting, May, 1836, and published as a note to that address, by Dr. J. Spaulding, of South Reading, Massachusetts.

Dr. John Hart was born in Ipswich, Mass., October 12, (old style) A. D. 1751. His father, John Hart, was a lawyer and a noted musician, and died many years since at the place of his nativity. His mother, Mary Hart, on whom devolved the first training of her son, was a woman of great personal charms, good talents, and eminent for purity; and spared no pains to impress on the mind of her son those traits of character for which he in after life became so distinguished. After having received a good preparatory education, for those times, he studied medicine at Ipswich, his native town, with Dr. John Calif, a distinguished physician of that place. At the age of nineteen he commenced his practice in Georgetown (now Bath), Me., and there continued in his profession till the commencement of the revolutionary war. At that time, when many were vacillating in relation to the grievances of the colonies, Dr. Hart, though young, took a decided stand; and as decision of character had been one of the most prominent traits of his youth, the following incident will show how it operated on this occasion. Dr. Calif, who was then his medical preceptor, being timid, and fearful of the issue of the revolutionary enterprise, advised his young friend, Dr. Hart, not to enter the service, as he would probably lose both his pay and his neck. But this did not frighten him; and he enlisted against the advice and remonstrances of one whom he respected. After about a year he returned on furlough and visited his medical patron, who advised him not to go back to the service, promising to obtain for him a surgeon's place in the British army, where he would be sure both of his pay and his neck. But his young friend was decided, and spurned the offer, saying, ' Sir, I will risk both.' After Burgoyne was taken, (and he was there) he said to his adviser, ' Sir, what do you think now.?' He first joined the army in Cambridge, in Col. Prescott's regiment, who fought at Bunker Hill. He continued in the army in 1775–6, and in 1776 went to New York; was stationed at Staten Island, and remained there till the enemy took possession of Long Island; then driven to the Highlands, remained there till Col. Prescott's regiment was disbanded. Then, a regiment was formed under the command of Captain Bailey, called the Second Massachusetts Regiment, to which Dr. Hart was appointed regimental surgeon, in which capacity he served till the war closed, in 1783.

After this he remained in a regiment, kept in reserve, under the command of Col. Henry Jackson, till July, 1784; having served his country a period of nine years and three months. Having passed through so many laborious scenes of warfare, he returned to Reading, (now South Reading,) in his native State, gladdened with the prospect of his country's peace, to take repose in the bosom of his friends, who thrice welcomed him as a patriot and republican. He however was soon solicited to enter into the active duties of his profession, when a field, large and broad, opened itself, which would afford ample opportunities for the exercise of that

knowledge in the healing art, which had been accumulating by practical experience during his nine
years service.   His practice soon became very extensive, not only in his own town and county, but
in the adjacent counties of Essex and Suffolk.   He
was one of the first, if not the very first, practitioners
in the county of Middlesex, who made use of mercurial remedies in acute and typhoid febrile cases; and
his success was such, by this course of treatment, that
the Middlesex Medical Association, formed about
1790, of which he was one of the most prominent
members, adopted his manner of treatment from that
period.   He has often told the writer of this sketch
that he felt sure of the life of his patient, when he
had evidence that the system had become affected
by mercurial action; his reasoning was that two diseased actions could not exist in the system at the
same time, and that, while the artificial diseased action produced by calomel was perfectly manageable,
the febrile diseased action might not be.   But whether he reasoned correctly or not, few, if any, physicians in New England ever took charge of a greater number of fevers, or treated them with greater
success.   In all difficult cases of this character, his
opinion was relied on as the last resort of human
skill.   In 1792, when Boston was visited with small
pox, and a general alarm was produced, not only in
Boston, but in all its vicinity, Dr. H. was called on to
take charge of hospitals, erected for the time being,
in Reading, Lynn, Boston and other places, for the
purpose of inoculation (the only remedy then known

to stay that awful pestilence,) and his skill and industry were such that he actually inoculated and carried through some thousands in the space of a few months, and in a number of the hospitals, without the loss of a patient. Having had great opportunities for the practice of surgery, during the revolutionary struggle, his judgment was considered decisive, and much to be relied on, in the most perplexing surgical cases; and frequently he was called to operate. In the department of midwifery, he was no less conspicuous, and in the course of his long practice he probably attended to more than three thousand obstetric cases. Possessing great firmness and resolution, blended with kindness and sympathy, he seemed peculiarly fitted to allay the anxiety attendant on such occasions; but when necessity required, the most responsible duties, by common consent, devolved upon him.

Dr. Hart was a strict observer of nature, and in viewing the cases, formed a theory of his own; he relied more on calomel, epicacuanha, and Peruvian bark, than all other remedies in the materia medica. He was exceedingly careful not to reduce his patients, after a few days illness, but on the commencement of disease, attacked the enemy with great boldness. He was a great enemy to depletion, and contended that the abstraction of blood diminished the power of overcoming disease, and he was so sanguine in this sentiment, that for forty years he rarely bled, and for the last twenty-four, not once. His aversion to quackery, nostrums, and specifics of all kinds, was almost proverbial, and had a weighty

influence with the younger part of the profession,
with whom he was often called to consult.   There
was a dignity and manliness in his character that
looked down with disgust on the little, low arts of
cunning and hypocrisy, adulation, and intrigue.   He
had no sympathy for such manœuvres, nor complacency in the actors of them.   He was open, frank,
unconcealed ; and seemed incapable of dissembling.
Although affable and familiar, he never descended to
any thing low and contemptible ; and so dignified
and commanding were his looks and demeanor, that
there were few, if any, but that felt respect for his
person, and awe in his presence.   As a physician,
he insisted on obedience to his directions, which in
most instances, by the unlimited confidence and attachment of his patients, were obeyed to the letter ;
but when they swerved from his advice, and disobey-
ed his injunctions, (choosing to follow their own reason) he felt a high sense of the neglect, and would occasionally permit such patients to ' *take care of themselves.*'   While Dr. Hart was engaged in a full tide
of practice, having reared a respectable family, with
industry, economy and a good reputation, and hoping
ere long to enjoy more leisurely the comforts of a
domestic life, he was called by the suffrages of his
townsmen to represent them in the General Court ;
in which capacity he served his town eight years.
He then sustained the office of Senator five years ;
and, during the time he filled these important stations, his constituents would scarcely release him
from the toils of his profession.   It may be observed,

that he was one of the first who had the moral courage to break up the advised custom of *treating* at representative elections. He was a living example of the value of the great temperance principles, as no man enjoyed better health, and few were more exposed to fatigue. He, probably, for the last forty years did not taste a drop of distilled spirits, and declared the same great principles, which, till late, the community have not been willing to acknowledge. He was long a member, and for many years a Counsellor, of the Massachusetts Medical Society, where he sustained a fair reputation among his compeers; also an intimate friend and associate of Gov. Brooks and Eustis, fellow patriots of the revolution. The Society of Cincinnati recognized him as one of the most active and distinguished members, and he sustained the office of Vice President of the Society at the time of his decease.

Dr. Hart was for many years an acting justice of the peace and of the quorum, which office he sustained till his death; the cases brought before him were numerous, and his decisions were so judicious, that all parties usually became reconciled to greater bonds of amity. He was also a justice of the Court of Sessions, which office he discharged with respectability. As a politician, he was a consistent, inflexible republican, ever sustaining 'the laws and the constitution.'

30

Dr. Abraham Haskell. Dr. Haskell was born in Lancaster, Mass., Nov. 16th, 1746. His father was a farmer in comfortable circumstances, had a numerous family of children, and was therefore enabled to do but little for each. The subject of this sketch gave early indications of his desire of having a profession, and, of course, of acquiring an education preparatory thereto. His father perceiving his fondness for reading and study, told him if he would study divinity, he would do all he could to help him through college. The son replied that he wished to study physic. Then, said the father, I shall do nothing more for you than for the others; and advised him to take the subject into consideration, and reflect upon the consequences before he decided. 'I have already made up my mind,' said the boy; 'I would rather forego all the honors and pleasures of a public education than renounce the thoughts of studying physic. I would rather follow my trade till I am free, and then trust to my own resources.' He therefore then returned to his trade, which was that of a shoemaker, and pursued it faithfully till he was of age. His father having then 'divided to him his portion of his goods,' he entered upon his preparatory studies with the Rev. Mr. Harrington, who was an excellent linguist, and Dr. Thayer's immediate predecessor in the ministry at Lancaster. He continued his classical studies till Dr. Harrington pronounced him fit to enter Cambridge College.

He then commenced the study of medicine under

the direction of Israel Atherton, M. D., of Lancaster,
one of the most noted practitioners of the county of
Worcester, at that time. He applied himself with
unabated diligence to the entire satisfaction of his
instructor. Having completed his course of studies,
he went to Lunenburg under the patronage of Dr.
John Taylor, who was in considerable practice, but,
being somewhat engaged in mercantile pursuits, was
desirous of quitting it. He soon began to acquire
the confidence of the people, and in the lapse of a
few years, as he became known, his calls were more
frequent, and his practice spread extensively into all
the neighboring towns. He remained in Lunenburg
till December, 1810, and during that period was frequently called in consultation, fifteen and twenty
miles, and sometimes farther. The roads being new,
and of course somewhat rough, his business was
very laborious; and in order to render it easier he
removed to Leominster, where he had done more
business, perhaps, than in any one town except Lunenburg, in which place he left his son as the principal physician. In Leominster his practice continued equally extensive as formerly, but less laborious;
and indeed there was no sensible diminution of confidence in the people towards him till he was between
seventy and eighty years old. A gradual failure of
the memory and the faculties was then perceptible,
as was common with people of his age; but still he
retained a good share of business as long as he resided in that place, which he left in his 88th year.
By the advice of his friends, his family, consisting of

himself, wife, and one daughter, he was induced to take up his residence with his son, who had a few years previous removed to Ashby in the county of Middlesex. When Dr. Haskell resided in Lunenburg, he was frequently called to Ashby to patients of his own, as well as in consultations, so that the people were almost as well acquainted with him as with their own physicians. Therefore, for the sake of giving the elderly part of the people an opportunity of once more gratifying their old doctor, and also for his gratification, his son would frequently carry him out to see his patients, and occasionally he would go alone in his son's absence. For, like most people in their dotage, he laughed at, or rather scorned, the idea that he was superannuated, and unable to discriminate and prescribe as judiciously as ever he could.

His health was at this time tolerably good, and his hand was so firm and steady, that he could use the lancet with perfect safety. This state of health continued through the summer of 1834. He was in the habit of visiting, sometimes alone, and sometimes with his son, an old gentleman whose toes and part of one foot were mortified. On the 9th of Nov. he was preparing to go and dress the foot, his son going another way; and after going out at the door, he seemed to be hesitating, and moving about as if he was in search of something. On being asked what he wanted, he instantly discovered, by an irregular and half uttered response, an imbecile and shattered state of mind. This imbecility daily increased, till he became perfectly idiotic. On the 16th, he lay in bed till after noon, then arose, dressed himself, and appeared perfectly composed, and restored to the full exercise of his mental faculties. After making some familiar remarks, he inquired the day of the month, and on being told the 16th, he expressed much surprise, for he thought it the 9th, and said, ' I have lost a week—why, this is my birth day, I am just 88 years old.' He continued rational through this day, but the next his mind was a little affected, and he gradually relapsed into his former state, and so continued till Dec. 13th, when he died.

Dr. Haskell was a very close student, and even unwearied in his application. While he was studying with Mr. Harrington, many was the night when he ' took no note of time,' till day light admonished him that he must retire to sleep and rest. By this manner his proficiency in the Latin and Greek languages was far superior to what falls to most people, who enjoyed higher privileges and better opportunities. His knowledge of them was so critical that he could very readily render into good English those Latin and Greek quotations with which medical books, especially old ones, abound. This love of study continued through life. He could read in the midst of his family, undisturbed by the common talk or the prattle of children. He procured and read almost every new medical work till upwards of 70 years of age. His memory was so strong and tenacious that he could state the opinion of almost any author on any subject, and confirm it by an immediate reference to his work. The collateral branches, also, as chemistry, botany, &c., engrossed no small share of his attention. Indeed, every thing that would add to his knowledge and enable him the more success-fully to combat disease in its varied forms was sought with avidity, and subjected to the test of experience before it was much used, or recommended as a re-medy to be depended upon. He was, therefore, rather fastidious in adopting the various *new fangled* medicines, as he demonstrated them, that were every now and then thrust into public notice. Experience abundantly taught him that they promised too much.

Early after its establishment he became a member of the Massachusetts Medical Society, and, it is be-lieved, contributed his full share to do away with the suspicions that were entertained against it, and to render it an honorable and useful institution in the eyes of the community.

The practice of physic was his forte, and he never interfered with the peculiar province of the surgeon. He extirpated very neatly and successfully a cance-rous breast; occasionally reduced dislocations and fractures, and united several hare-lips. But he always declined such cases, so far as he could, satisfactorily to his friends, because he was otherwise sufficiently employed in a way more agreeable to his mind. He also refused taking the lead in capital operations, yet his advice was frequently sought. His brethren re-gretted his unwillingness to pursue that branch of the healing art, because his calm, steady, persevering, undaunted resolution, conciliating address, pleasant manners,—in short, the possession of every requisite qualification seemed united in him, and pointed him out as a man peculiarly fitted for that purpose.

As he was habitually critical in his reading, so was he mathematically correct in his prescriptions. No hap-hazard compositions ever came from his hands. Every thing relating to his profession was done *secumdum artem*. By that means he learned how much reliance to place upon a particular remedy, to what to impart its efficacy, and where to alter it or substitute another in its stead. He never put much dependence upon book recipes. They might form the groundwork for his prescriptions; for he eagerly caught at every thing that promised usefulness, come from what quarter it might; and after subjecting it to the test of his long experience and sound discriminating judgment, would adopt or reject it accordingly. Prescriptions given in books, he said, were ordered under different circumstances from what our country physicians are accustomed to, as climate, situation, &c., and the remedies there recommended must be varied to suit the different forms the same disease would assume in different localities.

In his intercourse with his brethren he was always affable, communicative, condescending, and instructive. One who asked his advice frequently, for thirty years, said he never met him without learning something new. Never overbearing, he regarded the opinions of others, as he was ready to give his own. His pleasant, cheerful countenance never failed to inspire confidence in his patients, and his agreeable demeanor endeared him equally to the bystanders.

The great object of his capacious and well stored mind seemed to be directed to alleviating the sufferings and subduing the diseases of his fellow creatures. ' To do good and communicate,' was his governing principle. Interested motives had no resting place in his benevolent mind. All his acquaintances can testify to his indifference in pecuniary concerns. To command money enough to satisfy his pressing necessities, was frequently beyond his power. He had no disposition to make a fortune. He rather offended his friends by neglecting to send in their accounts, than by urging remuneration for his services; whereas had he possessed the common prudence and circumspection of many, which would have been justifiable, he would have acquired his thousands; and if he had practiced the foresight and shrewdness of others, he might have amassed his tens of thousands.

If there were any diseases in which Dr. Haskell, who knew so well how to prescribe for all, especially excelled, we might mention Midwifery and Fevers. His experience in the former was very great. In regulating the efforts of nature, he was neither too hasty, nor too tardy; but seemed to render artificial assistance just at the point of time when it was necessary. Among the several thousand cases which came under his care, it is said he never lost a woman in the time of child-bed, where he had the whole management. Always cheerful, and never impatient, he never failed of gaining the good will and approbation of his patients.

In fevers he was unusually successful. In his examination of a patient his inquiries were very par-

ticular. Not an irregular symptom escaped his observation. After obtaining all the information he
wanted, he calmly and deliberately pondered the case
in his mind, longer or shorter, according to its ur-
gency, and then made up his prescriptions; the
prominent symptoms demanding his first attention.
In this, as in all other cases, his acute diagnostic
powers soon pointed out to him the peculiar nature of
the disease; and on this ground, with his accurate
knowledge of the human system, he seldom failed
in his prognosis.

When the spotted fever was so rife in Petersham,
Barre, and several other towns in Worcester county,
the people were completely panic struck. Indeed,
the disorder attacked so suddenly, so violently, and
assumed such unusual appearances, and so severe,
and so frequently proved fatal, that even the physicians of those places and the vicinity, were not exempt from the general alarm and consternation. In
this state of extraordinary excitement, Dr. Haskell
was sent for, and many of the elderly inhabitants can
now testify with what calmness and patience he suffered the deprivations of sleep, food, and rest, and
with what unwearied diligence, perseverance and
attention he administered to the calls of the sick.
Nor was this all. The disease under his treatment,
which was very different from what had been pursued
before his arrival, was arrested in its progress in
many cases which the people considered hopeless; a
sober second thought therefore soon took the place
of a state of ungovernable fright and distraction, and
the senses of the people were restored to a state of

composure and calm reflection. In chronic complaints, tumors, abscesses and cutaneous diseases, he was uncommonly successful.

The publications of Dr. Haskell are not many. He wrote more for his own amusement and convenience, as a means of reference than for the public eye. He however read a dissertation on Croup before the Massachusetts Medical Society; another on Spotted Fever, and some remarks on inverted Uterus, which were all published in the Transactions of the Mass. Med. Society. He also published a paper with an elegant colored plate upon Icthyosis, in the New England Journal of Medicine and Surgery. He also delivered an oration on the 4th of July at Fitchburg, which was published. He delivered, also, several addresses before the Freemasons, but none of them were ever published.

He received the honorary degree of Doctor of Medicine from Harvard University, without any solicitation on his part. *Manuscript from his son, Dr. Abraham Haskell, Jan.* 1843.

Dr. PARDON HAYNES. The birth place of Dr. Haynes, late of Rowe, in the State of Massachusetts, was New London, Connecticut, where he was born on the 2nd of February, 1762. He moved from that place with his father to Hoosac, at the age of fifteen years. He served for a short period in the army of the revolution. He studied the profession of medicine with an older brother. He commenced practice in the town of Hebron, New York; but the manners

and customs of the people there were so uncongenial
to him, that he was induced to change his residence
for a home in New England. An intimate friend of
his directed him to Rowe, assuring him that that
place stood in great need of him. He visited the
place and concluded to remain there. His business
soon became quite extensive.

Dr. Haynes practiced his profession in Rowe and
the adjacent towns, for the space of forty-five years
with well deserved reputation, and with great success.
He accumulated, perhaps, as great a property by his
practice as any man in the country. His constitution was unusually firm. He had an indomitable
spirit of perseverance, and he faltered at no labor,
however severe. Dr. Humphrey Gould, of Rowe,
who has kindly forwarded me data from which the
following sketch is drawn, says, ' in the early part
of his practice he suffered great hardships and was
often exposed to imminent danger. He was frequently obliged to go by marked trees in his visits to
the sick, often at the peril of his life. On one occasion, riding in the night over a new cut path, in the
winter season, his horse fell with him, the place being sideling, his horse was brought up against a tree,
and fell upon him, and he was utterly unable to extri-
cate himself from his dangerous situation, remaining
thus exposed for a while ; fortunately a man came
along and relieved him. I have often heard the people of Reedsborough tell of being in the woods with
him, and thus exposed through a long winter's night,
till the light of day showed them on their way.'

Little do the physicians of the city know of the

hardships and privations of our physicians on our western mountains, during the long, dreary, and inclement winters. Frequently their only mode of conveyance is on foot, on Indian rackets or snow shoes, and all this for the paltry sum of one shilling a mile, even at which some of their employers find fault.

Small as is this sum, many of the physicians there make independent fortunes by it. Strange as this assertion may seem, it is nevertheless true. It is done by the most rigid habits of economy and self-denial of many of the luxuries of life.

Dr. Haynes never permitted any obstacle to prevent his visiting his patients at the appointed hour, if it was in his power to prevent it. He was often obliged to cross Deerfield river, which rises in Hoosac mountain, at the imminent hazard of his life. Dr. Gould observes, 'he would often swim his horse when the ice would beat the skin from his limbs. On such occasions his motto was, ' live or die, I will go through.' ' He was no surgeon, but a good and able physician, and particularly distinguished as a practitioner of Midwifery, in which department few excelled him. He was extremely regular in his habits. He rose in the morning at 3 o'clock, generally, in the active period of his life; devoted the stillness of the morning to reading; and usually, long before light, was upon his horse performing his daily round of business. He was ready at every one's call, rich or poor. He was a faithful friend, a kind parent, indulgent to a fault. His memory is still held in grateful remembrance by many who have received the benefit of his healing art. It was his inveterate practice, which grew upon him in consequence of the vast amount of business he was obliged to do while on his horse, to turn his head neither to the right hand, nor left, let him meet whom he might, unless particularly accosted. He commanded the Company in Rowe, when an office in the militia was honorable, and conferred distinction upon him who filled it. He was commissioned by John Hancock and Samuel Adams. On one occasion his Company was particularly distinguished by the venerable Gen. Mattoon, as the first and best disciplined upon the field, at a regimental muster. Dr. Haynes died Dec. 29, 1833, aged seventy-one years. His sickness was short, his mind unclouded. He died in the full faith of a Christian hope of a blessed immortality. He was a sincere believer in the Unitarian views of gospel truth.

My Address before the Mass. Med. Society.

DR. AMOS HOLBROOK. The data from which the following facts in relation to this distinguished physician are taken, are from the Boston Courier, as quoted by the Boston Medical and Surgical Journal of July 13th, 1842. They were furnished by a man thoroughly acquainted with the merits of the deceased.

Dr. Holbrook was engaged in the practice of medicine for nearly seventy years. Although he commenced the study and practice of his profession with but little previous preparation, yet he made up for these deficiencies of his early life by great experience and even skill, which he acquired in the American revolutionary army, and by a very extensive practice in Milton, Massachusetts, and the neighborhood, and by a remarkable devotion to the science of medicine, which he begun early in life, and which continued to the latest period of it. He was self-taught, as were many of the most distinguished medical men in America, but by an unconquerable love for his profession, he acquired a very high reputation, and he obtained the respect and esteem of his medical brethren and his patrons both at home and abroad. This reputation is of vastly greater importance than that obtained by many young men who, having completed their pupilage, think their education is finished, and scarcely ever afterwards procure a medical book, or record a medical fact. Men, to be useful in our profession, must yearly procure the latest and most approved works in it, and must be in the habit of recording the results of their experience and observation, or they will in a few years be more ignorant than they were when they commenced the practice of medicine. Without the use of books and recorded experience, physicians are apt to forget the details of practice in the course of three or four years. Genius and tact, without the aid of books, will soon shipwreck the best balanced mind, and in our profession lead to downright empiricism.

Dr. Holbrook was born in Bellingham, Massachusetts, on the 23d of January, 1754. Quite early in life he commenced the study of physic with his uncle on the maternal side, Dr. Metcalf, of Franklin. He completed his pupilage at Providence, Rhode

Island. He entered the army as a Surgeon's mate, at Cambridge, in the year 1775, in the regiment commanded by Col. John Greaton. In March 1776, after having passed a satisfactory examination, he was appointed a surgeon in the same regiment. He soon after accompanied this regiment to New York, and followed it to Albany, with the troops, which were destined to reinforce those who were engaged in the expedition against Quebec. The campaign in Canada proving unsuccessful, the army were compelled, after arriving at the mouth of the river Sorel, to retreat to Ticonderoga. At this place Dr. Holbrook was transferred to Colonel Joseph Vose's regiment, which he accompanied to New Jersey. In consequence of ill health he was obliged to apply for a discharge in March, 1777, and to return to Massachusetts. After this, by advice of Col. Vose and others, he went to Milton, in Massachusetts, where he established himself in the practice of medicine. An attack of Intermittent fever, probably contracted in the army, induced him towards the close of summer to undertake a sea voyage. He was fortunately enabled to procure the office of Surgeon in a letter of marque under the command of Captain Truxton, and he sailed for Europe, and visited France, where, being obliged to remain several months, he devoted much of his time and attention to witnessing the practice of the hospitals, and adding to his stores of practical knowledge. After this he returned to Milton, having been absent less than a year, with his health perfectly restored.

About this time Dr. Holbrook established tempora-

ry hospitals for the admission of patients who had
been inoculated for the small pox. He thus became
acquainted with the inhabitants of the town and surrounding country. Prepossessing in his appearance,
pleasing in his manners, possessed of great bodily
activity, and ardent and indefatigable in attention to
business, and in the pursuit of knowledge, he soon
found himself in a practice which gradually and constantly increased from year to year. He was indeed
eminently successful as a physician. His very presence in the sick chamber, and the soothing kindness
of his address, seemed to give hope to his patients,
and inspired confidence in their friends; while his
assiduous attentions to the sick of all ages and constitutions, and his sympathy with the afflicted, allevi-
ated suffering, and afforded consolation, when the resources of art failed to arrest the progress and fatal
termination of disease. He was always prompt to
answer every call, and much of his time was spent
in gratuitous service.

Dr. Holbrook, like many other respectable and
highly eminent physicians who have ever had an extensive practice, never became rich by the practice of
his profession. In one thing, however, like many
other benevolent physicians, he was peculiarly rich,
and that was in the gratitude and blessings of the
poor, whom he was always ready and willing to
assist in their distress. At a considerable loss in a
pecuniary point of view, he was particularly active
in introducing and promoting public vaccination in
the town of Milton, and that town was the first in
its corporate capacity to give to its inhabitants the

benefits of this most salutary protective agent from
the ravages of the small pox. Of the inhabitants of
this town, three hundred and thirty-seven of all ages
from the age of three months to seventy years, a
fourth part of the whole population, were vaccinated
by Dr. Holbrook in the year 1808. Of these, twelve
were afterwards tested by himself with small pox by
inoculation, and having successfully resisted an attack
of that loathsome complaint they were discharged as
safe from an invasion of that pestilence. He continued these public vaccinations in Milton for many subsequent years, and kept a register of the names of all
those who had successfully passed the disease. In
consequence of his benevolent exertions in this cause
and of his great reputation in other respects, in the
year 1811 he had the honor of being elected as a
foreign member of the Medical Society of London,
and of the Literary and Philosophical Society of
Preston in England. He was admitted a Fellow of
the Massachusetts Medical Society in the year 1800,
and resigned in 1832. He was a Counsellor in
the Society for many years. He was also Vice President of the Society for some time. The honorary
degree of Doctor of Medicine was conferred upon
him in 1813 by Harvard University.

'Blessed with a vigorous constitution, Dr. Holbrook was enabled, with little intermission, to endure
all the toils, by day and by night, of a laborious profession, till he was nearly 80 years old : after reaching this advanced age, and till within a few years of
his decease, though his strength was much impaired
by repeated and alarming attacks of sickness, and he

32

suffered daily from an incurable organic disease, he continued to yield to the solicitations of patients who required his services. For several months he had been conscious of increasing difficulty of respiration, especially on exertion ; but it was not till nearly the end of December that this became alarming to his family. The nature of his disease was now apparent to others, as it had been to himself, and under it he gradually wasted away. He occasionally took exercise in the open air, and on the very day before his decease he was able to ride out, and to tender an office of kindness to a young and suffering friend. His faculties, with scarcely diminished vigor, remained with him to the last moment, when, without a struggle, he expired at the age of 88.

Dr. George Holcombe. This distinguished physician was a resident of Allentown, Monmouth county, New Jersey. He was eminent as a physician, and when released from the discharge of those honorable public duties which his fellow citizens conferred upon him as evidence of the regard which they entertained for his talents and integrity, enjoyed an extensive practice. His mind, though well stored with the learning and observation of his predecessors and cotemporaries, relied less upon these adventitious supplies, than upon the application of its own fertile resources. Aided by these last qualifications, united to powers of quick perception and correct judgment, his practice was at once original, energetic and successful. His useful qualifications were well set off

by the talents he displayed for the ornamental branches of education, which in conjunction with great ami-
ability of character and urbanity of manners, rendered him an agreeable associate, and an ornament to
society. He received the degree of Doctor of Medicine, was a collaborator of the American Medical
Journal, and at the time of his death he was a member of the House of Representatives of the United
States Congress. He died at Allentown on the 14th
of Jan. 1829. *Amer. Med. Journal, Feb.* 1829.

Dr. EDWARD AUGUSTUS HOLYOKE, *the centenna-
rian.* It is a question with the public, whether the
life of a physician is favorable to longevity. Many
believe, that in comparison with the other professions
and occupations of men, that those of the physician
and surgeon, are not favorable to the attainment of
a great age. Certainly no class of men are subject
to so much bodily and mental fatigue, as that of the
physician with an extensive practice in the country.
The mental wear and tear of the constitution of eminent physicians in the city, are not less than in those
of the country. I have no data before me by which
I can draw the comparison between the health and
longevity of the farmer, for instance, whose employment is considered by many to be as healthy as that
of any other, and the physician, yet from the statistics before me, I am inclined to believe that the
practice of medicine is as conducive to health and
long life, as that of any other profession or occupa-

tion. In relation to this subject one remark should
not escape notice. In the profession of medicine
very many young men engage in the study of it,
with feeble and slender constitutions, from an erroneous opinion that none but the hardy and robust
should engage in the laborious occupation of agriculture. The reverse should be the fact, and none
but the most hardy should be advised to engage in
literary and scientific pursuits. Too many of our
young men fall victims to consumption from adopting
this course, who, otherwise, by laboring upon farms,
might be robust and vigorous. This cause undoubtedly operates against the longevity of the medical
profession in comparison with that of the farmer.
The following statistics, however, on a limited scale,
will show that the medical profession with all its
hardships, is not absolutely unfavorable to long life.

In the Massachusetts Medical Society, which up
to the year 1840 had contained about ten hundred
and sixty fellows, 1 died at the age of 100 years, 34
over 80 years, 50 between 70 and 80, 38 between
60 and 70, 37 between 50 and 60, 32 between 40
and 50, 32 between 30 and 40, and 6 between 20
and 30.

In Thacher's Medical Biography, in the names of
one hundred and forty-eight physicians whose ages
have been recorded, three have died between the
ages of 90 and 100, 23 between 80 and 90, 7 between 85 and 90, 27 between 70 and 80, 29 between
60 and 70, 22 between 50 and 60, 21 between 40
and 50, 13 between 30 and 40, and 3 between 20

and 30. By this it appears that almost one half of the deceased were over the period of three score years and ten, the age generally allotted to man.

The subject of our memoir was one of the favored few who arrived at the age of the patriarchs, or that of one hundred years, with almost uninterrupted health. From the memoirs of Dr. Holyoke prepared by the Essex South District Medical Society, and published in the 4th volume of the Massachusetts Medical Society, I have procured the materials for this notice. These memoirs were written by Dr. A. L. Peirson, of Salem, Mass.

'Edward Augustus Holyoke was the second of eight children of Edward and Margaret Holyoke, of Marblehead, Essex county, Massachusetts. His father was born in Boston, educated at Harvard College, where he was afterwards tutor, settled as a pastor of the second Congregational society in Marblehead, April 25, 1716, installed President of Harvard College 1737, and died in June, 1769, aged 80. His paternal ancestor came from Tamworth, on the borders of Warwickshire, England, and was among the grantees of the town of Lynn, where he settled at Sagamore hill, in 1635. President Holyoke was three times married; the first time to Elizabeth Brown of Marblehead, the second to Margaret Appleton, daughter of Col. John Appleton of Ipswich, and the third time to the widow of Major Epes, of Ipswich Hamlet. The subject of this memoir was the offspring of the second marriage, and was born August 1, 1728, old style. In 1742, he entered the Freshman Class, at Harvard University. He has preserved an account of his examination, and the sentence which was given him as a theme on that occasion, seems to have been a motto of his future life. 'Labor improbus omnia vincit.' From this period to the end of life, he was characterized by constant diligence, and assiduous attention to his studies. In 1746, he graduated, and in the following year he spent six months at Roxbury in teaching school, for which he received eighty-four pounds old tenor, $38 50 cents; out of which he paid his board at sixty-seven cents a week. In July, 1747, he commenced the study of medicine under the care of Col. Berry of Ipswich. This gentleman was the most distinguished practitioner of his neighborhood, although his being universally known, by his military title, does not speak highly for the estimation in which medical honors were then held. He finished his pupilage in April 1749, and then came to Salem, in June of the same year. This place has ever since been the scene of his useful and philanthropic labors. For the remainder of his life, he scarcely left the town, unless on business connected with the profession, and during his life he never wandered so far as fifty miles from the spot on which he was born. His longest journey was to Portsmouth, in 1749, at which time he was absent five days. In 1755, he was married to Judith Pickman, daughter of Col. B. Pickman, of Salem. This lady died in her nineteenth year, in 1756, soon after the birth of a daughter, which did not long survive her. In 1759, he was again married to Mary Viall, daughter of Nathaniel Viall, merchant of Boston. Upon this latter occasion, he was absent from Salem a week, which is believed to have been the longest visit he ever made from home, except in 1764, when he went to Boston, to be inoculated for the small pox. The length of this visit was occasioned by a custom which then prevailed, for newly married persons to devote a week to receiving the visits and congratulations of their friends, as the phrase was, 'sitting up for company,' a ceremony which Dr. Holyoke declared to one of the committee was 'very tedious and irksome.' By his second wife he had twelve children, most of whom died in infancy. Two daughters only survive; the widow of the late Mr. William Turner, of Boston, and the wife of Joshua Ward Esqr. of Salem. Dr. Holyoke perhaps was led to select this town as his place of residence in consequence of the death of Dr. Cabot, which occurred just at the time of his completing his pupilage; but so little were his expectations of employment realized that after two years trial, he appears to have had serious intentions of abandoning the place, in despair of success, and to have remained here only through fear of distressing his father if he returned home.

No man probably ever entered upon the business of his profession with more settled resolution and perseverance than Dr. Holyoke. He had youth and health, a constitution of mind and body eminently calculated for endurance of labor and fatigue, was reputed a good scholar for his time; he read the Latin language with great fluency, and he subsequently attained a familiar acquaintance with the French; he had as many opportunities of learning his profession as were common at that time, and was respectably connected and advantageously known. But notwithstanding these advantages, the medical profession abounded with discouragements, which, to say the least, are greatly lessened at this day. The standard of medical education was totally unsettled. Every one who chose to prescribe for the sick, was admitted to the rank of physician; the higher points of medical character, and the value of medical studies, were totally unappreciated by the bulk of the people; and the compensation for medical services was exceedingly small. His first visits were charged at 5 shillings, old tenor, about 11 cts. each. This was at a time when provisions bore nearly half of their present prices, and other necessaries of living were in like proportion. The periodical press did not then, as now, issue its regular current of observation and intelligence, and it was not till Dr. Holyoke reached the declining period of life, that this species of medical literature had given that impulse to the profession, which is so sensibly felt at the present day. It was rare, in the period of his meridian life, for any man to devote himself to medicine as a science, and pursue the profession without reference to other advantages, than those which appertain to medical and scientific character. During almost the whole period of Dr. Holyoke's life, the spirit of commercial adventure was the characteristic trait of almost all around him. There were many ways of rapidly attaining to wealth and distinction, that looked more inviting than the one he had chosen; and it shows his steadiness of purpose, and his characteris-

tic contempt for mere money, that during his whole
life he never appears to have been enticed to engage
in any of the enterprises which were undertaken by
others in the pursuit of wealth, or for a single day to
have laid aside his character as a practitioner of the
healing art. The following sketch is from the pen
of his intimate friend, and one of his eldest pupils
now living.

'He possessed much vivacity of disposition, accompanied with great agility of body, and when at
college was remarkable for his feats of activity. He
was reputed to have been a very good scholar.

The peculiar constitution of his mind led him to
cultivate and to be much attached to experimental
inquiry. He thought with Bacon that it was the only
road to discovery. He often expressed great aversion to hypotheses whether applied to medicine or
natural philosophy.

He made some original experiments more than
half a century ago, with ether and the thermometer,
by which he discovered the power of evaporation to
produce cold. And this was done before the discovery had been announced in America.

He was very attentive to his professional duties,
visiting with equal promptness the poor and the rich.
Few physicians in the United States have done so
much for the poor. When in the sick chamber his
manners were remarkably affable, and kind, but preserving a proper dignity of deportment. Such was
the success attending his practice, and his great
reputation, that it produced to him such a pressure
of business as sometimes scarcely permitted him to

33

take the necessary meals for supporting life. The following calculation conveys some idea of the extent of his business. He had filled 120 day books of 90 pages each, containing charges for 30 visits on each page, giving an average of over 11 visits a day for 75 years. And upon one occasion when the measles were epidemic in 1787 he made over 100 professional visits in a day for several days. And there was a period in his practice in which he could say there was not a house in Salem which he had not visited professionally.

In medical consultations he expressed himself with diffidence and caution, and with the junior members of the profession, was free from hauteur, and was communicative, and at the same time candid, and disposed rather to conceal than expose their errors.

His practice has been thought, in the use of mercury and opium, to have resembled that of the celebrated Darwin. For although he very often prescribed those active agents, yet it was, perhaps, in more cautious doses than they are generally administered at the present day. In pneumonic inflammation, and in cases of cynanche trachealis, the mercury was very liberally prescribed. In the latter disease he depended principally on the turpeth mineral. He was not averse, as he advanced in life, to the trial of new remedies, but might rather be said to be fond of such trial; but it was always done with great caution, to insure safety to his patients. He early gave the mineral solution, and was one of the first physicians in America that prescribed the Prussic acid.

Cheerfulness has been said to be conducive to

longevity, and such an influence it probably had in the subject of this memoir, in whom this quality of the mind abounded, and formed a most conspicuous trait in his character. But although he loved cheerfulness, his conversation did not admit of levity. The subjects which he most liked to dwell upon, in the society of his friends, were such as had a useful bearing on morals, the arts or sciences, for the advancement of the happiness of the great family of mankind. A learned professor said he always learned something new from the Doctor's conversation.

He was always a strong advocate for the truth of the Christian religion, and of the doctrine of immortality. And he adorned the religion he professed by his benevolent deeds, and most exemplary life.

The Doctor often regretted the want of greater advantages in his earlier medical education, and evinced by his diligence in reading the best medical authors, a desire to compensate as far as possible such deficiencies. He possessed great industry, for if he returned home but for a few moments he would snatch up a book and resume his studies. He was in the habit of importing, almost every year, from England, for some considerable portion of his life, the new medical books of merit. But his reading was not confined to medicine exclusively. He was well versed in Astronomy, and the several branches of Natural Philosophy and Theology and the Belles Lettres. He was truly a man of science, and the public manifested that they considered him to be, by his having been appointed the first President of the

Massachusetts Medical Society, and also President of the Academy of Arts and Sciences.

To his extensive science he united great urbanity of manners. The correctness of his conduct, prudence and politeness, were very remarkable. He was fond of society, which he enlivened by his wit, while he instructed his associates by a communication from the rich stores of his mind. For he was what Bacon has styled a *full* man ; and what was said of Dr. Mead, may be applied to him : ' Whose abilities and eminence in his profession, united with his learning and fine taste for those arts which embellish human life, long rendered him an ornament, not only to his own profession, but to the nation and age in which he lived.'

Dr. Holyoke had a good memory, and although his incessant calls prevented his devoting much time to reading, he seldom passed a day, for the first sixty years of his practice, without noting down some fact or observation calculated to augment his professional knowledge. His meteorological observations were recorded daily, almost without interruption, for eighty years.

The study of the book of nature has been the occupation of the enlightened physician in all ages, and a more complete method of pursuing this study can hardly be imagined than that of Dr. Holyoke. If his attendance upon professional practice had ever allowed him to have fully completed this plan, and prepared the general results of his observations for publication, he would have furnished a most valuable treasury of medical knowledge. He kept a memo-

randum upon his table, in which was minuted down
the name of every disease the moment he returned
from making a call, the more remarkable being the
subject of further memoranda, in which he ascertained by computation, the number of cases of every
disease. He also was diligent in obtaining correct
bills of mortality. He was thus enabled to inform
himself most completely of the changes which take
place in the frequency of occurrence, and the fatality
of diseases.

These observations, together with those of a meteorological character, formed a complete history of
the physical changes which came under his notice.

The manuscripts here alluded to, with the exception of those which were sent to the Massachusetts
Medical Society, were never intended for public
inspection, and are not left in a state to furnish a
connected history of the diseases of this vicinity.
But such a history might have been compiled from
them by the author himself, which would have resembled in character and value the celebrated commentaries of the venerable Heberden.

Dr. Holyoke devoted a portion of his time to the
study of Astronomy. The appearance of comets,
and remarkable displays of the Aurora Borealis, was
noted in his diary with much exactness, and published
in Silliman's Journal for 1827. In 1769, he made
an accurate observation of the transit of Venus over
the Sun's disc, and in 1782, the transit of Mercury
over the Sun's disc. The observation and recording
the changes of the weather, earthquakes, storms and
memorabilia, continued to be a favorite pursuit with

him as long as he lived. The well remembered
September gale of 1815, is noticed and recorded by
him, with much fidelity and exactness. The epidemics which occurred in his practice, were never suffered to pass without a cursory record of the principal facts connected with them.

Although for reasons which have been mentioned,
he did not often appear before the public as an author, he was not indifferent to the cultivation of
medical science among its professors. As soon as
the Medical Society of this State was formed, he
contributed his full share to their published transactions. He was one of the founders of the Society,
and also of the District Society of Essex, and was
a constant attendant at their meetings. To the
county society he bequeathed to their library some
of his most valuable books. He wrote the preface
to the first volume of the State Society's publications, and the first paper of that volume is his interesting account of the state of the weather, diseases,
operation of remedies, deaths, &c. in Salem, for
every month of the year 1786, and shows that he
must have been in habits of close observation, and
of noting down the occurrences he met with in
practice. Observations of the same kind, were
communicated for the years 1782, '83, '84, '85, '87,
and 1788. Every physician engaged in full practice,
as was Dr. Holyoke, at this time, will admit this to
have been no small labor.

The terrible epidemic sore throat of 1734–5, which
almost totally destroyed the infant population of the
north part of Essex county, was keenly remembered

for many years afterwards, and the attention of phy-
cians was directed to the inflammatory affection of
the throat and lungs, and the operation of remedies
the most efficacious in these dreaded and dangerous attacks. Hence originated a more complete acquaintance with the mercurial practice, than elsewhere obtained. An interesting letter of Dr. Holyoke on this subject was published in the 1st vol. of
the New York Med. Repository, and in the Appendix
to this memoir in the Transactions of the Society.

Although, as has been observed, Dr. Holyoke was
a cautious practitioner, he was not a timid one, and
never neglected to make himself acquainted with the
reputed powers of new articles which were from time
to time introduced into the materia medica, and with
the new modes of practice which were recommended by others. In the use of the Digitalis of the gum
Acarosides, of the Muriate of Barytes and of many
medicines of later date, he was one of the earliest
and most careful experimenters. His use of the Ac-
etate of Lead in restraining hemorrhages, of the oxy-
muriate of mercury in the treatment of scrofula, and
some forms of cutaneous disease, of small doses of
calomel in the ulcuscula oris of children, has led to
the establishment of modes of treatment attended
with the highest degree of benefit. There are several medicines which owe their introduction into use
entirely to him, and many in fact may be said to have
originated with him, as he was the first to settle the
best mode of preparation and administration. The
article so well known in this place by the name of the
‘white balsam drops,’ or fennel balsam, is a strong

solution of sub-carbonate of potash, with the addition
of a little essential oil of sweet fennel, and is a valuable diaphoretic and carminative, especially to children.
This was a favorite medicine during his whole practice.   He obtained his first knowledge of it from a
Mr. Wigglesworth of Malden.   Of a cheap method
of preparing the Salæratus, or Supercarbonate of
Potash he wrote an account for the Mass. Med. Society, which is reprinted in their appendix to vol. 4.
This article has in this neighborhood nearly superseded the common carbonate, both in medicinal and
culinary preparation.

Dr. Holyoke's prescriptions were, for the most
part, put up under his own inspection, either by himself or his pupils.   This practice was nearly universal, even in the large towns, till the commencement
of the present century, and if there were obvious
disadvantages in the necessity which called for so
much of the valuable time of the physician, there
were undoubtedly some benefits derived from con-
necting practical pharmacy with his more dignified
duties.   The practice still prevails among many of
our brethren in New York, and further south, and is
warmly advocated by a distinguished individual of
their number, Dr. Hosack.

Dr. Holyoke was intimately acquainted with the
qualities and preparations of all the drugs he was in
the habit of using, and was extremely neat and skillful in compounding them.   Although, perhaps, he
used a greater number of remedial agents than enter
into the prescriptions of the present day, he was by
no means infected with the polypharmacy which was

the prevailing fault of the physicians of his time. The following anecdote, related by one of his pupils, exhibits the simplicity of his practice. 'When I first went to live with him in 1797, showing me his shop, he said, 'there seems to you to be a great variety of medicines here, and that it will take you long to get acquainted with them, but most of them are unimportant. There are four which are equal to all the rest, viz., Mercury, Antimony, Bark, and Opium ; of these there are many preparations, however. Of Antimony I think I have used thirty.' These are his words substantially.' The same person adds, 'I can only say of his practice, the longer I have lived, I have thought better and better of it.'

In 1777 Dr. Holyoke applied himself to the business of inoculating for small pox. He had himself been inoculated in April, 1764, by Dr. N. Perkins, of Boston, and his careful minutes of this occurrence illustrate the customs and practice of that day. In March, 1777, he took charge of the hospital, which had been erected a few years before for small pox inoculation, and conducted through the disease three classes, amounting in all to about 600, with only two fatal cases occurring. But the loss of these two, less than the average number, one of which occurred in the first class of 200, affected his sensitive mind with so much anguish, as almost to occasion self-reproach, and a resolution to abandon the undertaking. During most of the period of his patients remaining in the hospital, he passed his whole time with them night and day, and many persons in this place, who were at that time under his care for inoculation, testify to

34

his skillful and assiduous attentions. He was an early vaccinator, and was in the common practice of it in the beginning of 1802, if not earlier.

As a surgical operator Dr. Holyoke had more than a mediocrity of talent and skill. He never appeared to have any extraordinary preference for this branch of his profession, but as a matter of necessity held himself qualified for all the usual demands of surgical treatment. In fact the opportunities for a display of surgical address are much less frequent in the population with which Dr. Holyoke has resided, than might be expected from its number. One of the committee has heard him say, there was a period of twenty-five years, during which he saw nearly all the important cases of disease and accident in the town of Salem, and yet never performed or witnessed an amputation of a large limb. This exemption from operations is to be ascribed partly to the character, the habits and occupations of the people. Agriculture and the fisheries were the principal pursuits, and the building of ships and houses the only mechanical employments in which there were likely to arise many occasions for surgical assistance. It must be allowed, too, that the period in which Dr. Holyoke held the lead of practice in this vicinity was characterized by a greater degree of *temperance* among laboring people, than existed in most large towns. Even at present, while it is acknowledged that the vice of intemperance has been of late years, (1829) a growing evil, it is believed there are few seaports in which there is a less number of sots, in proportion to the whole population. The extreme rareness of

Lithotomy is quite noticeable in this vicinity. The perfect purity of the water drank by the inhabitants of this town, is no doubt the cause of the infrequency of the disease requiring this operation. Notwithstanding, however, the infrequency of cases requiring surgical operations, such was the extent of Dr. Holyoke's practice that he was occasionally called upon to perform amputations, and other important operations ; and in these cases his promptitude and success were such as procured him a high degree of reputation. So late as December, 1821, when he was ninety-two years old, he performed the operation of paracentesis. In the management of fractures he particularly excelled. No man handled a broken limb with more tenderness and adroitness.

As an obstetric practitioner he was greatly esteemed, and upon this branch of his business he seems to have bestowed extraordinary attention. On his first coming to this place, this department of the healing art was entirely in the hands of ignorant midwives, and the physician was only called in extraordinary cases, or to rectify some of the blunders of these practitioners. He has preserved an account of the first forty-five obstetric cases which occurred to him. The first one on which he ' was persuaded to engage in, occurred in 1755, after he had been six years in practice, and it was not till four years afterwards that he makes the record of a case which was the first ' common, easy birth which ever came under his management.' Thus it happened that he was early taught to meet the *difficulties* of this branch of medical practice, and acquired a fertility of expedients, and dependence on the resources of art, which, no doubt, contributed to the safety of many a female in the hour of peril, after he became extensively engaged in attending to these cases. Between the years 1791 and 1801 the number of births which occurred in his practice was 946, viz. 494 boys, and 452 girls.

He received pupils during nearly all the period of his active practice ; and some of the most distinguished physicians of New England were educated under his care. Of the thirty-five pupils which he educated, thirteen are now living.

The period of the revolution was a trying one to the subject of this memoir, and he never loved to dwell upon the recollections of it. His feelings in the spring and summer of 1775, were intensely painful. In referring to that period, he said to one of his family, he thought he should have died with the sense of weight and oppression at his heart. He had sent his family to Nantucket, and the loneliness of his house increased the feeling of desolation. Most of his intimate friends and near connections favored the royal cause, and his own education had attached him to the established order of things, and his peaceful temper shrunk from the turmoil of a revolution. He thought this country destined to be independent, but he believed the proper period had not arrived, and that weakness and dissension were likely to follow what he considered a premature disunion. But in after times when referring to these opinions, he was wont, with his usual ingenuousness, to say that the event had proved that he was wrong in his prediction. He imputed to the revolution a change in the manners of the people, which will not be reckoned among its good effects. He thought there was a falling off in domestic discipline, and a relaxation of wholesome subordination among children, since the freedom of the colonies.

During this trying period, he kept steadily occupied in his benevolent duties, and such was his prudence, his inoffensive manners, and the universal respect for his virtues, that he did not meet with so much trouble as might have been expected from the unpopularity of his opinions. Although most distinguished men, who had adopted the royal cause, found it expedient to leave the country, it does not appear that he was ever impeded in the prosecution of his business for a single day. It does not appear that his practice was ever injured by the part he took in politics. He held a commission as a magistrate both before and after the revolution.

Dr. Holyoke was as little of a partizan in religion as in politics. He was firm and decided in his own opinions, but seems neither to have expected nor desired uniformity in christian belief. But although without any extravagant zeal, he was emphatically a *religious* man. He was a diligent student of the scriptures and continued to read the New Testament in the original until the last year of his life. For many years, he usually reperused this volume with great care, once every year. He was as constant in his attendance at church as his numerous engagements would permit, and in the most busy period of his practice, would so arrange his business as most commonly to find time for public worship on some

part of every Sunday. In deeds of piety and benevolence he was always active, and through life had
a systematic charity proportioned to his means. His
gifts were bestowed with the most scrupulous secrecy,
and from his intimacy in the families of all classes,
seldom misapplied. The widowed mother, and the
orphan children, were often relieved by a present of
money through the Post Office, which a grateful
curiosity has traced to Dr. Holyoke.

The loss of his hearing was the greatest privation
in respect to health which Dr. Holyoke suffered.
This for many years impaired his enjoyment of the
pleasures of society, for which he had so high a relish. When he was forty-five years old, his eyesight
required the use of convex glasses. These he used
for about forty years, when his eyesight gradually
returned, and at the time of his death it was so perfect as to enable him to read the finest print, without
the aid of glasses. In early life he could see with
much distinctness to a great distance, but after he
left off his glasses he lost this power, and for the last
few years, he has complained that objects at a distance
were multiplied, so that he could see four or five
moons, &c. An alteration in the refracting power
of the chrystalline lens, not uncommon in old age,
and which occasions the image to be imperfectly
formed upon the retina, might be considered the sole
cause of this imperfection of sight, or it was perhaps
connected with the state of the brain he so accurately
describes in the account of his own case.

After he had passed his seventieth year, although
at this time in full practice, he often expressed a fear

that he was too old for his employment, and that his powers of mind had failed him. In particular, for the last thirty years of his life, he was wont to lament his loss of memory, and say that he only read for amusement, and that his mind retained nothing. This, though true to a certain extent, his characteristic humility greatly exaggerated. He did retain the most important ideas which were traced in his mind, and kept up with the improvements in the practice of our art, to a degree most unusual for a man who had reached three score years and ten. Since he attained his hundredth year, he passed an hour in the study of one of his medical acquaintances, and was greatly interested in inquiring what had been the last accounts of the operations for the removal of urinary calculus, by the new operation of lithontripty. Only one week previous to his last confinement, in February last, he dictated a letter to a gentleman in Connecticut, who had written to him requesting his opinion in a case of schirrus, in which letter, Dr. Holyoke recommends the trial of Iodine, and gives full directions for its administration. Perhaps these incidents of his last days, exhibit in a sufficiently clear manner, what was the most distinguishing intellectual trait of his whole character. It was that he was always ready to receive information,—that he kept his mind open, so to speak, and never allowed prejudice, or the conceit of great acquirements, to prevent his examining and adopting any thing which claimed to be a novelty or improvement.

The circumstance of his arriving to be an hundred

years old, an occurrence so unusual to happen to any man, and of which it does not come within the knowledge of the committee that there are many authentic accounts of its having happened before to *eminent* physicians, was looked upon by the Doctor and his friends as an era of very great interest.*

The close of Dr. Holyoke's life was a period of quiet and calm domestic enjoyments, but not of sullenness or disgust. He received the visits of those

* Some eminent physicians have attained a great age, and several of them have their ages recorded at one hundred and upwards; but in almost all these cases, the contradictory accounts of authors give us reason to doubt the correctness of the statements. Some have stated that *Hippocrates* died at the age of 109, some at 104, and some at 99. *Ahoemon Abenzoar*, an Arabian physician and writer who flourished between the years 1630 and 1660, lived to 135 years. Some of the old writers doubt this. Belknap in his history of New Hampshire, says that Dr. John Huss of Durham, N. H., died in 1736, at the age of 108, and was very vigorous in old age. He mentions a death recorded in the newspapers of 1803, of Dr. *Hezekiah Miram*, of Ward, Mass., who died at the age of 100. He lived with his wife 78 years, and she survived him. In the Gentleman's Magazine, mention is made of the tomb of Dr. *Thomas Marwood*, of Honiton, in Devonshire, Eng., physician to Queen Elizabeth, who died in 1617, aged *above* 105. The celebrated *William Mead*, M. D., according to the same Magazine for 1781, died Oct. 28th, 1652, aged 148 years and nine months. He was but four years younger than the celebrated old Parr, but more than twenty younger than the well known prodigy of longevity, Henry Jenkins, the fisherman, who died at the age of 169. There are some even older, which we have no reason to dispute, recorded in the Welch chronicles. Ivan Yorath was buried on the 17th of July, A. D. 1621, aged 180. He was a soldier in the fight of Bosworth, and lived at Lantwitt Major, and he lived much by fishing. Elizabeth, the wife of Edmund Thomas, was buried the 18th day of February, in the year of our Lord God, 1688, aged 177.'

Cases of longevity are not rare among persons not distinguished for their mental powers, and the close of life with such is frequently a state of mere existence 'sans every thing.' A circumstance as remarkable as any connected with the longevity of Dr. Holyoke is, that he retained the power of using his intellect with vigor and energy, and of communicating his ideas intelligibly to the last of his days. His letters written after he was one hundred years old, prove this.

who waited on him to testify their respect for his venerable and virtuous character, with great affability and apparent satisfaction. He did not make the uncertainty of life and his being near the close of it an excuse for inaction. After he had completed his hundredth year, he commenced a manuscript in which he proposed to minute down some of the changes in the manners, dress, dwellings and employments of the inhabitants of Salem.

In summing up the character of our venerable friend, it is not too much to say, he was a perfect model of the general practitioner of medicine. His manners were equally removed from servility and arrogance. Free from dogmatism, and trusting to the mild dignity of his manners to enforce his precepts, nothing excited his displeasure more than the swaggering, *Radcliffe* style assumed by some men to impose an idea of their consequence upon the vulgar, who are sometimes prone to believe that excessive rudeness is a mark of genius, and that consummate insolence, is, not unfrequently, coupled with consummate skill. .These people he used to call ' medical bucks.'

His regard for truth was scrupulous and sincere, and this was obvious in his reasoning upon facts, for he was never known to form a deduction which required the sacrifice or modification of an important fact in the premises ; but he rather suffered his judgment to remain suspended, and waited for a farther insight into the operations of nature. From the same cause, a letter of recommendation or introduction coming from him, even in behalf of the most

35

valued of his friends, was sure to contain not one
word more than came within the scope of the author's personal knowledge and observation.

The respect in which his person and character
were held, by the inhabitants of this place, was almost enthusiastic, the whole of the present generation have been *taught* to look upon him with veneration, and to pronounce his name with affection and
respect. His name was sought for in every undertaking for the welfare of the community, as a sort of
passport to the confidence of his fellow citizens.
When a few years since some pilferer had taken from
his door post the thermometer which had been suspended there for so many years, from which he had
taken his daily observations of temperature, the act
was viewed as a sort of sacrilege, and it was generally agreed, that it could not have been the deed of a
Salem thief, for it was thought there could be none so
base, as not to respect the property of the Salem
patriarch. It is difficult to speak of the estimation
in which all classes united in holding him, without
being suspected of exaggeration, but it is certainly
safe to say that all who knew him regarded him as
having reached a height of moral rectitude, as elevated as was ever attained by uninspired human nature ;
and what his eulogist said of him was literally the
absolute conviction of his friends, ' that knowingly to
do wrong, in a single instance, would have required in
him as severe an effort, as the practice of elevated
virtue in most men.' This veneration must be
regarded as arising from the possession of some
peculiar and unusual moral qualities. He was ob-

viously less *selfish* than most men. His ready
generosity and the moderate competence with which
he always contented himself, prove this. But still
more peculiar was the perfect simplicity and singleness of heart which marked his moral conduct.
There was no *effort;* he *acted* right because he *felt*
right, and every one could see that the kindness of his
manner was a sincere expression of the kindness of
his heart. It was the perfect confidence which every
one had in the habitual rectitude and purity of his
intentions that induced persons of all ages and of all
classes to look upon him as a sympathizing friend to
whom they might intrust their most important interests. His sickness and expected death were the most
common topics of inquiry among the citizens of
Salem for some days previous to his decease; and
when this event took place, it was announced by the
tolling of all the church bells of the town, a mark of
respect never known to have been shown to any other
than the late Presidents of the United States. All
classes of persons thronged to his funeral to pay their
tribute of respect to his memory, and the eulogy pronounced over his remains by his pastor and intimate
friend, the Rev. Mr. Brazer, was a chastened effort of
genuine and touching eloquence, and a delineation of
his moral and religious character, which was recognized as faithful and just, by the crowded assembly
before whom it was pronounced. As that production is now before the public, we have avoided enlarging upon some points in regard to the character
of Dr. Holyoke, which are ably and fully expatiated
upon by his eulogist.

DR. DAVID HOSACK. My friend, Dr. J. W. Francis, of New York, the former colleague and partner of the eminent subject of this notice, has politely forwarded me the following elegant memoir of him.

Hosack, David, M. D., L. L. D., F. R. S. &c. Conspicuous among that class of individuals who have added distinction to the character of medical science, may be placed this eminent professor and practitioner of the healing art. By an exclusive direction to that pursuit which he deemed the most important of all studies, and by a long and severe discharge of its responsible trusts, he justly challenged public confidence in his skill, and secured a widely extended approbation.

The life of a practitioner of medicine of forty years devotion to his calling must necessarily involve many incidents ; our limits will embrace some of the most interesting.

David Hosack was a native of the city of New York, and was born on the 31st of August, 1769. His father, Alexander Hosack, was by birth a Scotchman, born at Elgin, in 1736, and came to this country with Lord Jeffrey Amherst, upon the siege of Louisburg. His mother was the daughter of Francis Arden of New York, and was born in 1743. David, their first child, and the subject of this sketch, after receiving his preliminary instruction in his native city, was sent to the grammar school of the late Dr. McWhorter of Newark, New Jersey, where, after pursuing the study of the Latin and Greek languages for some fifteen months, he was removed to the school of Dr. Peter Wilson, at Hackensack, by

DAVID HOSACK, M.D. LL.D.

W.C. Sharp's Lith. Boston

whom he was enabled to enter as a pupil in Columbia College, N. York, in 1786. In this institution he remained about two years and a half, when he proceeded to Princeton College, then under the control of the eminently learned and distinguished President Witherspoon. Here he received the degree of Bachelor of Arts, in 1789.

While in his attendance in the freshmen and sophomore classes of Columbia College, he was also engaged in the study of medicine and surgery with the late renowned Dr. Richard Bayley. At Princeton his medical studies were necessarily suspended. These, however, he promptly resumed upon his graduation in the school of Arts, and availing himself of the advantages which New York then possessed for private instructions, the medical faculty of the college having been dispersed by the revolutionary struggle, he attended the lectures of Bayley and Post on Anatomy and Surgery, those on the Practice of Physic, Botany, and the Materia Medica, by Romayne, those on obstetrics and the diseases of women and children by Bard. Clinical knowledge was afforded at the Alms House of the city by Moore, Kissam, Post, and Romayne. It is worthy of remark that a majority of these excellent instructors had been educated at Edinburgh, and that they pursued a plan of instruction for their pupils similar to that in which they had been taught in the Royal Infirmary at Edinburgh.

Young Hosack, solicitous of further improvement, now proceeded to Philadelphia, whose school had already acquired grear reputation from the active talents and personal skill of Shippen, Rush, Kuhn,

Wistar, Hutchinson and Griffiths. Here he received the degree of Doctor of Medicine in 1791, on which occasion he published an inaugural dissertation on Cholera Morbus, maintaining in this exercise, the somewhat peculiar views of Professor Kuhn. At the recommendation of Dr. Rush, Dr. Hosack commenced the practice of his profession at Alexandria, in Virginia, but after a year's residence in that place, though his success was sufficiently flattering to his ambition, he returned to his native city, New York.

In New York, it may be stated, he found many causes to operate in his behalf for the better exercise of his professional talents. The associates of his studies were here more abundant, his personal acquaintance with the inhabitants was comparatively large; he was ambitious to become known as a practical physician in the city of his birth, and here too was a wider field for the display of professional acquisition. Here he associated himself with many of the charitable and humane institutions which so remarkably characterize New York. As a member of the Humane Society, he published a pamphlet on suspended animation, one of the special subjects of the consideration of the society. His prospects improved, and he had reason to be well satisfied with the commencement of his medical career. Still he felt that all the opportunities for professional knowledge which he had enjoyed in his own country, fell short of what he might have possessed had he visited the schools of Europe. His father, desirous of gratifying his son in all reasonable demands, yielded to his solicitations, and the young doctor having soon arranged his business, set out for Edinburgh, as the great seat of medical and chirurgical science at that period. He ever spoke of this occurrence as the most advantageous one in his life. As an American graduate already invested with collegiate distinction, he was at greater liberty to indulge the bent of his mind in the prosecution of such departments of information as he most wished, and his letters of introduction to the Professors Gregory, Stewart, Duncan, Beattie, and others, enabled him to enjoy to the greatest extent, the instruction and the society of the eminent professional and literary men of that metropolis. Like every other scholar who has participated in the intellectual treasures of Edinburgh, his desires now led him to visit London, for still greater increase of scientific knowledge. The lectures of Andrew Marshall on Anatomy, the practical precepts of Pearson, of St. George's Hospital, the Anatomical and Surgical instruction of Earle and Abernethy, of St. Bartholomew's Hospital, the Botany of Curtis, of the Brompton Garden, and the zoological and botanical course of Sir James Edward Smith, President of the Linnæan Society, were sufficient to fill up every hour in profitable investigation. While in London, he drew up some interesting facts relative to the communication of the virus of the small pox to the foetus in utero. A paper of a more eminently philosophical character on vision, in which he was the advocate of the theory that the eye adapts itself to the view of objects at different distances by means of its external muscles, was also, at this time, drawn up by him, and obtained the approbation of the Royal

Society. It was published in their Transactions in 1794.

The same year, 1794, he returned to New York, and entered with renewed ardor upon the duties of his profession, which he continued to prosecute until within a short period before the close of his active and laborious life. In 1795, the Trustees of Columbia College appointed him Professor of Botany, and the following year he published a syllabus of his lectures. His old teacher, the venerable Dr. Samuel Bard, being now about to withdraw from the practice of physic, a connection was formed between him and Dr. Hosack, which continued for four years, when in 1800, Dr. Bard retired to his country residence, leaving Dr. Hosack in the possession of an extensive and lucrative practice.

During the prevalence of the malignant yellow fever in New York in 1795, '6, '7, '8, and 1801, '03, '05, '19, and 1822, he was actively engaged in encountering that direful malady, and was earnest in enforcing, as the most effective mode of relief, the sudorific plan of treatment. On this disorder he has written many papers, in all of which he contended for the distinctive or specific character of the disease when compared with the several forms of indigenous fever, and that *sub modo*, it was of a contagious nature. By the death of Dr. W. P. Smith, Professor of Materia Medica in Columbia College, that branch was also assigned to Dr. Hosack, and the joint Professorship of Botany and Materia Medica were discharged by him until the dissolution of the Medical Faculty of that Institution in 1813. The active interest which Dr. Hosack took in furthering the organization of a new medical school in New York, is familiarly known to all who have studied the progress of medical affairs in that city. In this new institution he was the master spirit of its success, and when by the union of the two rival faculties of Columbia College and the College of Physicians and Surgeons, there were now concentrated in one school the eminent teacher in both, the career of that establishment, as second only in numbers to the older school of Philadelphia, was universally admitted. Anatomy was held by Post, the practice of Physic and Clinical Medicine by Hosack, Chemistry by Macnevin, the Institution of Medicine and Midwifery by Francis, to whom also was assigned Medical Jurisprudence, upon the death of Dr. Stringham; Surgery was taught by Mott, and Clinical Medicine by Hamersley. The learned Mitchill gave full instruction in Natural History and the Materia Medica. With such a list of experienced Professors, the college enumerated more than two hundred students attending its lectures, many of them coming hither from the remotest parts of the Union.

Unfortunately, however, dissensions between the Trustees of the College and the Faculty found admittance within their walls, and the anomalous system of government which controlled the Institution not admitting of an easy reconciliation, the Faculty gave up their commission in the spring of 1826, and withdrew from the responsible duties of teaching. The elaborate report of the Regents of the University, touching the difficulties under which the college had labor-

36

ed, exonerated the Professors from all censure, and
the board of regents passed a vote of approbation
in April, 1826, for ' the faithful and able manner in
which the faculty had filled their respective chairs as
instructors and lecturers in the said college.'

Dr. Hosack, with Dr. Mott, Dr. Francis, Dr. Macnevin, and several other of his colleagues in the University, now laid the foundation of another school of
practical medicine and surgery. The lamented Dr.
Godman of Philadelphia, occupied the chair of Anatomy, and Chemistry was held by that practical teacher, Professor Griscom. This school proved a powerful and successful rival to the College of Physicians
and Surgeons, but after four years of triumph, was
abandoned on account of legislative enactment in
behalf of the College of Physicians and Surgeons,
and restrictive ones in relation to the Rutgers Faculty. These legislative measures, while they threw embarrassments in the way of the continuance of the last
named Faculty, did not, however, prove so advantageous to the College of Physicians and Surgeons as
was anticipated, inasmuch as the number of medical
students attending the State College was diminished
to less than one half that which attended when competition existed between the rival institutions. The
monopoly of instruction seemed to be more odious
to the students than to the law makers. Dr. Hosack
after this period, 1831, withdrew from all public
teaching.

The writings of Dr. Hosack embrace many subjects, medical and philosophical, and of a general
interest. We have already noticed some of them.

In 1810, in conjunction with his then pupil, John W. Francis, afterwards his associate in business for many years, he projected a new medical journal, entitled the Medical and Philosophical Register, which was continued for four years; it embraced a large amount of original materials on the state of science in this country, and many papers of a practical character in physical and surgical science. The most valuable, perhaps, of the papers of Dr. Hosack are on the Yellow Fever, in his correspondence with the late Dr. Chisholm, of Bristol, in England, including his strictures on Contagion and Infection. His practical exposition of the nature and treatment of Hives, or Croup, is well known, and highly appreciated. To all solicitous of information concerning the history and progress of medical affairs in the United States, his discourse before the Rutgers College will be studied with peculiar interest. But it is deemed unnecessary to enumerate his various individual papers, inasmuch as they are to be found in his Medical Essays, in three volumes, octavo, which he published in 1824—1830. In 1819 he published a system of Practical Nosology; a second edition, much improved, appeared in 1821. Besides these writings, more immediately of a professional nature, he is the author of a discourse on Horticulture, and on Temperance, and Biographical notices of Drs. Rush and Wistar. His memoir of his lamented friend, De Witt Clinton, is a production which will ever command the regard of every friend of the system of Internal Improvement, which ennobles the state of New York.

It may easily be inferred from the record already

made of the labors of Dr. Hosack, that his life was
one of great industry and untiring application. For
a long period of years at the head of medical practice in his native city, his time was necessarily almost
wholly absorbed in the clinical exercise of his profession. When to this it is considered that for about
twenty years he was one of the physicians of the
New York Hospital, and for thirty years a distinguished professor of practical medicine, we cannot but
admire the zeal he displayed and the services he has
rendered his fellow men. As a collegiate instructor
he had scarcely a rival; as the eloquent expositor
of medical science he ever commanded a deep and
general attention, equally by his copious stores of
clinical wisdom and by the clear and pertinent
language in which he imparted the rich treasures
of his experience. A posthumous publication in one
volume octavo, on the Practice of Physic, recently
appeared, edited by one of his pupils, Dr. H. W. Ducachet.

Dr. Hosack was honored with testimonials of distinction from many learned and philosophical societies,
both abroad and at home. He was, while in Europe,
made a Fellow of the Linnæan Society of London.
His Alma Mater, Princeton, conferred on him the degree of Doctor of Laws; he was enrolled a Fellow
of the Royal Society of London in 1816, and in 1817
the Royal Society of Edinburgh conferred on him a
like distinction. He was early made a member of
the American Philosophical Society.

Dr. Hosack was nearly through the whole of life
in the enjoyment of excellent health; his constitution

had a natural tendency towards plethora of the blood vessels which he was cautious in guarding against by the use of antiphlogistic means; yet at an advanced period of age he suffered occasionally from its effects. By undue exposure in the early part of the winter of 1835, to the extreme cold of the season, he was suddenly seized with giddiness, and fell, upon entering the door of his residence. It proved a fatal apoplexy.

All that friendship or professional aid could impart, was given, but full consciousness never returned to him. His friends, Drs. McLean, Wilkes, Francis, Stevens, and his son, Dr. Alexander E. Hosack, were almost constantly with him. After about four days illness, he expired on the evening of the 23d of December, 1835, in the 67th year of his age. The funeral ceremonies were such as comported with the services he had rendered his fellow citizens, and his eminence as a laborer in behalf of the interests of mankind.

The manuscript correspondence and papers which Dr. Hosack has left, have been recently deliverd to his surviving friend, the Rev. Dr. Henry W. Ducachet, M. D., from whom is expected an ample memoir of this distinguished individual, whose abilities few men are better able to appreciate or more highly to admire.

DR. LUKE HOWE. The following brief sketch of the life of Dr. Howe, was read before the New Hampshire Med. Society, at their annual meeting in

June, 1843, by James Batcheller, M. D. of Marlborough. The Society passed a resolution to have
it published in the Boston Medical and Surgical
Journal, from which this is taken.

Luke Howe, the subject of the following memoir,
was born at Jaffrey, N. H., March 28th, 1787. His
father, the late Dr. Adonijah Howe, was a respectable and much esteemed physician, and a worthy and
very exemplary citizen. He commenced the practice of medicine in Jaffrey, soon after the town was
incorporated. He had four sons, all of whom received a collegiate education. Three studied the
profession of medicine and became eminent. The
youngest son studied divinity ; but the period of his
earthly existence was short. His early death was
deeply lamented by the church and parishioners over
whom he was settled. The whole family, consisting
of four sons and three daughters, are now, with the
exception of one daughter, numbered with the dead.

Dr. Luke Howe did not commence his literary
studies till twenty years of age. Up to this period,
he had been engaged in, and felt somewhat attached
to, agricultural pursuits. He however changed his
views, and commenced preparing himself to enter
college with a most commendable degree of industry
and perseverance. He entered Dartmouth College
as Sophomore, in 1808, and graduated in 1811.
Soon after leaving college he commenced the study
of law in his native town, with Samuel Darkin,
Esqr. He spent also considerable time in the office
of the Hon. Samuel C. Allen, of Northfield, Mass.,
who was for many years a member of Congress.

He closed his legal studies in the office of the honorable and distinguished Nathan Dane, of Beverly, Mass. He commenced the practice of law in Jaffrey, with the prospect of becoming distinguished. But he had been in practice but about a year, when his brother, Dr. Adonijah Howe, Jr., who was associated with his father in the practice of medicine, was suddenly removed by death. This truly grievous dispensation disappointed the hopes and expectations of the father, who, being in the decline of life, was anxious to resign his business into the hands of his son. He strenuously urged and importuned his son Luke to relinquish the practice of law, and commence the study of medicine. The son finally yielded to the solicitations of his father, and commenced the study of physic with him. He attended medical lectures at Boston and Hanover, and received the degree of M. D. from Dartmouth College, in the year 1818. He associated himself in business with his father in Jaffrey, where he continued till his death.

In the few brief remarks I have to offer in relation to Dr. Howe, as a physician, I do not wish to exhibit him as the wonder of the age in which he lived, or as far outstripping all his cotemporaries. Could he speak from the grave, he would denounce such a description as false and fulsome flattery. I wish simply to describe him as he was—a very industrious, studious, investigating, discriminating, and faithful physician—highly beloved and esteemed by his patrons. The limited circle in which most country physicians move, usually prevents their fame from being published to any great extent, let them be ever so meritorious. A single meritorious act, performed by a city physician, will probably be chanted by tens of thousands, and pass from city to city; while similar or superior acts of the country physicians will be, perhaps, merely noticed by a few friends in the immediate vicinity to the transaction. There are many traits in the character of Dr. Howe, highly commendable and worthy of imitation.

In his intercourse with neighboring physicians, his conduct was in an unusual degree honest, frank, gentlemanly and confiding. He never was guilty of an attempt to shake the confidence of friends in the attending physician, by significant nods and jesuitical innuendoes, of which some physicians, claiming a high standing, are guilty. I will hazard the assertion that there was not a physician favored with his intimate acquaintance, who was not his personal friend. He possessed an inventive genius. He was not content invariably to walk in the old paths marked out by his predecessors, but would occasionally step aside as a bold pioneer, in pursuit of new discoveries and improvements. He had considerable taste for surgery, but his local situation was unfavorable for extensive surgical practice, being in the immediate vicinity of one of the most distinguished surgeons in the State, between whom and himself, I am happy I can truly say, there existed the most intimate and cordial friendship. Dr. Howe felt no desire to place himself in the position of a rival. He however performed a few cases of amputation, and was frequently called to cases of fracture and dislocation. During the last years of his life he became associated with a young

physician as partner, which gave him more leisure to
pursue his favorite inclination of attempting to make
improvement in the apparatus used in certain surgical
operations. He has invented several new kinds of
splints, calculated for fracture of the femur, tibia and
fibula, the fore arm, and also the clavicle. He invented a new truss; also what he terms the semicir-
cular tourniquet. He attempted some improvement
in the abdominal supporter. They will, doubtless,
prove a valuable acquisition to the store of the medical knowledge of the country. Of these modes,
most of them, I believe, have been exhibited before
the New Hampshire Medical Society, and received
due commendation as constituting valuable improvements. The Trustees of the Mechanics' Association
of the city of Boston presented Dr. Howe with a
silver medal in commendation for the valuable articles
which were exhibited and examined by them at a recent fair. A few years since Dr. Howe published
in the Boston Medical and Surgical Journal, a description of the articles he had invented, with the
mode of application, and various valuable suggestions. It was also published in a pamphlet form, with
accurate plates. His apparatus for fracture of the
tibia and fibula, which he terms 'the posterior con-
cave splint,' is a most valuable improvement, and
ought, in my opinion, to be universally adopted, as it
fulfills all the indications more certainly than any other
method; mitigating, in a great degree, the suffering
of the patient, as he can leave his bed every day if
he desires, and is almost sure to prevent displacement.
1 wish every physician would try it. His semicircu-

37

lar tourniquet has one peculiar advantage, as by it we can effectually compress a single artery, and leave the circulation of all the other vessels of the limb unimpeded. Dr. Howe frequently contributed valuable articles for the Medical Journal, showing much research, and a discriminating mind.

He devoted much time to investigating the disease peculiar to clergymen, which he termed the ' Minister's Ail.' The result of his investigations he read before the State Society at their meeting in June, previous to his death. This article showed much laborious research, and embodied many practical facts and observations. Dr. Howe sustained through life a character for strict moral honesty and integrity. He at various times held many minor offices, the duties of which he discharged to the satisfaction of all. At the time of his death he was President of the New Hampshire Medical Society.

He was actively engaged in the various humane enterprises of the day, having for their object the elevation and amelioration of the human family. The cause of temperance received a great share of his benevolence. He drafted the first set of resolutions that were adopted by any medical society on the subject of temperance, and presented them to the western district of the New Hampshire Medical Society. He delivered many lectures upon the subject.

His fees for medical services were low, especially to the poor. On the subject of religion, he was a believer in those doctrines termed evangelical. Some eight or nine years before his death he made a public profession, by uniting with the Congregational

Church. His Christian walk and conversation proved him to be a sincere and devoted member. He was a very affectionate husband, and a most kind and indulgent parent. He was not a blank in society. He had no leisure for idleness. It was a maxim with him to fill up time with duties. He spent his whole time in visiting the sick, perusing his library, and contemplating new methods of improvement in the profession. He felt a deep interest in the elevation of the profession, and was a deadly enemy to quackery and empiricism, in whatever form. He had no faith in the secret nostrums of the day, comprising the whole family of the popular patent medicines. Some might have thought him too severe in his denunciation, but those best acquainted with him knew he was influenced by a sincere regard for the welfare of the community, rather than any unworthy motive of self-interest. He was in favor of a thorough education preparatory to the commencement of the study of medicine. This, connected with a more thorough study of the profession, would, in his opinion, be the most effectual means of discountenancing empiricism, and preventing its increase.

After all, Dr. Howe laid no claim to perfection; he also had his faults. But this is only saying that he was a man, subject to the imperfections, the passions, the temptations and weakness of poor, frail, dependent human nature. But it may be truly said that he restrained, overcame and counteracted many of the evil propensities of our nature, when thousands fail in the conflict.

The final, closing scene was sudden and unexpect-

ed. He visited Boston and Andover, enjoying an
unusual flow of spirits. At Andover he read his
dissertation on the disease peculiar to clergymen,
before the faculty and students of the Theological
Institution, which excited much interest. The students, as an expression of their high respect for the
author, and for the valuable suggestions contained
in the address, wrote a letter of thanks to Dr. Howe,
expressing in the most kind and flattering manner
their high appreciation of the value of his discourse.
Their letter was received by his friends on the day
of his funeral. During his pleasing journey to Boston and Andover, he was under constant excitement,
receiving the gratulations of friends, and many testimonials of regard. He arrived home on Wednesday
evening, and considered himself in usual health. In
the morning he complained of a little indisposition;
but he dressed and left his bed every day during his
sickness. No dangerous symptoms were discovered
till Tuesday morning of the next week, when Dr. Ri-
chardson, his partner, who had visited him frequently,
discovered symptoms unfavorable, and indicating danger. I was requested to visit him. This was on the
ninth day of his sickness. I did not arrive until 11
o'clock, P. M. I found him in the arms of death.
He recognized me, told me he supposed he was dying, reached out his cold hand, and affectionately
closed mine, as the last token of friendship and
remembrance. His spirit took its flight December
24, 1841. On his death bed he enjoyed the unspeakable consolations of religion, and departed in
the full belief of a glorious immortality. His funeral

was attended by an unusual number of his medical brethren, and a large concourse of his immediate friends and townsmen, who evinced their deep sorrow by signs more expressive than words.

DR. THOMAS HUBBARD was born at Smithfield, near Providence, in Rhode Island, where his father resided as an innkeeper, in the year 1776. While he was about 16 years of age, his father having died, the care of the establishment and the oversight of the concerns of the family, consisting of a widowed mother and several children, all younger than himself, devolved upon him. The duties which were thus thrown upon him, at a period of life when most young men are scarcely competent to take care of themselves, were performed with great judgment and skill, and evinced the same energy and decision which characterized him through life. At this time he acquired a fondness for agricultural pursuits, an employment which he continued with much gratification until his removal to this place. What his early education was, I am not informed, though it is known that he pursued the study of the languages and of mathematics, for a period, most probably a short one.

His professional instructor was Dr. Albigense Waldo, a surgeon of considerable reputation, who had acquired most of what he knew of the art, by his practice in the army. Dr. Hubbard, however, derived the greater part of his knowledge from the diligent study of the best medical books, and from his own observations. He was a most diligent student, not only when preparing for his profession, but during his whole life. His library was a valuable one, especially in works on surgery, and his habits were to spend a portion of every day, even when engaged in a most laborious practice, in availing himself of the knowledge which it afforded. I have often heard him remark, that the physician who neglected his books, would lose more by forgetfulness than he would acquire by observation, and would be less skillful at fifty than he was at thirty years of age. His written lectures bear the strongest marks of his great industry. He obviously revised with care every subject, each successive year ; and at each revision, added in the form of notes and interlineations, the results of his reading and observation. This course of diligent study, aided by a strongly retentive memory, stored his mind with the most valuable information. I know not the man whose knowledge of the best practice of the best Surgeon, is more intimate and exact.

Having prepared himself for his profession, he commenced the practice of it upon the death of his preceptor, Dr. Waldo, in the year 1795, before he was twenty years of age. He met with opposition at first, on account of attempting to unite the practice of physic with that of surgery. It seems to have been the custom of that part of the country, as it had been extensively elsewhere, for the surgeon to confine himself to that branch only, and to call in the aid of a physician when it was thought necessary. This plan Dr. Hubbard always reprobated, believing that the union of the two professions in the same person was better suited to the wants of a scattered population. Whatever opposition there was, seems soon to have subsided. His practice became extensive and very laborious, reaching not only all the eastern part of the State, but also the bordering towns of Rhode Island and Massachusetts. There is the fullest proof of the success of his practice, especially in surgery. His qualifications as a surgeon were of a high order. Though not early instructed in anatomy, he was in the constant habit of dissection, and thus gained the [requisite anatomical knowledge. He was prompt and decisive in forming an opinion of the cases which were presented to him, and equally so in advising and performing such operations as he deemed necessary. His vigorous and well trained intellect, enlightened by long experience, grasped the strong points of a case, both as they were at the time, and as they would become if neglected. He always advocated an early resort to surgical operations, not timidly and hesitatingly waiting until its necessity was more obvious, at the expense of the health, and perhaps the life, of the patient. In operating, he was cool, deliberate and collected.

The same promptness and energy which marked his character as a surgeon, controlled his practice as a physician. Employing but few remedies, and those of an active kind, he was thoroughly acquainted with their effects, and used them with great judgment and skill. He had great confidence in the remedial power of active medication. The object at which he aimed was to break up disease in its forming stage, or to control it by agents stronger than itself. This trust in the power of remedies he was in the habit of expressing strongly to his patients, and thereby secured that confidence on their part which is so efficient an aid to the physician in the cure of diseases.

His energy and promptness sometimes gave a degree of peremptoriness to his manners, which, if unattended by kindness, might have been unpleasant. This was seen, however, to be prompted by the desire to enforce a strict observance of that course of treatment which he knew was for the benefit of the patient, and as such was duly appreciated.

In his intercourse with his patients he was frank and undisguised, and entirely above those little tricks and concealments which indicate a weak or dishonorable mind. The same frankness also marked his conduct towards his professional brethren, and all others with whom he associated. The free expression of opinions uprightly formed, he believed to be the right and duty of an honest man ; a right which he claimed for himself, and to the exercise of which by others he was unusually tolerant.

During the thirty-four years which Dr. Hubbard spent in Pomfret, his time was fully employed in the faithful discharge of his professional duties, as well as those which devolved upon him as a good citizen and a kind and upright man.

He was several times chosen Representative, and once Senator in the State Legislature. He was also appointed President of the Connecticut Medical Society, and held the office till he declined a re-election. He was active in the promotion of such institutions as were designed for the benefit of the afflicted.

The Asylum for the Deaf and Dumb, the Retreat for the Insane, and the State Hospital, each in its turn received his efficient aid. In the last year of his life he was active, under the authority of the Legislature, in procuring information, and in devising plans preparatory to the establishment of a hospital for the insane poor. The fatigue and exposure, while on a journey connected with this object, appeared to excite the disease which terminated his life.

In the year 1829, Dr. Hubbard removed from Pomfret to New Haven, and assumed the duties of Professor of Surgery, in the Institution at that place, and for nine years he performed these duties with great zeal, industry and success. As an instructor, he was plain, simple, strait forward, abounding in correct principles and illustrative facts, without any attempt at the niceties of style, or the graces of manner. Unbewildered himself by theoretical discussions, he spent no time in making theories of his own, or in marring those of others. His remark was, that if young men were desirous of theories, they could find enough of them in the books, and that his business was to teach them by facts how to distinguish and cure diseases. Possessing a memory wonderfully retentive, he embodied the accumulated facts, and the rich experience of his professional life, in the course of his instructions, thus giving them authority and force. His lectures were highly useful, and deservedly acceptable.

He died June 16, 1838, of a disease of the stomach and bowels, of which he had suffered several

38

severe attacks. *Introductory Lect. of Dr. Knight, of Yale College, published in the Boston Med. and Surg. Journal.*

DR. DAVID HUNT. Dr. Hunt was son of Dr. Ebenezer Hunt of Northampton, a very distinguished physician, who died in the year 1820, at the age of 76. Dr. David Hunt was born at Northampton, Massachusetts, in the year 1773. He studied the profession of medicine principally with his father, and commenced the practice of it in his native place, soon after he became of age, and continued the practice of it there, until he died in the year 1837, at the age of 64 years. He was a very respectable practitioner, and a good scholar. He received the honorary degree of Doctor of Medicine from Yale College in the year 1818. He was a Fellow of the American Antiquarian Society, and I believe of the American Geological Society, and of the Physico-Medical Society of New York. He was a distinguished mineralogist, and was one of the first physicians in America who ever devoted much attention to it. His cabinet of minerals was rare, and very beautiful and large, for a private individual. He was on terms of intimacy, and maintained a constant correspondence with the late Dr. Bruce, Professors Silliman, Cleaveland, Hitchcock, and several other of our celebrated and most distinguished mineralogists and geologists. He had a large, select and valuable medical library, and he spent many of his leisure hours in it. In early life he was rather wild, but this wildness did not lead him to acts of wickedness. His sprees were got up more for the sake of fun and hilarity than for mischief. On one occasion he was seen riding through the streets of Northampton with a large bush or limb of a tree tied to his horse's tail. His minister, the Rev. Mr. Williams, met him and said to him, 'Why David, I thought you had sowed all your wild oats.' 'And so I have, sir,' said he, 'and I am now bushing them in.' His fund of anecdote was inexhaustible, and he has been known to keep his friends in a continual peal of laughter for hours, in listening to him.

The productions of his pen were not numerous. I recollect but one medical paper of his, which was ever published in any of our medical journals, and that was on a case of poisoning by lead, which was published in the New England Journal of Medicine and Surgery.

He was admitted a Fellow of the Massachusetts Medical Society in the year 1813. He was, for many years, an officer in it. He resigned in 1833, four years before his death.

DOCTOR EBENEZER HUNTINGTON, of Vergennes, Vermont. Doctor J. A. Allen has published the following sketch of Dr. Huntington, in the Boston Medical and Surgical Journal for Jan. 11th, 1844.

Ebenezer Huntington, the subject of this memoir, was born in Windham, Connecticut, May 21st, 1763. His father was a practising physician in that place,

but subsequently entered the ministry in Worthington,
Massachusetts.   Ebenezer, before he arrived at the
age of 21, commenced the study of medicine with
Dr. Bradish, of Cummington, in his adopted state.
Having completed his pupilage with his instructor,
he commenced the practice of his profession in Ches-
terfield, Mass., at the early age of 22.   After having
remained in that place two years, he removed to
Vergennes.   To this place he came in January, 1789.
At this time the place was new, and contained only
one framed house.   The inhabitants were sparsely
scattered over the adjacent country.   For some years
Dr. Huntington, as he once told the writer of this
article, was one of the three physicians only, who
then resided on the west side of the Green mountains
within the precincts of Vermont.   Consequently his
ride was very extensive ; his labors and exposures as
a practising physician were excessively trying and
fatiguing.   But he engaged in those labors, and encountered the severe trials incident to his profession,
at this early period, with a resolution seldom surpassed and truly commendable.   He appeared to enjoy
himself most when he could most relieve the sick.
His constant desire to relieve the sick and suffering
is well remembered by a large circle of surviving
friends.   His constant readiness to endure fatigue and
privation, either by night or day, to relieve pain and
disease, is a trait of character well deserving special
commendation.

His professional opinions were always expressed
with candor, frankness, and free from ostentation ;
and if, on any occasion, he committed a mistake, his

ingenuous and honest avowal of it could not fail to excite in the breast of every one, sentiments of admiration for his honesty of purpose. It is believed, however, that his mistakes were as rare, and his imperfections as few, as usually fall to the lot of man. In his family he was a sample of excellence. Few if any instances can be found in which all the endearments of domestic life appeared to be enjoyed with such perfection. In the social circle he was humorous, remarkably happy in the narration of anecdotes, and always avoiding, with the most scrupulous exactness, every thing which bordered on vulgarity.

By his good judgment, kind feelings and courteous deportment, he acquired and retained, in an eminent degree, the confidence and good will of all who knew him. He was emphatically 'the poor man's friend.' He continued in the practice of medicine at Vergennes, nearly forty-five years. He became extensively and favorably known, and was regarded as a safe and successful practitioner.

Few men have enjoyed such opportunities to amass an estate as he ; and yet he was content with a handsome competency. In reply to the inquiry, why he did not collect his dues, he said, ' I never could find time.' His time was not his own. It was devoted to the glorious purpose of doing good to the afflicted. He was fully conscious that the more charity, compassion and condescension with which he treated the poor, the nearer he approached to the greatest and highest of glories—an imitation of his adorable Savior.

For a considerable period he was President of the

Vermont State Medical Society. And subsequently, for a series of years, he was President of the Addison County Medical Society. In 1826, being recommended by the Faculty of the Vermont Academy of Medicine, now the Castleton Medical College, the honorary degree of Doctor of Medicine was conferred on him by the Corporation of Middlebury College.

For many years he was an active and efficient member of the Congregational Church at Vergennes. He died Dec. 4th, 1834, aged 71 years. His last moments were moments of peace. He gave the most cheering evidence to all who witnessed his departure, that the Divine Redeemer, the great Physician of souls, in whom he trusted in life and health, was his refuge and support in death.

DR. SHIRLEY IRVING, was born in Boston, November, 1758. He was the grandson of Gov. William Shirley, and son of John and Catherina Irving. He was an eminent physician, and practiced in Portland, then in the District, now in the State of Maine. He entered Harvard College, in 1773, but in consequence of the disturbance of the American revolutionary war, he did not complete his collegiate course there. He however received the honorary degree of Master of Arts, from that college in the year 1810. He studied the profession of medicine with Dr. Lloyd, of Boston, and afterwards established himself as a physician in Portland, where his professional services were justly appreciated, and for a great many

years he enjoyed the approbation and confidence of
the public. In the latter period of his life, his health
was extremely feeble in consequence of an affection
of the lungs, a complaint under which he had labored
for many years, and which had been gradually sap-
ping the springs of life, he in a great measure abandoned the laborious duties of his profession, and returned to Boston, where he died in July, 1813, in
the 55th year of his age.

' In an obituary notice, published at the time of
his death, he is represented as having been eminently
a good man; distinguished for his unbending integrity and affability; and for that rare endowment, a
most placid and agreeable temper,—such an one as
was never seen ruffled by accident, or distorted by
passion.

' His character was remarkably symmetrical; yet
if any one virtue predominated, it was benevolence,
and that of the most active kind. He rather sought
out than shunned misfortune; and when it was discovered, *he never passed by on the other side.* He
was a learned and scientific man, but without the
slightest tincture of dogmatism or pedantry. Such
was Dr. Irving; and he insensibly attracted and attached to himself all who came near him. It is said
he never had an enemy, and as he was highly respected while living, so his death was greatly lamented, and his memory was embalmed in the affections
of a numerous circle of relatives and friends.—*Alden's Family Record, Columbian Centinel.*

Dr. Ansel W. Ives. The subject of the following notice was, for many years, my most intimate friend. He was a medical classmate of mine in Columbia College, in 1812–13, a class from which have proceeded some of the most eminent men in America. Dr. Ives was my room mate, and for many years preceding his death, we maintained an uninterrupted correspondence. I can, therefore, most cordially subscribe to the truth of the subjoined remarks in the American Medical Journal of May, 1838.

'Dr. Ansel W. Ives, our collaborator, was born in Woodbury, Conn., on the 31st of August, 1787. His father was a respectable farmer of that place, who, having a large family, and very limited means, was unable to give his children even an ordinary education; and the third child, at the early age of nine years, was bound apprentice to a farmer, until his nineteenth year; his time was spent in agricultural employment, except a few months in which he was permitted to pass a portion of each day at an ordinary school. A taste for knowledge and literary pursuits, which may almost be considered innate, in some measure compensated his want of early advantages. From his early age, he always carried a book in his pocket, and never lost occasions for study afforded by opportunities of labor. So industrious a reader was he that before the expiration of his apprenticeship, (as he informed the writer) he had perused all the books he could borrow within five miles of his master's residence. At the age of nineteen, having qualified himself to keep an elementary school,

he commenced teaching, which he pursued for several years with credit to himself and advantage to his
employers. Continuing at the same time with the
greatest zeal, his plan of self-instruction, he soon
found himself sufficiently advanced to commence the
study of a profession; and having chosen that of medicine, he entered a student with Dr. North, an eminent physician residing in New London. On removing to Fishkill, in the State of New York, he continued his studies with Dr. Barto White, a distinguished
physician of that place, and completed them in the
office of Dr. Valentine Mott, graduating in the College of Physicians and Surgeons of the University of
New York, in the year 1815.

Dr. Ives carried into the practice of his profession
the same zeal and industry which had heretofore so
distinctly marked his character, and though for several
years his means were limited and precarious, he soon
acquired a large share of public confidence and professional employment, which continued steadily to increase, till his exertions were paralyzed by the disease
which terminated his life. Dr. Ives devoted a large
share of his time to the instruction of others; and
many of his pupils are witnesses of the zeal and
fidelity with which he discharged that responsible
duty. He also contributed largely to our Medical
Journals, and some of the papers, especially that on
Humulus Lupulus, gained him much credit both at
home and abroad. He republished, with notes and
additions, Paris' Pharmacologiæ, and Hamilton's observations on the use and abuse of mercurial remedies, and also a description of the Epidemic Influenza,

39

which prevailed in the northern and eastern States, in the year 1815; indeed his whole time was spent in improving his mind, or making himself useful to his fellow men.   In 1827, he became a member of the Presbyterian church, and from that period devoted a large portion of his time to religious and charitable institutions ; being always ready to work, a great deal of labor in preparing reports, &c., fell to his share, and was always cheerfully performed.   Of the sincerity of his religious faith, his consistent life, his exemplary patience, under almost intolerable pain, and truly christian death, afforded the best evidence.

Dr. Ives was in person above the middle height, well formed, with an intelligent eye, his manners were prepossessing, and he possessed a fund of humor and anecdote, which made his company acceptable to his associates, and often dissipated the gloom of the sick room ; his constitution was good, and he enjoyed a fine share of health till he was attacked, in Feb. 1837, with neuralgic pain about the left hip, which gradually increased in duration and violence, till his sufferings for hours together were almost beyond endurance.   About five months from the attack, the hip and thigh began to enlarge, which they continued steadily to do, with augmented pain, till Feb. 2nd, 1838, when death relieved him from his agony.   On dissection a large tumor was found on the left ilium, extending downwards under the left gluteus muscle, pressing on the sacro sciatic nerve, and bones of the pelvis, which were carious, and on that side separated from each other, and a collection of matter on the inner surfaces of the ilium, with

traces of extensive and severe periterreal inflammation, which was probably the immediate cause of his
death. F. U. J.'

DR. JAMES JACKSON, JR. The subject of this notice was son of Dr. James Jackson, of Boston, one
of the most distinguished physicians in New England,
if not in our country, who is still living in a green
old age, admired and beloved by all who know him.
Long may he continue, and may the evening of his
life be as calm and serene, as the course of it thus
far, has been useful and happy. The following notice
of his son is principally selected from a memoir of
him by an afflicted father, prefixed to a volume of
his letters and cases, written principally to his father
at Boston, while he was in London and Paris, completing his medical pupilage. I take this opportunity
to return to my friend, Dr. Jackson, my sincere
thanks for the presentation of this interesting volume
to me. It is a most interesting work, containing 444
pages, octavo.

'The following pages contain a memoir of the life
of my late son, James Jackson, Jr., M. D., with extracts from his letters, and a selection from the medical cases collected by him, principally in Paris. I
have been induced to print these cases by the solicitation of those who knew how he had collected
them. I have been induced to write the memoir, in
consequence of the suggestion of those who knew
something of him, and whose opinions I respect.
In some points, the task has been grateful to me:

sad, though it may seem, for a father, I thank God
that I have been able to maintain my cheerfulness,
and to attend to the common occupations of life, since
the deplorable loss which I suffered, in his departure
from this world.   But every hour he has been in my
mind.   In every occupation, in almost every conversation, however little others could see the connection,
his image has been before me.   It has been a beautiful image, and has not checked any pleasure, nor
even any gaiety, in which I thought he could have
joined.

Under any circumstances, I might seem an improper person to give his history, and my statements may
be deemed scarcely worthy of credit.   Who will believe that I shall be impartial ?   I can say, however,
that I would not willingly be guilty of exaggeration,
if it were only for respect to the love of truth, which
formed the most distinguishing trait of his character.
He loved me, as few sons love their fathers.   Of this
I have had constant and ample proofs.   But he loved
truth better, and would not subscribe to any opinion
because it was mine, though he was quite willing, in
his conduct, to submit to my direction and control.

But if I draw a fancy picture, while I design to
paint the character of my son, if that presents a
young man who devoted his time most assiduously
to the acquisition of useful knowledge, who cultivated at the same time his best moral affections, and
acted from the highest love of virtue, and who thereby secured the friendship of the wise and good, the
fiction at least, may have some good influence on the
young and inexperienced.   At least it may lead them

to reflect on the immutable connection between virtue and happiness.

The subject of this story was not indeed rewarded by long life. But in this age will it be maintained that long life is the greatest of blessings? This is a topic on which I shall not enlarge; but I will only say for myself, which I do most sincerely, that I would not have added a year to my son's life by an allowed indulgence in a single vice.

The history of my son's life is very simple, and it may be told very briefly. He was born on the 15th of January, 1810, graduated at the University in Cambridge, in 1828, and then engaged in the study of medicine. This he did under my direction, and as my pupil. He continued as such till the April of 1831, and during this time he attended the medical lectures of our University, and saw the practice of the Massachusetts General Hospital. In the spring of 1831, he went to Paris, where he arrived in May, and remained till July, 1833, except during a visit of six months to Great Britain and Ireland, in the spring and summer of 1832. He reached home at the end of the summer of 1833, and graduated as Doctor of Medicine, in the University, in February, 1834. He was now prepared to engage in practice, and took rooms for himself in Franklin Place. He was thus brought to the starting place of active life, and under circumstances the most flattering and the most grateful, when he was arrested in his course. Exactly at this point he was arrested. His arrangements being made, he sent an advertisement to the public papers, which appeared on the 5th of

March, and on that day he was taken sick, so as to lodge at my house, instead of occupying the rooms which he had just announced as his residence. This sickness was his last, and he died on the 27th of the same month, being in his 25th year.

Thus cut off before he had yet been tried in the serious business of life, and having passed his brief course without encountering any of the trials to which many men are subjected, it would seem that his story could hardly afford any details of interest, except to his own family. And yet he did excite an interest during his life, in very many friends, abroad as well as at home, and that of the warmest kind; and his loss has been deeply mourned by those, whom I never saw, and to whom he was recommended only by his own conduct. There must, then, have been something in him to have excited this interest, which I shall call deep and ardent, disregarding the imputation to which I subject myself of a blind partiality. This something was in his character. If he is to be commemorated, it should be by delineating that character; and while doing this, I shall be led to detail, though it may not be in exact order, the events of his life, as illustrating it. Any friend in pursuing this course would be thought liable to run into eulogy, instead of giving a true description of the subject of his discourse; a fond father must certainly be subject to this suspicion. Those who know the truth in this case, must decide whether this suspicion is justified by what follows. I may, however, promise that I shall not attempt to write coldly, while I shall endeavor to keep in mind that my business is not to display my own feelings toward the beloved subject of my discourse, but to draw a picture of one whose features are more perfectly engraved on my mind, than on that of any one else.

From his earliest age, my son always manifested great cheerfulness of temper, and gaiety of heart, so that he was never long depressed by trouble of any kind. He was always ready to sympathize with those about him, and he loved to engage their sympathy in return. He was not contented without constant action, except when engaged in study, or other occupation. These characteristics are common enough in boyhood, and did not distinguish him among his fellows at that stage of life. It was by myself only, perhaps, that his indomitable gaiety of heart was then noticed; though I also remarked, very early, that his mind was capable of being engaged on the most solemn subjects. From these characteristics he was often boisterous and annoying to those around him, but he was so good natured that they could not be angry with him. He had very little ambition to gain distinction, or to be a leader among his comrades, but delighted to join in their sports on terms of equality, as anxious that they should be pleased, as to have his share of the sport. He was agreeable to his young friends without being distinguished among them. His schoolmaster loved him; but had to punish him continually for the sin of laughing, of which he could not break him, however. He would strive at times to get a high rank in his class to please me, for he always loved me most ardently; but he seemed no otherwise to value the distinction. Once,

when a little boy, he had kept the head of his class
for two or three days, and then a younger boy got
above him.   I reproached him for permitting this.
But he said, with great naivette, that the other boy
'ought to be at the head sometimes.'   I hardly gave
him credit, at the moment, for this generous wish for
the gratification of his rival; but his companions in
later life will agree with me in believing that it was
the result of that interest in the happiness of others,
which he manifested more and more strongly as long
as he lived.

In college his ready sympathy led him at first into
the company of those who were most gay, and for a
few months he joined in their pastimes.   At the end
of six months, the excellent President gave me warning that my son had become intimate with those
whose company was most dangerous.   This would
have caused me great distress, but that happily my
son had recently given me the same information, and
had told me that he had discovered his danger; in
fact, as soon as he perceived the views of his associates, he no longer sympathized with them; he had
broken with them.   He now formed an intimacy with
one who encouraged all his virtuous aspirations, and
he began to cultivate, upon principle, a purity of
heart, of which the fruits were in all his subsequent
life.   He was not led into habits, nor into any feeling of austerity.   Gaiety, he could not dismiss; it
was ever springing up in him.   He was guilty of imprudence like others.   But he constantly studied his
duty; he cultivated more and more the best principles of action, and from year to year, his standard of

excellence was placed higher and higher. He never attained a distinguished rank in his class, by an exact attention to his collegiate duties, a circumstance which I do not mention in commendation. Yet without my knowledge, until long afterwards, he established for himself certain rules of action, and habits of industrious study, from which he seldom deviated subsequently, and was really storing his mind with valuable knowledge. I was not aware of his industry, though I thought that I watched him closely, till he had left the college. He did not tell me of it, though he was very open and ingenuous in telling me his feelings and his errors. When he began the study of medicine, under my eye, he gave himself to it with an energy and industry that surprised me. I thought at the moment, that he was resolved to make up for past negligences, but that his zeal would soon abate. I did not yet understand him. Subsequently, my only apprehension was from his too great devotion to his studies, which constantly went on increasing. I presumed that the temptations to pleasure in Europe, would draw him off from laborious study quite enough; but not so; there, even more than here, he spent his strength without reserve, in his professional pursuits; though he meant to keep himself within the limits of safety. The only temptation which he could not at all resist, was that furnished by the invaluable opportunities, there offered to him, for the increase of useful knowledge.

When he went abroad his reading on professional subjects had been so extensive and his habits of attention so well formed, that I thought him fully prepared to avail himself of the advantages he might derive from the excellent schools of Paris, London, and Edinburgh. I dared not then say so, even in my own family, for I feared the evil consequences of too much praise ; but I regarded his acquisitions as very extraordinary for a student, and therefore, let him go at an earlier period than that in which I commonly advise young men to take the same step. Those who are acquainted with medical literature, will believe that I did not overrate his diligence, after considering the following statement. Before the termination of the second year of his pupilage, he went through the Epistles of Morgagni on the seats and causes of diseases, as translated by Alexander, in three thick, quarto volumes. He took notes of what he read, and as he went on, compared with it, the invaluable work of Baillie, on morbid anatomy, another quarto, with the plates accompanying it. This he did indeed in the quiet of the country, but he took proper time to exercise, and did not seem to me more industrious than at other periods. He however completed the whole in seven weeks. Nor did he read this work, as a task, without possessing himself of the contents of it. He read it with great interest ; and he fixed in his mind so many of its details, that by the aid of his short notes he was able to refer to it afterwards. Thus I find in his early autopsies in Paris, which he entered in his common place book, many references in the margin, to cases in this great store house of post mortem examinations. Indeed, I have not been acquainted with any one, who was so intimate with the details of this work, as he was.

Immediately after this, and before his second year of
medical studies was terminated, he wrote a long dissertation on pneumonia, in doing which he consulted
all the writings on the subject which he could get at,
both those expressly on it, and those which embraced
it with other subjects in systematic works. This dissertation gained him the Boylston Medical Prize from
a committee, among the members of which was Dr.
Ware. Dr. Ware spoke to me of this work at the
time, in terms of great commendation, and I confess
that when I read it, I was fearful that it would be
supposed I had rendered assistance in the preparation
of it, which in such a case, would have been improper. But, in fact, I had only pointed out the sources
of information, and had made some general remarks
on the subject, as I should in conversation with any
pupil. I was aware that he was writing on the subject, but thought at the time, it was only an exercise
as a member of the Boylston Medical Society, not a
dissertation for a prize.

I have stated these things as examples of his industry. I may add, that in the period of his medical
studies, before he went to Europe, scarcely two years
and a half, if I deduct the time employed on journies,
he had read a very large proportion of all the valuable English standard works on medicine, and very
many in the French, frequently and carefully consulting older works in other languages when referred to,
especially when facts were concerned. At the same
time he had engaged as fully as most others in dissection, in its proper season ; he had seen much of disease elsewhere, particularly at the House of Industry,

where Dr. Fisher was then physician, and frequently invited him when there was any thing particularly interesting ; and he took notes of lectures of every thing which came under his observation, especially of the autopsies which he attended, so that he had covered twelve hundred folio pages of his common place book, when he left home.

It was thus prepared that he went to Paris, there to take care of himself when just past twenty-one years of age. Thus far, except two or three journies, he had lived in a limited circle, under the eyes and care of his friends. At college, even, he resided principally in a private family of the first respectability, and of the greatest moral worth, where he had been allured by kindness to submit to wholesome restraints, and to the friendly feelings of wisdom and experience. I could not dismiss one so inexpressibly dear to me, without anxiety, though satisfied that it was wise that he should go. The following extracts, will show something of the state of his mind, and of my own. They will bring before the reader the true feelings and principles which then reigned in his heart, and if I may write about him at all, I see not why I may not produce them.

Dr. Jackson then goes on to give more than 430 octavo pages of letters and cases recorded by his talented son, which shows him to be second to no young man of his age in America, and which will amply repay the reader for the perusal of them, and which show a giant mind just bursting into resplendent day. He died on the 27th of March, 1835, aged 24 years.

Dr. Thomas C. James. The Philadelphia Casket
for March, 1830, has the following notice of this distinguished Obstetrician. It was written previous to
his decease.

'Thomas C. James, M. D., an eminent practitioner in Philadelphia, and Professor of Midwifery in the
University of Pennsylvania, was born in Philadelphia,
in the year 1766, and received his education at
Friends' Grammar School, under the tuition of the
celebrated Robert Proud, author of the History of
Pennsylvania. It was there his genius was more
fully developed for that course of study to which he
was afterwads led by inclination, and for which he
was eminently qualified by the highest talents, and
the most amiable disposition of mind.

After finishing his school education, he commenced
the study of medicine under the worthy Dr. Adam
Kuhn, then Professor of Materia Medica, and of
considerable eminence in the profession. With him
he remained as a student of medicine till the year
1788, when, with the most flattering prospects, he
graduated in the University of Pennsylvania, being
then in the 22d year of his age.

It was not unusual, at that day, for young physicians, ere they commenced practice, to visit foreign
places, and frequently to embark on long voyages;
to enable them to add to the general theory of their
profession, that practical knowledge so needful to
perfect professional skill, and which could be obtained
only by personal observation and experience. Accordingly, in the year 1788, Dr. James was entered

as surgeon on board the ship Sampson, Capt. Howell, on a voyage to the Cape of Good Hope and China.

The character of the young physician was established for skillfulness, and especially for that humanity and gentleness of disposition, so essential to the character of a physician, and for which, at a more advanced age, and through its successive periods, Dr. James has been eminently characterized.

In the fall of 1790, Dr. James embarked for Europe, and arriving in London, he had free intercourse with some of the most eminent men of the faculty, and daily added to his stock of knowledge. His industry in acquiring information on every subject connected with his profession, and his attention to the means so amply afforded by the most eminent London practitioners, to whose personal acquaintance his amiable disposition and distinguished talents gained him access, could not fail of their effect upon the mind of one so ardently devoted to medical science. He walked through St. George's Hospital, at that time attended by Drs. John Hunter, Home, Baillie, Fordyce, Osborne, Clarke, &c. From London he went to Edinburgh, in Scotland, where he spent the winter of 1791–2, in the earnest pursuit of general literature and medical science; and returned to Philadelphia, in the summer of 1793, in time to witness the ravages of the malignant epidemic of that year.

The talents and success of Dr. James have distinguished him even in a city noted for producing many eminent physicians. Though unambitious and unpretending, and rather retired in his public character, his qualifications well established with the faculty, and in the esteem of his fellow citizens, were too conspicuous not to be duly appreciated. Accordingly, in 1811, we find him promoted to the Professorship of Midwifery, in the University of Pennsylvania; to which distinguished and responsible station he was elected by the Trustees of that Institution.

Dr. James was descended from highly respectable settlers in his native State of Pennsylvania; and by the mother's side, grandson of the worthy and much esteemed Thomas Chalkley, from whom he derived his name—formerly an eminent minister of the Society of Friends, well known, and gratefully remembered for his christian piety, and his various useful writings.

The situation which Dr. James occupied as Professor, was the meed of his professional labors. We remembered him when in the humble ranks of a practitioner, devoting his talents at the risk of his life, in the cause of humanity. As attending physician of the Welch society, of which he was an active member, his philanthropy has been tested by numerous instances of devotedness, in the arduous duties of a profession where no honors were to be won, nor applause to be gained. It was in the mansion of disease and death—the Hospital on Schuylkill, when so many of the unfortunate emigrants from Wales were placed by the Welch society, during the prevalence of an epidemic which raged among them in the year 1805, that Dr. James gave unequivocal proof of his medical abilities and charitable feelings.

At that dreadful period, when the wretchedness of the sick and dying stranger was aggravated by extreme poverty, and the appalling apprehensions of virulent contagion, Dr. James was the constant attendant—the skillful physician—the kind and sympathizing friend ; and to whose assiduous exertions, under Providence, the survivors were indebted for the prolongation of their existence.

In his Obstetric practice, Dr. James stood unrivaled, and may deservedly rank at the head of the profession. With a practice of nearly forty years, he acquired and retained the respect of his fellow professors, and the confidence of his fellow citizens ; with whom also his patronage was at once liberal and extensive, the results of a long and extensive practice.'

The following additional remarks in relation to the life of Dr. James, are from a paper read before the College of Physicians of Philadelphia, by Hugh L. Hodge, M. D., and published in the American Medical Journal for July, 1843.

' Dr. James died July 25, 1835. His death though sudden, had been long expected by himself and friends from the evident decline of his health, and from the premature approach of those infirmities which too surely indicated the decline of life.

We all knew him. We all loved and respected him. It could not be otherwise. The senior members of this college, of which he was President, viewed him as a friend and brother, who had been always their chosen companion, and their fellow laborer in all the duties of this society, and of the profession to which they were alike devoted. The younger members looked on him with love and veneration, for he had been their medical teacher, their friend, their counsellor, and, as far as practicable, their benefactor. His example had always been presented as most worthy of imitation. And when he departed, they felt, and still feel, as if one important link in that golden chain which binds this generation to the past, was, unfortunately for them, severed. The college has lost one whose devotion to its interests had been sincere and long continued ; and whose virtues, age, and experience had deservedly placed him in the most prominent station in its power to bestow.

The most striking trait in the character of Dr. James, was unfeigned modesty and diffidence. His conversation, his intercourse with his friends, with his professional brethren, and even with students of medicine, his whole deportment indicated that he did not rest upon his own sentiments, with that implicit confidence which would induce him to promulgate his opinions, or to insist on their correctness or importance. He paid great deference to the opinions of others, and would hence submit to the guidance of those of an opposite temperament, really believing they must be better informed than himself. This native modesty, pervading his whole intellectual and moral nature, had the most decided influence on his professional course, and on his present and future reputation.

Nevertheless, Dr. James, however reluctant he might be to promulgate his sentiments, or even to express an opinion, possessed a mind too powerful and too well furnished, not to form positive opinions on almost every subject to which it was directed, whether in literature or science. Those only, who

41

enjoyed his confidence, who were admitted into the favored precincts of his private friendship, could discover how positive and correct were his sentiments; how discriminating his opinions respecting men and things; and yet, how anxious to avoid having his views known, whether for praise or criticism.

As a man, Dr. James was also remarkable for great dignity, combined with mildness of disposition, and gentleness of manners. He was entirely free from any thing approaching hauteur or stateliness; yet no one could look on him without feelings of respect, which were excited by his venerable appearance, and by the native simplicity of his manners. He was affable and condescending to all, and never in the latter years of his life, manifested undue excitement under the most trying circumstances. This gentleness of character, was greatly the result of his own efforts; for gifted by nature with a warm heart, and a sprightly imagination, he was prone in early life, to be excited when any dear friend or darling opinion was assailed. In subsequent years, he had so fully obtained the government of his passions, that no one even suspected that he could ever have been under their influence; a victory this, more difficult of achievement, than those which have conferred celebrity on many of the heroes of the world. This self-command was the result of high moral and christian principles. To the important subject of Christianity, he devoted much attention. He studied the Bible as the source of all correct knowledge on religious subjects, not only in his native language, but in the original Hebrew and Greek, and in the Latin,

French, and German versions. He examined the various readings, the commentaries of different authors, and the creeds of different sects of Christians. He ventured even within the perplexed mazes of theology, and endeavored to elicit information and sound doctrine from the obscurities of theological metaphysics. His mind, however, was too strong to become confused by sophisms, and his heart too sincere in the love and pursuit of truth, to be lost in this extensive investigation. He returned from these excursions, ladened with good fruit; and after much inquiry among the living and the dead, he rested with child-like confidence his hopes of immortal happiness on the simple declarations of the Bible, and his life was governed by the principles of it.

In 1794, Dr. James accompanied the Western expedition as Surgeon of the 'McPherson Blues,' and on his return, presented his friends with a copy of a very animating song which he wrote on a drum head, at a time when great gloom pervaded the corps. It had a fine effect on their spirits, was set to music, and was sung through the camp for a long period.

Under the signature of P. D., he published in the Port Folio for 1801, versified translations of the Idyls of Gessner, which were regarded by good judges to be entitled to 'much, and some to high praise for poetical merit,' as well as exhibiting his accurate knowledge and fine perception of the German language and idiom.

The imagination of Dr. James was, however, restrained by strong good sense, and by devoted attention to practical duties. Nevertheless, literature was his delight and recreation. He kept pace with the publications of the day, and amidst the interruption and toils of an arduous and self-denying profession, succeeded in gratifying his taste, and refreshing his spirit, by continual recurrence to these fountains of unalloyed pleasure. These intellectual gratifications were derived not merely from publications in his native language, but from those in Latin, Greek, French and German, with all which his knowledge was considered as so intimate, that he could fully appreciate their merits and enjoy their most delicate allusions; thus keeping up an active interest in the republic of letters, and a peculiar fitness for intelligent and cultivated society.

Intimately associated with these intellectual gratifications, was the interest he manifested in the history of his native State, and the character and conduct of the early settlers, in the products of the soil, and especially in the richness and variety of its mineral productions. He was among the first to perceive, and rightly to estimate, the great value of the coal formations, so numerous and varied in Pennsylvania, having commenced the use of anthracite coal in his own house, as early as 1804, and having published a memoir on its original discovery, in the second volume of the Transactions of the Historical Society. He was among the founders of the society for commemorating the landing of William Penn, and also of the Historical Society of Pennsylvania. To these he devoted much of his leisure, took a warm interest in their success, and rejoiced in every new development of the original character and policy of the early settlers, in every discovery relating to the physical and moral character of Pennsylvania.

It does not appear that Dr. James ever devoted much attention to the exact sciences. He was in the proper meaning of the term a philosopher,—a lover and supporter of science ; but irrespective of those branches which are involved in his profession, he left to others minuteness of detail, and contented himself with mastering the general principles and lending his influence for the support of scientific men and institutions. Being early made a member of the American Philosophical Society, he at one time attended its meetings, acted as its secretary, and was interested in their transactions; but afterwards he but seldom appeared, and, it is believed, never contributed any paper except on medical subjects to their publications. He preferred the seclusion of his study to the bustle of the society, and the lighter walks of literature to the rougher paths of science.

As a practitioner, he was remarkable for his knowledge, and for his judgment in the selection and application of remedial measures, rather than for the novelty or boldness of his prescriptions. He was well read in his profession, learned in the opinions and practices of others, well imbued with all that collateral information so important for all professional men, especially for the physician ; and interested in every thing suited to advance the interests of the profession, to enlarge the boundaries, or to increase the efficiency of medical science. He was a scientific physician, not governed simply by authority, or by the experience of himself or others, but regulated by principles derived from anatomy, philosophy and pathology.

As an obstetrician, he was chiefly. known to the inhabitants of this city, and of our country; and great are the obligations under which society is placed to him and a few of his cotemporaries, who, by their talents, education, learning, manners and accomplishments elevated and adorned a department of the profession which had been unaccountably neglected, and was, in this country, especially, in a degraded condition.

As a practitioner of obstetrics, Dr. James manifested the same kindness and benevolence of disposition, the same prudence, discretion and judgment, for which he was distinguished as a physician, and which gave him an eminent station as an accoucheur. As an operator he was also skillful and prudent; occasionally also bold and decisive when the circumstances of the case demanded his assistance. His natural diffidence of himself, his fear of responsibility, his deference to the opinions of others, prevented, however, his obtaining that self-command, and that composure essential for the greatest eminence in the operative department of obstetrics. Nevertheless, a large proportion of our physicians resorted to him for assistance in cases of difficulty and danger, with the happiest results.

As a teacher of obstetric science, his success was also great. Commencing a system of instruction when no medical school patronized this department

of the profession, when the prejudices of the community were greatly in opposition, and when even practitioners of medicine thought any peculiar union on
this subject unnecessary, Dr. James succeeded in securing the attention of a very respectable portion of
the pupils who then resorted to Philadelphia for medical instruction, and soon obtained an influence in
favor of tocology, by which the practice was rendered more efficient and extensive, and the importance of the science suitably acknowledged by the
establishment of an independent professorship. Occupying the situation of Professor, he was well and
advantageously known to the full classes which annually resorted to the University of Pennsylvania. In
him they beheld the accomplished obstetrician, one
whose mild, sociable, but dignified deportment, not
only gained their respect but their affection; who
not only secured for himself attention and confidence, but for his science the devotion and interest
which it so justly deserved.

As a lecturer it is not pretended that Dr. James
was perfect; the critic might say that from the native
peculiarities of his character, especially from that
modesty and self-diffidence, that respect to the opinions of others, even of mere tyros in their profession, he wanted that boldness and decision, that
spirit of enthusiasm, that air of originality and self-
confidence so interesting and impressive in a teacher,
so calculated to fix the attention and impart instruction. Nevertheless he was an excellent teacher. His
lectures were handsomely and classically written;
they were copious, abounding in matter rich in illus-

trations, and indicating a mind of superior cast, well cultivated and enriched with literary, as well as scientific attractions. If he wanted originality, he was well versed in the opinions and discoveries of others; if he was deficient in spirit and boldness, his compositions evinced great taste, much reading and laborious attention to his subject, so that every lecture was a full and satisfactory essay on the subject, treated with suitable references to acknowledged authorities. His delivery, it may be inferred, was not very impassioned; he wanted more energy, and more vigor in his voice and composition, yet he was always interesting from the mild dignity of his appearance and manners, and from the good sense and superior mental and moral character which marked the man and his productions.

Hence he was a successful teacher. This is not the proper occasion to analyze the doctrines which he taught, or to examine the medical or chirurgical treatment which he recommended in the practice of obstetrics. Suffice it to say, that receiving his early impressions from distinguished English teachers, his views were founded mainly on British obstetrics. He examined, however, the productions of the French and other continental schools, followed their writers into scientific detail, and those minute instructions regarding the mechanism of labor and the treatment of parturition therewith necessarily connected, which has distinguished the French obstetrician, and so elevated the science of tocology. Profiting by all this accurate information, Dr. James still in his teaching and his practice, yielded to the influence of the English, rather than of the French, authorities, either from the influence of early impressions, or from a decided conviction of the superiority of the former.

Unfortunately for the medical profession, as well as for the greater perpetuity of Dr. James' reputation, he has not appeared before the public as a medical writer. The results of his accurate observation and extended experience have, with some minor exceptions, perished with him. This is to be regretted, for it seems hardly possible that the experience of a long life, devoted to the observation of diseases, to the details of a profession so varied, yet so imperfect, as that of medicine, should not have furnished abundant material for the improvement of his science, as well as for the amelioration of human suffering, especially when elaborated by a mind so well constituted, and liberally furnished. Our regrets are unavailing, but this negative example should induce all of us, who are actively engaged in professional duties, to make that record of our experience and observations, which when age or ill health prevents active exertion, may be promulgated as our mite to the cause of science, and the interests of humanity.

DR. HORATIO JONES of Stockbridge, Mass., was son of Capt. Josiah Jones of that place, and grandson of one of the first persons who were chosen for the companions of the first Missionary and Schoolmaster to the Housatunnuc Indians, the Rev. Mr.

42

Sergeant. He was born in the year 1770, and died
on the 26th of April, 1813, at the age of forty-three
years. He entered College at New Haven, at an
early period of his life, and continued his studies
there with so much zeal that his sight began to be
seriously impaired, and his physicians were fearful
that amaurosis, or gutta serena, might entirely deprive him of vision. He was, therefore, obliged to
abandon his studies for a while, and being of a most
active disposition of mind, he, with several others,
went to what was then called the Genessee country
for the purpose of laying out lands, as a surveyor.
His health and sight were here reinstated, and he
soon returned to his studies, and entered as student
of medicine in the office of the celebrated Dr. Sergeant of Stockbridge.

Before commencing practice as a physician, he
was engaged for awhile in business as a Druggist in
his native town. His daughter, Mrs. Fairchild, now
of Middletown, Connecticut, from whom I have
many of these facts, states that she does not recollect
how long he continued in this business. She only
knows that he commenced practice at Pittsfield,
Mass., where he remained a little more than a year.
Dr. Sergeant, his former preceptor, was at that time
in want of a physician of talent and principle to
succeed him in business, being himself in the decline
of life, invited him to settle in Stockbridge, which
invitation he accepted. In the winter of 1805–6,
probably a few years after he commenced practice in
Stockbridge, he went to Philadelphia for the purpose
of improving himself more particularly in the depart-

ment of surgery. He spent one winter there, and
attended the various courses of medical lectures in
the medical department of the University of Pennsylvania. He afterwards returned to Stockbridge,
where he remained till the time of his death.

He became a member of the Mass. Medical Society in the year 1804. He received the honorary degree of Master of Arts from Williams College, in
1810.

Dr. Partridge of Stockbridge, from whom I am
indebted through Mrs. Fairchild, for many facts in
relation to the life of Dr. Jones, observes that ' he
was a man of science, eminent in his profession, a
good operator in surgery, active, sociable, and very
popular, indefatigable by night and day to give relief
in cases of distress and danger.' Mrs. F. says, ' It
is often remarked to me that there was that in his
manner which seemed to add efficacy to the medicines which he administered, and that his visits were
often acknowledged to be beneficial to his patients,
when he made no prescription. I recollect a striking
expression in a short article published in some periodical a few years since, written by Miss Sedgwick—
a description of the burial ground in Stockbridge, in
which she speaks of him as our ' beloved physician,
who gave us smiles instead of drugs.' Another striking trait of character, which I have often heard spoken of, was his unremitted attention to the poor,
even when he knew he could secure no pecuniary
reward.'

The following just notice of Dr. Jones was written by the Rev. Mr. Curtis, now Chaplain in the Pri-

son in Charlestown, Mass., and published in the Farmers' Herald, in Stockbridge, at the time of his decease, will be read with much interest.

'On Tuesday, April 27th, 1813, his funeral was attended by an immense concourse of people, from this and the neighboring towns. Divine service was performed at the meeting house, where a sermon was delivered by the Rev. Dr. Hyde of Lee. Of the sermon it is but an ordinary tribute of justice to say, that it was peculiarly appropriate, impressive and solemn.

To give any thing like a just delineation of the character of Dr. Jones, the writer feels himself wholly incompetent. The community, however, and his numerous acquaintances and friends are capable of forming a just estimation.

As a man he combined in himself all those excellencies and virtues, which constituted him just what the excellent and virtuous wished him to be. As a scholar, he was eminent. Possessed of a mind vigorous and comprehensive, his advances in whatever was the object of his attainment, were much more than ordinary. Not contented with a superficial view of subjects and things, his researches were deep, thorough and effectual. His knowledge was extensive, and of such a kind as qualified him for the most extensive usefulness. As a physician, it is no more than justice to say he had but few equals. In addition to his extensive medical knowledge and skill, he possessed more than any other man we have ever known, the talent of rendering himself pleasant, easy, and agreeable to the objects of his professional attention. There was something in his manners, which, though indescribable, could almost restore the sick to health, and would induce a smile of complacency even on the pale cheek of the dying.

In his attention to the sick, he was indefatigable. He spared no pains. Without any regard to his own ease or quiet, he devoted all his time and talents to the service of the public. He possessed the entire confidence of all, and his eminent services, rare talents, and unusual success, justly entitled him to it. The loss of the community in the death of this distinguished man is irreparable.

As a friend, companion, husband, father, how shall I speak of him? On this subject let me spare those feelings already wounded to death. He was above all praise, and certainly above our poor praise. ' When such friends part, 'tis the survivor dies.'

But the most distinguished trait in his character, and one on which the minds of his bereaved friends will dwell with the greatest complacency and delight, remains unmentioned. He was a *Christain.*

During the winter past he had experienced, as is humbly hoped and believed, that change of heart, which seemed alone wanting to complete a character already so excellent and amiable.

Eight days before his death he was very violently seized with the prevailing epidemic.* His friends had long been fearful of the event, as he had for two months previous, been, without intermission, attending upon those who were sick with this complaint.

*Pneumonia Typhoides, I believe.—S. W. W.

If the Dr. lacked in any thing, it was in prudence as respected his own health. This he did not seem to regard. He literally wore himself out for the safety and health of others, and fell a sacrifice to his benevolent exertions. But his sickness afforded him an opportunity of exhibiting to the world a most glorious example of the power and triumph of the religion of the gospel. Several days before his death his prevailing sentiment was that he should not survive; yet his mind seemed fully prepared for the event. He was perfectly calm and tranquil. His strong and lively faith bore his soul above every thing like fear. It pleased the Sovereign Disposer of events to continue to him the unimpaired exercise of his reason to the last. His reason, and what strength he had, he employed in glorifying that God and Savior, who, by his grace had prepared him for glory. The scene was the most interesting and solemn that can be imagined. A heart of stone must have melted, and the most hardy infidel been confounded. As he drew nearer and nearer the close of life, his joys and prospects continued to brighten; and when he found all earthly objects fading from his view, and the light of eternity opening upon him, he cried 'Lord Jesus receive my spirit,' and fell asleep. 'Let me die the death of the righteous, and let my last end be like his,' must have been the language of every heart present.

Doctor Jones has left a wife and little daughter, a number of brothers and sisters, and a numerous train of relations and friends, to lament his death. Never before have we seen as many real mourners for the death of an individual. The whole town and vicinity are literally in tears. His virtues, worth and services, will long be held in grateful remembrance. Why such a man should be removed, is to us mysterious, but of this we may rest assured that the Judge of all the earth has done right.'

Dr. David King was born at Raynham, Massachusetts, in the year 1774. He graduated at Brown University during the Presidency of Maxy, in 1796, and pursued his medical studies under the direction of the venerable Dr. James Thacher of Plymouth. In 1799 he came to Newport, and began the practice of his profession.

In the early part of his professional career, his attention was drawn to the consideration of the vaccine disease, then first introduced into the United States. Regarding it as an invaluable discovery, he proceeded, notwithstanding the strong opposition of popular prejudice, to benefit his fellow citizens by the application of the early discovered principles in his science. In thus early adopting the views of the immortal Jenner, and carrying them out in practice, he displayed a decision and independence of mind which strongly characterized him through life.

Having acquired the habits of a student during his collegiate course, he vigorously applied them to the attainment of a thorough knowledge of his profession. In this he was aided by the valuable library of the late Dr. Center, which came into his possession soon after his settlement in Newport. His mind was

eminently practical, and endowed with those patient
powers of exertion which are necessary to arrive at
truth in any science or art. His professional knowledge was therefore such as to give him a just claim
to the attentions of his fellow citizens; this, added
to the kindness of his heart, his correct deportment
and unassuming manners, opened to him, almost from
the first, an extensive practice. The exercise of a
sound, discriminating judgment in his medical practice, and the study of the standard works in his profession, furnished his mind with principles to guide
him in the treatment of the various forms of disease.
The possession of these elevated him above the
sphere of the routine practitioner, and gave him in
cases of difficulty, manly confidence in the resources
of his own mind. The University at which he was
educated, evinced its high estimation of his professional character, by conferring on him in 1821, the
honorary degree of M. D.

For several years he held the appointment of surgeon to the detachment of United States troops,
stationed at Fort Wolcott. In 1819, during the prevalence of the yellow fever in this place, his great
skill and experience were actively and successfully
called into operation in repelling that terrible malady.
At that time it was the part of humanity to refute the
errors of those who regarded that disease as invariably and certainly propagating itself, and as exposing
those who attended upon the sick to almost certain
death. Not admitting the contagious character of
the disease, he attributed it to a more general and
pervading cause, and by his intrepidity and free per-

sonal exposure, attested his confidence in the truth of his theoretical views.

Ardently attached to his profession, he was ever ready to promote all useful and liberal plans which might contribute to the improvement and elevation of its character. He was one of the earliest promoters of the Rhode Island Medical Society, in which he successively held the offices of Censor, Vice President and President. He was elected President in June, 1829, and continued in that office till July, 1834.

In August, 1834, he suffered an attack of paralysis, brought on from the exertion of the discharge of his professional duties. Since then, his constitution gradually failed until his death, Nov. 14th, 1836. When he had then been thus struck down in the midst of active life, the attachment of the community to him was most signally exhibited. Throughout the community there was an universal conviction that society had lost a benefactor, and an invaluable member. In the extensive circle of his own patients there prevailed a feeling of personal loss, which no other person could supply. Few men have lived more respected, or died more lamented. His monument is in the hearts of the community.—*Bost. Med. and Surg. Jour.*

DR. FREDERIC GORE KING died at New York, April 24th, 1829, in the 28th year of his age. Dr. King, the youngest son of the late Rufus King, was born in England, in the year 1801, during the period

43

in which his father was minister to that country.   He
came with his father's family to the United States
when very young, and immediately commenced his
education, pursuing his studies with zeal and ability,
and evincing the possession of no ordinary talents.
He entered Cambridge College, Mass., with great
credit, and at the conclusion of his academic course,
left it with increased reputation.   He now returned
to New York, and commenced the study of medicine
under the direction of the late Dr. Post; he early
evinced a partiality for the study of anatomy, and
pursued it with corresponding zeal and success.   At
his graduation, he defended an inaugural dissertation
on Neurology, a part of which was published in the
second number of the third volume of the New York
Medical and Physical Journal, edited by Drs. Francis
and Beck.   This essay, which in its historical sketch
exhibits great research and familiarity with the ancient writers in medicine, was but the precursor of a
greater work on the same subject, which it was his
intention to have published, and from which much
valuable information might have justly been anticipated.   After the attainment of his medical doctorate,
he married the daughter of his preceptor, a mutual
attachment having subsisted during his studies.

A brilliant career now opened upon him, and he
entered upon it with zeal and enthusiasm, that held
forth a certainty of the highest professional distinction.   He had hardly commenced, before he was called upon, in the double capacity of brother and physician, to accompany his brother's wife to the Havana.
After a short absence he returned to New York, from

whence he was again summoned to proceed as speedily as possible to England, to accompany home his venerable father, whose enfeebled constitution had sunk under the accumulated privations and difficulties of a mission to England. On his return, he prepared again to engage in professional occupations, when he was required a third time to cross the Atlantic, as professional adviser to his wife's sister, whose health required a winter's residence in Italy. The melancholy termination of this visit to the lady, whose death took place soon after her arrival in Italy, left him at liberty to prosecute his travels in Europe. He visited different parts of Italy, examining every thing worthy of observation in the arts and sciences generally, as well as enriching his mind with stores of professional knowledge. He visited France, and during his stay at Paris, enjoyed the greatest opportunities of improving himself in his favorite study of Anatomy. Here he added to his library a valuable collection of French authors on the different departments of medical science. In the fall of 1825, he returned to New York and resumed the practice of medicine. During the severe epidemic fever which visited the neighboring country during that season, he attended the family of his elder brother, then residing at Jamaica, Long Island, and there contracted the disease, from the effects of which he seems never entirely to have recovered ; it aggravated a pulmonary attack, which he suffered while in Italy. During the succeeding winter he was obliged to confine himself to the house the greater portion of the time, harassed by a severe cough ; this continued without much intermission, until the month of March, when he was attacked with hæmoptysis. His friends, who included a numerous and extensive circle, now became seriously anxious about him; every exertion that domestic or fraternal solicitude, or the highest professional aid could suggest, was faithfully tried, to arrest the ravages of his fatal malady; they proved of no avail, but to afford a melancholy consolation to his afflicted family, of having rendered him all the assistance that human means could afford. For a short time after the cessation of the hemorrhage, strong hopes were entertained that his naturally vigorous constitution would triumph over the disease; these hopes were of short duration, no material improvement resulted, and the disease proceeded with steady and rapid progress to a fatal termination. During his illness, eager inquiries were constantly made, and an anxiety pervaded the community, to obtain intelligence of the state of his health.

His sympathy with the sufferings of his patients, and his anxiety to relieve them; the mildness of his manners, and the mildness and benevolence of his disposition, will be long remembered by those who came under his professional care. Though so early removed, he has not lived in vain; his example yet remains to stimulate our medical youth who are pressing forward in the narrow path of high and honorable distinction.

Dr. King was among the first selected by the Atheneum to give popular lectures; this duty he discharged the first year, by delivering four lectures on phrenology; the succeeding year, being again appointed, he lectured on the structure of the human voice, in which he gave a highly interesting view of the science of music. The National Academy of Design, with the laudable view of affording instruction to young artists, selected Dr. King to give a course of lectures on anatomy; the members of that association affectionately remember the interest he took in their welfare, and the pupils the valuable instruction he imparted to them. After his graduation, he spent one year in the New York Hospital, as house surgeon, and was immediately after appointed demonstrator of anatomy to the College of Physicians and Surgeons, Dr. Post being at that time Professor of that branch; during this period he gave a very instructive course of lectures on the preparations contained in the Museum.—*J. M. P., the Am. Med. Journ.*

DR. JOHN LEE. Dr. Lee was born at Amherst, Mass., about the year 1786, and died in 1813. The following notice of him is an extract from an address which I delivered before a literary society in Deerfield, of which Dr. Lee was a member—in the year 1813.

To show forth the private virtues of Dr. Lee, it may be necessary to give a slight sketch of his life. Little is known of the early part of it, except that the greater part of his first twenty years, was devoted to his favorite pursuit of agriculture. To this his attention was devoted with assiduity, and perhaps it was owing to his great exertions and persevering industry, that he was attacked with a weakness at the breast, and bleeding at the lungs, which threatened to terminate in that lingering and distressing complaint, the pulmonary consumption, to which he was always predisposed. By the advice of physicians, and in conformity with his own feelings and judgment, he was induced to try traveling, and residing upon the sea-board.

He returned with renovated health, and in a few months from this period, he commenced the study of physic in my father's office, with Dr. Saxton and myself; his persevering diligence and correct acquirements in the elementary branches, evinced beyond a doubt, the germ of future usefulness. Day after day, by his industry, did he suffer the glow of health to fade upon his cheek, and night after night, did he 'trim his midnight lamp, and hang o'er the sickly taper.'

He saw, from reading, the necessity of being thoroughly versed in the profession before entering upon the responsible duties of it. He shuddered with horror when he saw the audacious strides of charlatans and empirics, and subscribed with pain to the truth of the remark, that an ignorant pretender, from his imposing upon the too easy credulity of the multitude, would always obtain more business than a regular bred and accomplished physician. This remark is verified by daily experience in our too easily gulled American people. Most fully did he agree with Darwin, that 'Ignorance and credulity have ever been companions, and have misled and enslaved mankind.'

Much as he dwelt upon the necessity of indefatigable industry in obtaining a correct knowledge of his profession, he still believed with Klapp, that 'theory, without practice or experience, is a floating bubble, which with inflated grandeur, may serve to catch the eye or the fancy, until its momentary form or existence bursts into airy nothing ; and practice without the guide of science is downright jargon or empiricism.' As he approached the termination of his pupilage, as if susceptible of more than ordinary impressions, his anxiety, for many a weary night, deprived him of rest. He felt the full force of the arduous task in which he was engaged, and the high responsibility of it. After searching through a number of towns in Vermont and New Hampshire, and most of the towns in the old county of Hampshire, in Mass., for a place to establish himself for future usefulness, he at length commenced practice in the town of Ashfield, in the county of Franklin, in this State. Circumscribed as was his business here for a time, he had the pleasure of seeing it daily increase, and his prospects brighten.

When that awful scourge which has devastated so fair a portion of our country, that scourge, the ravages of which we have so much to deplore, which has deprived so many of us of parents, of near and dear connexions, and of friends, first appeared in his vicinity, all his vigilance and anxiety were awakened to avert its impending destruction. But alas! the mandate of Jehovah summoned him to appear before his majestic throne in the midst of his usefulness, and in all the vigor of his mental strength, to join in higher offices, and to reside throughout the never ending ages of eternity, with more congenial spirits.

A young man of worth and usefulness, surrounded by his helpless babes, being dangerously sick, awakened all his feelings. So great was his concern for him, that the day before his own attack was spent with him, administering to his comfort and ease, and endeavoring to restore him to usefulness, to his family, and the world. On Tuesday, the 5th of April, he rode in the storm, three miles from his boarding house, to visit his patient. He was much indisposed before he left home, and unfortunately, wet his feet on the road. He was immediately taken with violent cold chills, and excruciating pain in his side. A large fire was made, but it seemed to operate but little towards removing the chills, for he frequently observed, ' I freeze one side while I scorch the other.' The pain in the side growing more severe he bled himself, but with no alleviation to his distress. Attempting to return home, his complaint increased upon him with so much violence, that he was obliged to stop at the first house he came to, where he again bled himself, and immediately sunk into a state of faintness.

In four or five days a messenger was dispatched for my father and myself, about fourteen miles distant, and we immediately attended, but alas! we were too late to save him. Never shall I forget the momentary joy he expressed upon my entering his room, nor the anxiety that we should summon all our skill to arrest the mandate of death. His looks still dwell upon my mind, and his image is imprinted there. He clung to life, for he had many attachments to it; nevertheless, in his addresses to his Heavenly Father, he exclaimed, ' not my will but thine be done.' At this time he appeared to express great anxiety for his patients, and in his muttering delirium, he was constantly engaged in the practice of physic, demonstrating that his attention while in health was devoted exclusively to his profession. On the night preceding his dissolution, he was attacked severely with bleeding at the nose, which prostrated his strength irrecoverably. His spirits were now fast retreating to the ' last citadel, the heart.' Religion now supported him. He expressed a fear for the tremendous change, but observed that he thought he was not without a well grounded hope. He fixed his eye upon the throne of God, and at six o'clock his spirit departed, we trust, to everlasting rest. That body which so late was animated with light and life, is now a mass of senseless clay; that eye which so late beamed with resplendant lustre, is now dimmed by death.

To use the language of Ames on the death of Hamilton : ' The tears which flow on the fond recital will never dry up. My heart, penetrated with the remembrance of the man, grows liquid as I write, and I could pour it out like water.'

Dr. THOMAS G. LEE. Dr. Smith of the Boston Medical and Surgical Journal of Nov. 9th, 1836, observes, that it is with unfeigned sorrow that we record the death of this excellent physician and philanthropist, who, had he lived to the common age of man, would have taken an elevated rank in society In the very beginning of his usefulness, he fell a victim to professional responsibilities. He had not a physical organization fitted to undergo the fatigues he felt himself called upon to endure. We knew enough of his character to admire it; and with regard to the moral constitution of his mind, it was such as to exert the happiest influence on all within the circle of his official acquaintance. The McLean Asylum, over which he presided, has indeed suffered a severe loss. The Board of Trustees, in continuing his salary to the widow, till the first of April, 1837, have done a memorable act, highly honorable and praiseworthy. Dr. Lee was a correspondent of this Journal, and his writings exhibit evidence of much research and industry.

The following communication from Dr. Samuel B. Woodward of Worcester, where he died, so completely anticipates what we were preparing to say, that no apology is necessary for inserting it in this place.

Died, at the residence of his friend, Dr. Woodward, in Worcester, Mass., on the 2nd of October, 1836, Thomas G. Lee, M. D., Physician and Superintendent of the McLean Asylum for the Insane, aged twenty-eight.

Dr. Lee's health had been declining for some weeks previous to his leaving the Asylum. A bowel complaint, with daily paroxysms of fever, had reduced his strength and depressed his spirits. During this period, however, he exerted himself to do the duties of his station, till his appetite wholly failed him, his sleep departed, and he found himself worn down, dispirited, and so extremely susceptible, that common incidents in the Institution agitated him in such a manner as to render him unfit longer to continue. Under these circumstances he left for Worcester, where he arrived late in the evening of the 15th of October. His friends were all impressed with his sickly and emaciated appearance. He led them to suppose, however, that he had been slightly indisposed, and had commenced a journey for the re-establishment of his health. He conversed a short time with cheerfulness and animation, and retired to rest. In the morning following, he complained of not sleeping, and a total loss of appetite ; he, however, proposed to go with his friend through the wards of the extensive establishment for the insane, and continued his walks, notwithstanding the remonstrance of his friend, for nearly four hours. He then complained of great fatigue, and went to bed. Toward evening he arose, but complained of not having slept, and appeared exceedingly ill. From this time, all his former symptoms returned with tenfold violence. The symptoms of malignant disease were rapidly deveoped. His mind and nervous system were at first clearly disturbed. During the whole period of his sickness, the disease of the bowels made steady progress, and showed that local danger existed in the digestive organs, which years before had been subject to alarming disease.

Under the influence of remedies, after some days his sleep became quiet, and delirium left him. But the disease of the bowels went steadily on, and pointed but too truly to the fatal result which took place on the morning of the 29th. The last two weeks of his illness, his sufferings were severe. When informed that remedies would probably be unavailing in his case, he settled his worldly affairs with the composure of one who was preparing for a temporary journey, expressed his gratitude in the most feeling terms to all who had attended him in his illness, took leave of his friends, and resigned himself to the will of his Heavenly Father, in the full confidence of the Christian's Hope.

The death of Dr. Lee is a severe public calamity. In the situation which he occupied for a few months only, he gained a high reputation for himself, and increased the honor and raised the character of the Institution, which for years had been deservedly high. His qualifications of mind and heart were admirably fitted for the station, and he fulfilled the duties of it with great acceptance to the officers who controlled it, and the inmates and their friends who were interested in his success. He commenced these duties with that diffidence and distrust which are evidences of merit. His youth, his inexperience, and his feeble health, were urged by him, in correspondence with his friends, as reasons why he should not assume the responsible duties of superintendent of an institution, the character of which was high, the superintendent of which was a man of great attainments and deserved reputation in the management of the insane. He was, however, persuaded not to decline. The result has shown that the selection was most judicious, and most happy for the interests and prosperity of the institution.

In the management of the insane, Dr. Lee possess-

ed that trait which belongs to but few men. His
mind was active to discern, and fruitful in expedients
to satisfy, the expectations of his patients, and gain
their confidence. His feelings, naturally ardent, became deeply interested in each patient under his care.
His whole mind and soul were devoted to the welfare
of the institution, and the success of his efforts to
restore to health and reason the victims of insanity,
was so great as to keep him in a state of continual
excitement. This his friends foresaw, and warned
him of the consequences. His benevolence knew no
boundaries but the accomplishment of the ultimate
object of his wishes; and no personal labor was
spared and no privation interfered where his sense
of duty called. Such a mind wore bright, but could
not wear long. It was of such delicate structure as
to be exceedingly susceptible, and with a physical system naturally slender, and rendered still more delicate by disease, it is not surprising that it should produce excitement, resulting in serious injury to health.
Such was ever the condition of Dr. Lee while in situations of great responsibility. While in the Retreat
at Hartford, the assistant of the distinguished Dr.
Todd, from whom he acquired much of his knowledge of the treatment of insanity, his zeal and ardor
in this cause of humanity, brought upon him, as has
already been mentioned, an attack of disease which
seriously threatened his life, and resulted in such a
state of his general health, and particularly of his
nervous system, as induced him, at the solicitation of
all his friends, to resign his place. Such was its effect in the present case. And it is not too much to

say that he fell a victim to his efforts in this cause of
benevolence.

Dr. Lee was beloved by every one who knew him,
because his character and deportment was uniformly
lovely.   In his intercourse with mankind, he was
frank, open and honest.   Few men were so concilia-
tory, and yet so firm and decided.   He carried his
point with all, in and out of the institution; effected
what he wished, and yet gained the confidence and
even the affection of those who might be supposed
unfavorable to his plans.   Sincerity and love of truth,
were prominent traits of his character.   He loved his
friends, and delighted in refined and polished society.
His heart was ever ready to sympathize with the distressed.   To make all around him happy, was the
greatest pleasure of his life.

His career was short, but brilliant.   He has gained
a name which will be remembered while the institution which he superintended shall remain a monument of christian charity and benevolence.   In all
this, I am quite sure the directors of that Institution
will acquiesce.   In selecting a successor, they will be
most happy if they can find the same high qualifications in an individual who is willing to spend his life
and be spent in the cause of humanity.

Within a few days I have received the following
additional particulars concerning Dr. Lee, from Dr.
Woodward.

He was born in Berlin, Connecticut, December,
1808.   His parents were respectable, and the father
for many years was a Magistrate and Judge of Probate in the District.   After a good academical educa-

tion, he spent a year in the Military Academy of Capt. Partridge in Middletown, then commenced the study of medicine with Dr. Gridley, of his native town, who was my pupil, and is now a Senator in the Legislature of Connecticut. Afterwards he completed his studies under the instruction of Drs. Eli Ives and Knight, of New Haven, at which seminary he received the degree of M. D. in 1830.

Almost immediately after his graduation, he received the appointment of assistant physician at the Retreat for the Insane in Hartford. In that school of instruction, under the tuition of the master mind of Dr. Todd, he formed habits of thinking, and received instruction from lips eloquent, on all subjects connected with the profession, and particularly on whatever related to Insanity.

Dr. Lee remained in this situation nearly three years, during which time a friendship was formed between this highly gifted preceptor and admiring pupil which lasted and increased in ardor till this great and good man was gathered to reap the reward of a life well spent.

Dr. Lee lost his health, and was constrained to leave a post in which he delighted to act, and for which by the highest qualifications of mind and heart he was peculiarly fitted.

He married Miss Susan Clarke of St. Johnsbury, Vermont, in 1834, with whom he lived scarcely two years, before his death, and left no children.

DR. LEWIS FIELD LINN. Mr. Benton from Missouri, of the United States' Senate, in Congress, December, 1843, thus announces to the Senate, the death of his distinguished colleague, Dr. Linn, which is an elegant delineation of his life and character.

' Lewis Field Linn, the subject of this annunciation, was born in the State of Kentucky, in the year 1795, in the immediate vicinity of Louisville. His grandfather was Colonel William Linn, one of the favorite officers of Gen. George Rogers Clark, and well known for courage and enterprise in the early settlement of the great West. At the age of eleven, he had fought in the ranks of men in the defence of a station in western Pennsylvania, and was seen to deliver a deliberate and effective fire. He was one of the first to navigate the Ohio and Mississippi from Pittsburgh to New Orleans and back again—a daring achievement, which himself and some others accomplished for the public service, and amidst every species of danger, in the year 1776. He was killed by the Indians at an early period, leaving a family of young children, of whom the worthy Col. William Pope (father of Gov. Pope, and head of the numerous and respectable family of that name in the west) became the guardian. The father of Senator Linn was among these children; and, at an early age, skating upon the ice near Louisville, with three other boys, he was taken prisoner by the Shawnee Indians, carried off, and detained captive for three years, when all four made their escape and returned home, killing their guard, traversing some hundred miles of wilder-

L. F. Linn.

Engraved for the Democratic Review.

from a Daguerreotype in the National Miniature Gallery N-York

of Anthony Edwards & Chilton

J. & H. G. LANGLEY N-YORK.

ness, and swimming the Ohio river. The mother of Senator Linn was a Pennsylvanian by birth, her maiden name Hunter, born at Carlisle, and also had heroic blood in her veins. Tradition, if not history, preserves the recollection of her courage and conduct at Fort Jefferson, and the Iron banks, in the year 1781, when the Indians attacked, and were repulsed, from that post. Women and boys were men in those days.

The father of Senator Linn died young, leaving this son but eleven years of age. The care of an elder brother supplied, as far as such a loss could be supplied, the loss of a father, and under his auspices the education of the orphan was conducted. He was intended for the medical profession, and received his education, scholastic and professional, in the State of his nativity. At an early age he was qualified for the practice of medicine, and commenced it in the then Territory, now State of Missouri, and was immediately amongst the foremost of his profession. Intuitive sagacity supplied in him the place of long experience, and boundless benevolence conciliated universal esteem. To all his patients he was the same—flying with alacrity to every call, attending upon the poor and humble as zealously as on the rich and powerful ; on the stranger as readily as on the neighbor ; discharging all the duties of nurse and friend as well as physician, and wholly regardless of his own interest, or even his own health, in his zeal to serve and to save others.

The highest professional honors and rewards were before him. Though commencing on a provincial theatre, there was not a capital in Europe or America in which he would not have attained the front rank in Physic or Surgery. But his fellow citizens perceived in his varied abilities, capacities and aptitude for service in a different walk. He was called into the political field by an election to the Senate of his adopted State. Thence he was called to the performance of judicial duties, by a federal appointment to investigate land titles. Thence he was called to the high station of Senator in the Congress of the United States—first by an Executive appointment, and then by three successive, almost unanimous elections. The last of those elections he received but one year ago, and had not commenced his duties under it—when a sudden and premature death put an end to his earthly career. He entered this body in the year 1833—death dissolved his connexion with it in 1843. For ten years he was a beloved and distinguished member of this body ; and surely a nobler or a finer character never adorned the chamber of the American Senate.

He was my friend ; but I speak not the language of friendship when I speak his praise. A debt of justice is all that I can attempt to discharge—an imperfect copy of the *true man* is all that I can attempt to paint.

A sagacious and a feeling heart were the great characteristics of Dr. Linn. He had a judgment which penetrated both man and things and gave him near and clear views of far distant events. He saw at once the bearing—the remote bearing of great measures either for good or evil ; and brought in-

stantly to their support, or opposition, a prompt
and natural eloquence, more beautiful in its delivery,
and more effective in its application, than any art can
bestow. He had great fertility of mind, and was
himself the author and mover of many great measures—some for the benefit of the whole Union—
some for the benefit of the great West—some for the
benefit of his own State—many for the benefit of
private individuals. The pages of our legislative history will bear the evidence of these meritorious labors to a remote and grateful posterity.

Brilliant as were the qualities of his head, the
qualities of his heart still eclipsed them. It is to the
heart we look for the character of the man; and
what a heart had Lewis F. Linn! The kindest, the
gentlest, the most feeling, and the most generous,
that ever beat in the bosom of the bearded man! and
yet, when occasion required it, the bravest and the
most daring also. He never beheld a case of human
woe without melting before it; he never encountered
an apparition of earthly danger, without giving it defiance. Where is the friend, or even the stranger, in
danger or distress, to whose succor he did not fly,
and whose sorrowful case he did not make his own?
When—where was he ever called upon for a service
or a sacrifice, and rendered not, upon the instant, the
one or the other, as occasion required?

The Senatorial service of this rare man fell upon
trying times—high party times—when the collisions
of party too often embittered the ardent feelings of
generous natures. But who ever knew bitterness or
party animosities in him? He was, indeed, a party

man—as true to his party as his friend and his country; but, beyond the line of duty and of principle—beyond the debate and the vote—he knew no party, and saw no opponent. Who among us all, even after the fiercest debate, ever met him without meeting the benignant smile and the kind salutation? Who of us all ever needed a friend without finding one in him? Who of us all was ever stretched upon the bed of sickness without finding him at his side? Who of us all ever knew of a personal difficulty of which he was not, as far as possible, the kind composer?

Such was Senator Linn in high party times here among us. And when he was here among us, he was every where, and with every body. At home among his friends and neighbors; on the high road among casual acquaintances; in foreign lands among strangers; in all and in every of these situations, he was the same thing. He had kindness and sympathy for every human being; and the whole voyage of his life was one continued and benign circumnavigation of all the virtues which adorn and exalt the character of man. Piety, charity, benevolence, generosity, courage, patriotism, fidelity, all shone conspicuously in him, and might extract from the beholder the impressive interrogatory,—*For what was this man made?* Was it for the Senate or the camp? For public or for private life? For the bar or the bench? For the art which heals the disease of the body, or that which cures the infirmities of the State? For which of all these was he born? And the answer is, for all. He was born to fill the largest and most varied circle of

human excellence; and to crown all these advantages,
nature had given him what the great Lord Bacon
calls a perpetual title of recommendation—a countenance not only good, but sweet and winning—radiant
with the virtues of his soul—captivating universal
confidence; and such as no stranger could behold—
no traveler even in the desert could meet, without
stooping to reverence, and saying, ' Here is a man in
whose hands I could deposit life, liberty, fortune, hon-
or.' Alas! that so much excellence should have perished so soon! that such a man should have been
snatched away at the early age of forty-eight, and
while all his faculties were still ripening and developing!

In the life and character of such a man, so exube-
rant in all that is grand and beautiful in human nature, it is difficult to particularize excellencies, or to
pick out any one quality or circumstance which
could claim pre-eminence over all others. If I should
attempt it, I should point out, among his measures for
the benefit of the whole Union, to the Oregon bill;
among his measures for the benefit of his own State,
to the acquisition of the Platte country; among his
private virtues, to the love and affection he bore
to that brother—the half brother only—Governor
Dodge of Wisconsin, who only thirteen years older
than himself, had been to him the tenderest of fathers. For twenty-nine years I had known the depths
of that affection, and never saw it burn more brightly than in our last interview, only three weeks before
his death. He had just traveled a thousand miles
out of his way to see that brother; and his name was

still the dearest theme of his conversation; a conversation strange to tell, which turned not upon the empty and fleeting subject of the day, but upon things solid and eternal—upon friendship and upon death, and upon the duties of the living to the dead. He spoke of two friends, whom it was natural to believe that he would survive, and to whose memories he intended to pay the debt of friendship. Vain calculation! Vain impulsion of generosity and friendship! One of those two friends now discharges that mournful debt to him; the other (Gen. Jackson,) has written me a letter expressing his 'deep sorrow for the untimely death of our friend, Dr. Linn.'

It was then resolved that as a token of respect to the memory of the late Lewis F. Linn, the Senators wear crape on the left arm for the space of thirty days. And immediately after, the Senate adjourned.

The following extract from a letter dated Washington city, Dec. 30, 1843, from the Hon. Thos. H. Benton, accompanying the splendid and correct lithograph of Dr. Linn, was received on the 2d of Jan. 1844. I hold myself under the deepest obligations to the honorable Senator for his polite attention, and for his kind assent to the publication of the above memoir.

'Dr. Linn died of an affection of the heart—a stoppage of the circulation—and had lived in dread of it for a dozen years, and never sleeping a night at home or abroad, stationary or traveling, without having some person in the room, with directions to awaken him if they heard him give any notice of distress.'

Through the politeness of my friend, James H.

Relfe, M. D., Member of Congress from Missouri, I am enabled to furnish more particular information concerning the lamented Dr. Linn. His brother-in-law Gov. Henry Dodge of Wisconsin, and now a delegate in Congress from that Territory, has also kindly furnished me with many valuable documents concerning him, of which I avail myself and for which I return him and Dr. Relfe my sincere thanks. Among other memorials which were forwarded to me by Dr. Relfe, was a funeral discourse on the life and character of Dr. Linn, by the Rev. John H. Linn of St. Louis, from which many of the following facts are taken.

Col. Benton has already stated that at an early age Dr. Linn resided in Kentucky, where he was born. ' At that time this was a border country. The emigrant's axe was just gaining its first trophies. The yell of the savage had not yet died away from the distant forest. A way had not been open to refinement. The soil had not yet been taxed to supply the imaginary wants of human society, for such demands are few and simple, and always readily and abundantly supplied. The riotings and excesses of luxury were not known, and no contributions for its insatiate appetite had, as yet, been levied. The high claims of honor, held sacred and inviolate, and not the mere restrictions of law, regulated the intercourse of man with his fellow. There, breathing an atmosphere uncontaminated by the baneful presence of oppression and deceitfulness, of fraud and force, his manly and chivalric spirit flourished on the food afforded, and assimilated more and more to the objects of its contemplation. Inclined to study and reflection, his walk, if not with God, was among the sublime and ennobling forms of his greatness. Upon the prairie he stood, and along the banks of the beautiful Ohio he wandered, feeling not only the existence, but the presence of his and their Creator. Thus attended, thus surrounded, he advanced towards the era of his majority. We claim for him no academic or collegiate honors; for Academies and Colleges were then scarce thought of in the country west of the Alleghanies; but even at that period his intellect may be thought worthy a comparison with those who may be regarded as favored with more imposing facilities. Superior in strength and singleness of purpose, and in the dignity of his whole moral character, it only remained to be tried whether his mind had capacity to take high intellectual rank.

At the requisite age he began the study of medicine under the instruction of Dr. Galt of Louisville, Kentucky; and, it was there he made more extensively those acquisitions, not only in science, but in the habits of study, which often lie at the foundation of character as subsequently developed, but which so eminently qualified him for future usefulness. At the request of his half brother, Henry Dodge, the present Delegate from the Territory of Wisconsin, he visited the Territory of Missouri, as early as 1812. He returned, however, to Kentucky, to resume the study of his profession, and when prepared to practice, revisited and settled in St. Genevieve, about the year 1815. From that time to the period when he was appointed one of the Commissioners under the

act of Congress of 9th July, 1832, to investigate and
report on the French and Spanish claims, he devoted
himself with great assiduity to the study and practice
of his profession.

Warm and generous in his friendships, none could
surpass him in his sympathy for the afflicted and suffering, and thus controlled, his attentions were unremitting. To skill that was seldom baffled, there was
added this essential qualification of a successful physician—a benevolent heart; a heart that feels his patient's pain as if it were his own; that looks on the
woe-stricken countenance of a wife, and resolves
that, if possible, she shall be saved from the desolate-
ness of widowhood; that looks on weeping children,
and resolves that no energy shall be spared in saving
them from the orphan's destitution; that looks at a
father's and mother's anguish, and resolves that with
God assisting, he will save their child.

It was the enthusiasm of this benevolence that
diffused over the whole character of Dr. Linn a
sacred splendor—adorned and imbued his whole
behavior. Never did the love of ease, study, or
friends, present a single temptation to confine him to
his books, or detain him with the society of his companions, or at the convivial feast, when he should be
watching by the couch of sickness. His manners,
always natural and easy, rendered him not only acceptable to all, but so prepossessing and delightful
that it was absolutely impossible for any, however
circumstanced in life, to feel uneasy or restless in his
company. Hence the most unreserved confidence
always subsisted between him and his patients; and

46

the memorials of his tenderness and skill are to be found in the gratification of all classes of society in the entire southern portion of our State. For, however much dissimilar views upon religion and politics may affect the state of society generally, it never lost Dr. Linn one friend, or made him less studious or anxious about their wants.

His reputation as a physician had become so extensive, and the demands upon him so frequent—and he was one of those to whom an appeal was never made in vain—that apprehensions in relation to his health, from fatigues and exposures, induced him to accept the appointment of Commissioner under the act of July, 1832. To discharge the duties of his office, he removed to St. Louis in 1833, and though the practice of his profession was not entirely abandoned at this, or any other subsequent period, we find him entering a theatre upon which he not only sustained himself creditably, but secured an enviable distinction.'

The following remarks from the St. Louis Republican, will show the estimation in which his professional brethren in Missouri held him. ' The professional brethren of Dr. Linn will all bear testimony to his learning and skill in his profession. For its practice he seemed to have been especially calculated by nature. There never has lived a physician in this country, who has acquired a higher or more enviable reputation than he did. To his great abilities he united untiring zeal with the most unbounded charity. The highest testimony that can be given in his favor, is to be found in the esteem and sincere re-

spect entertained for him by all classes of persons in
the counties of St. Genevieve, Madison, Perry, and
St. Francis, in which he practised as a physician for
many years. There is no doubt that he impaired his
health, and abridged his life by a too close and rigid
discharge of the duties of his profession. His reputation extended over most of the southern counties of
the State. He was called upon to visit the sick at
all seasons of the year, and frequently compelled to
travel from fifty to sixty miles on horseback, over
rough roads, and not unfrequently in the night.
Sometime before he abandoned his practice, he began
to feel his constitution giving way, and he became
satisfied of the necessity of changing his mode of
life, if not altogether abandoning the practice of his
profession.'

The Rev. Mr. Linn, continues in his address; ' It
is said by a celebrated Athenian commander, that it
was a reproach to a General to have it to say of any
event—' I had not expected it.' Such censure
could seldom attach to Senator Linn. The success
of all that he undertook, evinced the versatility of his
mind and the energy of his whole character; and if
in the political world he had left no other monument
of his wisdom and prudence, than recommending the
policy to be pursued by the Government of the United States in confirming grants to the French and
Spanish claimants, he would have been entitled to a
high place among sound and practical financiers.
But having thus been thrown within the confines of
political life, without design on his part, unimpelled
by ambition, and uncontrolled by selfishness, a wider

sphere of usefulness was opened before him.' Senator Benton has so ably delineated his character above, as a statesman, that I shall not follow the Rev. Mr. Linn, in detail, upon this subject. He, however, observes, ' He sought his country's good, not his own promotion. He was scarcely ever provoked to personal invective, but when such circumstances did occur, his sarcasm was bold and withering. It was evident to all that he sought not to defeat and confound his opponents, much less to degrade them in their own estimation, or in the opinion of others, but with a look, manner and language which bespoke his own candor and sincerity, to lead them to his conclusions, and his competency was only paralleled by his faithfulness and untiring industry. Says Mr. Buchanan, the distinguished Senator from Pennsylvania, in a letter of condolence to his family :—' He was indeed every thing which constitutes a man : mild, amiable, and benevolent of heart, he was yet the very soul of chivalry and honor. Possessing uncommon talents and extensive information, he was one of the ablest and most useful members of the Senate, and yet he ever seemed unconscious of his own great powers. His loss to his personal and political friends in that body is irreparable. No man in the country can supply his place. He was the rock against whose firmness the storm might beat, but beat in vain ; and he was ever as prompt and decided in sustaining his friends, in their hour of need, as in defending himself. And yet in him the elements were so combined, that his political opponents were all his friends.' He adds—and it is a noble tribute—' Beyond all question, he was the most popular man among his fellow members in the Senate of the United States.'

The basis of his well formed public character was his private virtues. The impressson left upon the mind of every one who had intercourse with him for a single hour, was, that he possessed honesty which could not be corrupted—integrity which could not be moved by prosperity, nor shaken by adversity. His stern and inflexible moral principles were written upon every lineament of his strongly marked countenance—upon every word that fell from his lips, and upon every action of his life, whether as a citizen or public servant.

As the result of this last trait, he was possessed of decision of character. He knew, he felt he was right, and then was never moved from his course by trifles. When any thing was to be done, he was unwearied till its completion ; and this was the case whether one object, or a multiplicity of cases pressed upon him. But he was never obstinate ; for his decision, energy, and unyielding perseverance were controlled by the native, unaffected benevolence of his heart. And to the presence of these benevolent affections, he was largely indebted for that graceful and easy politeness, that unassuming suavity of temper, which were so conspicuous in his intercourse with society, and which so justly and eminently entitled him to the uniformly and universally recognized appellation— ' the peace loving Senator.'

We have followed Senator Linn through his comparatively brief but distinguished career ; in boyhood acquiring those habits of mind and body that indicated the promise of his usefulness to the world ; in his profession, with a mind richly stored with general as well as professional information, with a heart alive to all the tender and generous sensibilities of our nature, throwing the drapery of kindness over the chamber of affliction, lighting up a milder sun under the sky overcast with the clouds of misfortune, and searching out the causes of distress that he knew not. Like Job he was eyes to the blind, and feet to the lame, a father to the orphan, and the widow's friend.

Says my correspondent, 'Could the world have seen Dr. Linn's house when his death was made known at St. Genevieve, then indeed would his worth have been appreciated. The rich and poor filled his house and yard, from the town and country, to learn if the melancholy news was true—that their friend, their kind physician for many years, who never charged the widow or the poor man for his individual services—their benevolent fellow citizen, who had so often put in jeopardy all he had on earth to save their property, was indeed gone from them forever. Even the poor Africans, whose sick beds Dr. Linn had watched over many a long and weary night, were seen kneeling around the heart broken widow and orphan children, begging to know if they could serve them in any way. Surely such heartfelt affection for any man, such profound sympathy for his family, could not be manifested more strongly for any person, than was evinced by those who followed him to his last home.'

At the call of his country, he promptly relinquished his profession, and entered upon the duties of a public servant; as a Commissioner satisfactorily adjusting antagonist claims, involving important private and public interest; as a Senator standing forth on this great theatre, acknowledged by all, a great and good man, lending the energies of his mighty mind, to defend the institutions of his country from all assaults, both within and without. Devoted to the interests of his constituents, he showed himself a faithful and industrious Representative.

But while the memorials of his tenderness shall thus be gathered up by his friends in private life; while love and affection mourn him, yet not as those who mourn without hope; while the memory of his devotedness to this wide spreading valley is long and tenderly cherished; while Oregon shall in her orphanage, inquire who will now defend her honor, her character, her interests; the records of the Church will testify to his virtues, his spirituality, his devotion to his God. Early and favorably impressed with the truths of the Christian religion, a close study of these truths produced, under the influence of the Holy Spirit—as it was to be expected in a mind honest and sincere as his, a firm and steadfast faith as to its divine origin, and its infinite interests and obligations. And his attachment to the fundamental verities of the Bible became firm and exemplary, and grew in strength and influence to the very close of his life. His avowed and decided preference to the Rev. Mr. Cookham, then chaplain to Congress, and pastor of one of the Methodist churches in the city of Washington, induced him in the winter of 1839, to wait upon the ministry of that great and good man, whose melancholy fate he deplored so deeply, and with whose sainted spirit he is now enjoying delightful communion before the throne of God. On the 5th day of April, of that year, he joined the Methodist Episcopal church, and from that period to the day of his death, devoted much of his time to religious purposes, to the study of the Bible, and the perusal of religious books.

For the last several months he was peculiarly thoughtful and heavenly minded. A temporary but severe indisposition early last spring left him with the radical and permanent impression that he should not long survive. This impression he often communicated to his family, always accompanying it with a desire to have his worldly affairs well arranged, and himself in preparation for another existence. 'On the 28th of last April,' says my correspondent, 'late at night he desired that his household should be called together, and with his wife and children by his side, kneeling in a most devoted and fervent manner he dedicated himself and them to the great Head of the Church—that whether they lived they should live unto the Lord, and that whether they die, they should die unto the Lord, that whether they live therefore or die, they should be the Lord's.' That solemn scene will not soon be forgotten. An offering was laid upon that altar, the perfumes of which have left a delightful fragrance behind, and in years to come when memory shall recall that scene, how like an angel shall he rise up from the dominions of death, the very personification of love, of generosity, of kindness, of friendship, of truth and heavenly ardor. But in an effort to delineate his religious character, I find myself invading that sacred enclosure, the domestic circle, where every step must wring out tears and press the bleeding hearts of the widowed and father- less ones. Oh! would to God that I could now re- tire and let the guardian angel with a feather plucked from his own bright, silvery wings, describe the scenes of reciprocated tenderness and love that made his home an earthly paradise. The image is present to my own mind with all the glowing freshness of life. Here are combined, like nestling seraphs, the graces of moral beauty, the breathing forms of holy friend- ship and mutual love. The majesty and dignity of giant mind turning aside from the world, eager to do it homage, bending in admiration over the gentle flower at his side, while the cherub faces and merry tones of early childhood, exhibit such a vision of felicity as to be cherished, loved, almost adored— while upon this already hallowed scene religion throws its radiance, like a stray sunbeam, piercing the drifted cloud and opening upon another day.

This state of uninterrupted domestic bliss was the result of the happy and appropriate marriage in 1828, of Dr. Linn and the only daughter of Mr. John Relfe, a lawyer of distinguished abilities from the State of Virginia, who died in early life, leaving but two children, Mrs. Linn and Dr. James H. Relfe, now a Representative in Congress from Missouri. Of his immediate relations, Dr. Linn left one own sister, a half brother, Hon. Henry Dodge, and a half sister, Mrs. Nancy Sefton, with their families, to all of whom he was tenderly attached, and among whom

47

he felt and made no distinction. Of a large family of children Dr. Linn left but two, a son and daughter, to mourn their loss, and soothe by their society and sympathy the aching heart of a widowed mother. God bless thee, Augustus! God bless thee, Mary! Yours is a rich inheritance—in your veins is coursing in blending currents the blood of a patriot and a christian. Upon your destinies rest the blessings of a sainted father. In your behalf is enlisted the sympathy of the Church. Hearts, fond hearts are beating high for you—prayers warm and earnest are offered up for you. Voices, glad voices will welcome you at the threshhold and cheer you through the pathway of life. Go, be ornaments of society—go, and may that God who has promised to be a father to the fatherless, shield and protect you! Go, imitate the virtues of one loved and lost! go and let the dawning graces of youth reflect, as in a mirror, to the anxious eye of your widowed mother, the light of him who was her protector through life—whose tenderness and care constituted her sum of happiness, and who, connected with this, has only one other source of comfort—the religion of Christ. An illustration for condolence and comfort is furnished us by the last words of that distinguished statesman, whose melancholy fate our country will never cease to deplore—Alexander Hamilton—' Remember,' said he, with the utmost composure, to his wife almost frantic with grief, ' remember, my Eliza, you are a Christian.'

The accounts published of the last moments of Dr. Linn, are substantially, though not minutely cor-

rect. Up to the evening of the 2d ultimo, he was
in the enjoyment of unusually good health. Having
just arrived at home, on the day previous, after an
absence of twelve days, he was busily engaged in arranging some private papers, intending on the next
day to visit St. Louis. During that day he had indulged much anxiety in relation to a private paper
of considerable importance that he apprehended had
been mislaid. Late in the afternoon, in stooping to
search a trunk, he raised his head suddenly and asked
Mrs. Linn, who had been assiduously engaged in
assisting her husband, if his face was not very much
flushed, as he felt exceedingly dizzy, and there seemed to be a general determination of blood to the
head! The painful sensation, however, passed off,
and he resisted the suggestion that he should be bled
during the evening, and to a late hour at night he
was engaged in correspondence and in conversation
with his family, whose society, he said, never seemed
so sweet as on that evening. When he retired he
was indisposed to sleep, but did not complain of being unwell. As the morning dawned, he remarked
that he felt unusually sleepy. His wife, who had
been accustomed to watch over him with sleepless
vigilance for years, when there was the slightest indication of indisposition, or undue nervous irritation,
proposed to write the letters that he had dictated, and
watched over him, that he might not be disturbed by
the approach of any one. Whilst thus employed, she
frequently turned and gazed upon him to see if he
was awake—but he slept on gently and quietly as an
infant. Having finished the correspondence, and

being much fatigued and oppressed for want of sleep,
she concluded that she would lie down by his side,
to be ready, when he awoke, to wait upon him her-
self, as he had affectionately requested. As she drew
aside the curtain to look again upon the calm and
tranquil features of her loved husband—quick as
thought, a dark, death-presaging shadow passed over
his face. For a moment she was transfixed. It was
not the painful apprehension that she was watching
by the bed of death that converted that fearful expression into the precursor of dissolution. Others
might have seen it, and no fear been started, but a
woman's love, a wife's tenderness marks the first indication of death, and, sleepless and vigilant she is ever
found ready to catch upon her lips the last faint
breath. With Mrs. Linn vigilance had become habitual; a moment's relief suggested that all her fears
might have been groundless. But another look, and
though her loved husband still breathed on, confirmed
her fears that life, gradually sinking down into the
horizon of death, was throwing its melancholy, farewell rays in golden beauty over the unconscious sleep-
er. The agonizing cry soon filled the chamber of
the dying husband and father, not only with the inmates of the family, but sympathizing friends, among
whom was Dr. Sargeant, who providentially passed
the house at that moment, and who was by his bedside only to see him draw a few faint breaths; and
then, without a struggle or a sigh, he exchanged a
life full of honors on earth for a life full of glory at
the right hand of God.

Dr. WILLIAM JAMES MACNEVEN. The editor of these biographical sketches is indebted largely to the interesting memoir of this eminent individual, as published in the second series of the lives of the United Irishmen, written for Dr. Madden, the author of that work, and drawn up with consummate talents and feeling, by his accomplished surviving daughter. Judiciously to abridge that memoir, and add what further particulars private friendship may supply, is all that can be attempted in this biographical sketch.

J. W. FRANCIS.

William James Macneven was born at Ballynahowne, county of Galway, on the 21st of March, 1763. He was the eldest of four sons. At the age of ten or twelve years he was sent for by his uncle, Baron Macneven, to receive his education in Germany, a custom very common in catholic families, and rendered necessary at that time by the operation of the penal laws. Young Macneven received an excellent classical education at the college at Prague; subsequently, he passed through the medical college there, and finished his professional studies at Vienna, where he graduated at the age of twenty, 1783. He now returned to his native country and commenced the practice of physic in Dublin. With youth, health, superior abilities and education in his favor, and good family connexions, he had a fair and prosperous career opened before him; and had Ireland been in a happier condition, or could selfish motives have deadened his love of his unfortunate country, his eminence in his vocation must have been secured. His political associations, however, were of a nature which he deemed vital to the interests of his country, and though much absorbed in matters of a public nature, he nevertheless continued the practice of his profession and mingled in society as usual. We must refer to the political annals of the times for his principles and actions, during a most eventful period. His intimacy with Lord Edward Fitzgerald, with Tone, with Emmet, and others; his arrest on the 12th of March, 1798; his confinement in Kilmainham, and subsequent removal to Fort George, are among the foremost occurrences most worthy of detail. While in his long imprisonment, he rendered his situation the less irksome by the vigor and activity of his mind. Books were his greatest resource. Among his studies we find that he gave great attention to the writings of Ossian, many of which he translated from the original Gaelic, a language with which he was perfectly familiar. After the liberation of the state prisoners from Fort George, he passed the summer and autumn of 1802 in traveling through Switzerland on foot, and wrote an account of his journey, called ' A ramble through Switzerland.' He also visited his relations in Germany in the course of that year.

In 1803 he went to Paris, and either in that year or the following, entered the French army as a captain in the Irish brigade. He entertained the idea of an attack upon Ireland by the French, and in enrolling himself in the service of France he conceived he was only in another way devoting himself to that cause which he had espoused elsewhere. Disappointed in these hopes he at length resigned his commission, and in June, 1805, set sail from Bourdeaux for New York, where he arrived on the 4th of July following.

He lost no time in presenting his letters, and declaring his intentions of becoming an American citizen. He fixed upon New York as his permanent residence, and immediately entered upon the practice of physic. His most intimate friends, and who continued such through their lives, were Mr. Emmet and Mr. Sampson. The confidence which each reposed in the other was of the most unbounded kind, nor was that confidence ever interrupted through their long lives for a single day. Dr. Macneven soon found the place he had chosen for the scenes of his future life, to be well calculated as the best theatre for his operations, and as a practitioner he met with the kindest consideration of his countrymen, and with the public at large.

In 1810 he was married to Mrs. Jane Margaret Tone, a lady well qualified to appreciate his high merits, the widow of an eminent merchant of New York, and daughter of Samuel Riker of Long Island, by whom he had a considerable family, three children of which at present survive, as also his accomplished widow. The excellence of Dr. Macneven's constitution was so great as to give him the enjoyment of almost uninterrupted health until he had arrived to quite an advanced period of existence. In March, 1838, he was attacked with severe illness and lay some days dangerously sick, but the attack at length terminated in a severe fit of the gout. His health was so impaired by this illness, as to render the practice of his profession both irksome and injurious to him, and he determined on retiring to the country. On the 25th of November, 1840, he received a severe injury of the leg, which, together with a shock from a fall, occasioned him a long and painful illness. From this time his strength gradually failed him, and on the 12th of July, 1841, he breathed his last. ‘He was throughout his life,’ says the elegant biography of his daughter, ‘a consistent and enlightened Roman Catholic, and his examination of other creeds tended only to confirm him in that persuasion. Twice during the winter of 1841, he received the communion from his friend, the very Reverend John Power, and, on the morning of his death, the last rites of the church were administered to him by the Right Rev. Bishop Hughes.’

The Editor will conclude the account with the ensuing letter addressed to him, from Dr. Francis of New York, a gentleman long associated with Dr. Macneven in the same collegiate institution.

‘If extensive learning, rare attainments, great natural abilities, and long service in the cause of medical science,’ says Professor Francis, ‘have claims to your consideration, few will be found more fairly entitled to notice in your contemplated biography than the late Dr. Macneven. It was my happiness to be well acquainted, for a long series of years, with those very remarkable men, William Sampson, Thomas Addis Emmet, and William James Macneven. The renown of the first two is already well established ; the general knowledge, the lively fancy, and brilliant wit of Sampson, the immense intellectual stores, forensic powers and oratory of Emmet, are almost proverbial. The warmest friendship united Dr. Macneven with these his most intimate friends and countrymen; nor can the closing scenes of their eventful lives ever be erased from my memory, when, as a medical prescriber, associated with Dr. Macneven and others, the last attentions were paid to their physical sufferings and departure. Few final separations were more impressive than those which took from Dr. Macneven these enlightened and distinguished characters.

Upon the organization of the College of Physicians and Surgeons in 1807, Dr. Macneven delivered at their opening session a long course on clinical cases, as they occurred in the New York Almshouse, of which, with the late Dr. Hosack, he was an associate physician. In 1808 he received the appointment of Professor of Midwifery from the hands of the Regents of the University. Upon the reorganization of the College in 1811 he was appointed Professor of Chemistry, and in 1816 Materia Medica was added to his chair. This arrangement was continued until 1820, when they were again separated. In 1826 he resigned his Professorship in the College of Physicians and Surgeons, and, with his colleagues who withdrew at the same time from the institution, received the thanks of the Board of Regents, for the faithful and able manner in which they had filled their respective chairs as instructors and lecturers in said College.

In the November following, (1826), he commenced

48

an elaborate course of instruction on the Materia Medica in the Rutgers Medical College, which institution, with a majority of his former associates, Drs. Hosack, Francis and Mott, and Drs. Griscom and Godman, was now organized in New York at an expense of twenty-two thousand dollars, and opened for the better promotion of medicine and its several auxiliary departments of knowledge. The success of this new school exceeded his most ardent anticipations, as well as those of his fellow laborers. It continued its operations with increased renown, and gave promise of results most beneficial to science. After four years, however, its doors were closed by legislative enactments, and in 1830 Dr. Macneven ceased his functions as a public teacher.

It will be perceived that for more than twenty years Dr. Macneven was engaged as a professor of medical knowledge, and it would be withholding the tribute becoming his memory not to affirm that during that long period he was most assiduous in contributing with zeal and ability to promote the soundest interests of a responsible and important science. He left the state school, which he had helped to rear, in a condition of great prosperity, both in respect of character and in the number of students, and which at the commencement of its career had yet to secure the approbation and support of the profession. He withdrew from it because of its anomalous government—its intestine feuds with professors and trustees —the absurd restrictions capriciously adopted by its rulers to diminish the qualifications of candidates for the highest honors of the science, ere they were vest-

ed with collegiate testimonials legally to assume the
practice of the healing art. With his colleagues generally he was unwilling to endure the reproach of
abetting, in any wise, incompetency in the proper attainment of those who sought the medical doctorate.
How ably he enforced the strongest views in behalf of
medical learning in the candidate for medical honors,
how enlarged was his policy in the several measures
required to build up a great school of medical and
physical science, will best be learned by the perusal
of the documents on the subject, many of which are
preserved in the third volume of Dr. Hosack's Medical Essays, and several of which papers were the
emanations of Dr. Macneven's pen during the acri-
monious warfare waged against the college for a
number of years prior to the resignation of his official duties therein. Nevertheless, from the result of
tried experience he felt persuaded that another Medical Institution might be organized, more simple in its
government and more effective in its triumphs. He
had the happiness to find that public opinion sustained him, and with the same ardor which marked his
career twenty years before he resumed the chair of
Materia Medica in the Rutgers Medical Faculty, organized by the resources of its founders. The monopoly of instruction was, however, sustained by
additional legislative enactments; difficulties were
thrown out as to the validity for practice of the diplomas conferred on the candidates for degrees in
the new college, and, after four years of great promise he beheld his favorite object defeated, and this
second school closed by the constituted patrons of

learning, according to the spirit of laws especially designed to protect the State establishment from the inconvenience which might arise from competition in teaching.

That these enactments extinguished a medical school of great promise ; that legislative supremacy, characteristic of a people of the most benighted times in mental culture, interposed its power to the detriment of the precious interests of humanity, is conceded by many of the warmest advocates of those monopolizing laws ; and their argument for change of opinion is well sustained in the humiliating fact that the State school, with all its flourish of Regency power and ample support from legislative bounty, has dwindled in renown and in numbers to an almost nominal institution.

Dr. Macneven was learned as an instructor, and ample in his expositions. In chemical philosophy he was universally admitted to hold a high rank. Close attention to the progress of discovery enabled him with each returning term of the College to improve his lectures and add new illustrations to experimental truths.

Besides his ' Rambles in Switzerland,' his pieces of Irish History, and numerous political tracts which his eventful life occasioned him to publish, Dr. Macneven was the author of a highly esteemed essay entitled ' An Exposition of the Atomic Theory,' published in 1820, which was received with favor both at home and abroad. He also edited an edition of Brande's Chemistry, which met with extensive circulation. As co-editor of the New York Medical and

Philosophical Journal, he published two or three papers on subjects strictly medical. In 1812 he was appointed by Gov. Clinton Resident Physician of New York, and in 1840 he received the same honor from Gov. Seward. He was a member of the New York Literary and Philosophical Society, in whose Transactions he published his paper on the Mineral Waters of Schooley's mountain ; and in 1823 he was elected a Fellow of the American Philosophical Society of Philadelphia. During the prevalence of the Asiatic Cholera in New York in 1832 he was selected by the municipal authorities as one of the Medical Council of the city, and notwithstanding the reports which were published by official sanction, during that crisis, he assured the writer of this hasty note of his conviction that the disorder was a *nova pestis* in the country, and that its progress through the land was best explained by considering it a specific disease, and regulated by the laws of a sub-modo-contagio.

Sufficient has been said to show that the life of Dr. Macneven was one closely devoted to knowledge and its promulgation. The love of books was a leading passion with him, and no medical man among us surpassed him in the acquisition of languages. As a classical scholar his claims were unquestioned. He spoke German and French with the same facility as English ; and in the Italian, unlocked with delight the treasures of Dante and Ariosto. His native tongue, the Irish, as it was the first he had learned, so through life he conversed in it with fluency.

As at the funeral of his friend, Thomas Addis

Emmet, so that of Dr. Macneven was honored by a large attendance, both of adopted and native citizens ; and, as at the burial of that illustrious man there was but one feeling which pervaded all hearts, and one sentiment uttered by all lips, so at the interment of Dr. Macneven, all felt that learning had lost a distinguished ornament, real knowledge a true disciple, the charities of life an ardent friend, and patriotism one who had sustained martyrdom in her glorious cause.'

DR. NILES MANCHESTER. Died suddenly on the 15th of June, 1843, at North Providence (Pawtucket), Dr. Niles Manchester, aged 65, formerly 1st Vice President of the Rhode Island Medical Society. Dr. Manchester was born in Johnson, and commenced his professional career in North Providence forty years since, where his practice has been successful and extensive till within the last two years, when declining health compelled him to retire. He was faithful and conscientious in the discharge of medical duties, and enjoyed the respect and confidence of a wide circle of employers in the neighboring towns, where he was often called in consultation. In accurate diagnosis he met with few equals among physicians educated in his day, and his kind and soothing manner in a sick room rendered his visits peculiarly agreeable.—*Bost. Med. and Surg. Jour.*

Dr. Elisha Mather. Both the father and grand-father of Dr. Mather were natives of Northampton, Massachusetts, and they were both very eminent physicians. It is a subject of much regret that we have not biographical notices of these distinguished men. The elder Dr. Mather was cotemporary with the celebrated Dr. Pyncheon of Springfield, and Dr. Thomas Williams of Deerfield, Mass. These three physicians were almost the only ones of any note in the three counties of Franklin, Hampshire and Hampden, in the early settlement of the county. These three counties were united in one by the name of Hampshire county, till about the year 1816, when they were divided into three, bearing the above names.

The subject of the subjoined notice, Dr. Elisha Mather, was born at Northampton in the year 1792, and died on the 24th of April, 1840, aged 48 years. He was a judicious and respectable practitioner. He joined the Massachusetts Medical Society in the year 1824, and was a Counsellor and Censor in it for many years. He continued his fellowship till the time of his death. The Hampshire Gazette gives the following notice of him.

'In noticing the death of this good man and physician, it is not our object in this obituary to analyze particularly his character, or describe minutely the elements of which it is composed; but generally, to bear testimony to his high standing in his profession, and the excellency of his character. Dr. Mather was, undoubtedly, more self-taught than most of his professional brethren. He was indebted to his talents, his industry, and his application, for the rank which he attained. In all the various branches of his profession he was entitled to entire confidence. With the structures and functions of the different parts of the human system he was most intimately acquainted, and seldom surpassed in accuracy of anatomical knowledge. His practice was invariably founded upon physiological and pathological principles. He always thoroughly investigated the cause of diseases, and applied his remedy accordingly ; and though the public as a mass may not have awarded him that reputation as a physician to which he is justly entitled, those most competent to judge of his qualifications (the medical profession) have duly appreciated his great worth.

In his deportment he was neither forbidding nor imposing, but was affable and accessible to all ; so that his younger brethren could always approach him without being apprehensive that they should be overpowered by his feelings of superiority.

In his domestic relations he was greatly endeared. His conduct in his family was marked by the greatest purity and tenderness ; and he here experienced his greatest happiness. As a Christian he was exemplary, and no one doubts that he possessed the leading characteristics of a christain character.'

Dr. Samuel Mather was another of the distinguished medical men of his time in Connecticut, in the town of Windsor. He was born in or near Boston, about the year 1680, and is supposed to be of the same family of Mathers as the celebrated divines of that name who resided in Boston and the towns in its vicinity. Dr. Mather graduated at Harvard University in the year 1698, and received the degree of Master of Arts some time after. He studied his profession with Dr. Hooker of Hartford, and received a license to practice medicine from the Legislature of the State. He was the cotemporary and intimate friend of Elliot, and greatly distinguished as a scholar and physician. He died in the year 1743, aged 63 years. No man at the time stood so high in public confidence, or had so extensive a medical practice in the State, as Dr. Mather. He visited every section of country in a circuit of forty or fifty miles as a counsellor, and was as greatly venerated for many excellent virtues, as for science and skill as a physician. He left a number of descendants; amongst others Dr. Samuel Mather, formerly of Windsor, and more recently of the city of Hartford, a distinguished and successful accoucheur, was his grandson. Dr. Charles Mather died in Hartford, in 1822, at the age of 80 years.—*S. B. W., in the Bost. Med. and Surg. Jour.*

Dr. JOSEPH W. McKEAN was son of the late Professor Joseph McKean of Harvard University, and was born in 1800. No announcement could have been more surprising than the death of Dr. McKean, of this city, Thursday evening, April 2d, 1839. We have known him many years, and appreciated the many excellent qualities which gained for him the

49

personal friendship of a wide circle of acquaintances.
While we sympathize with the afflicted family of relatives in this melancholy dispensation of Divine Providence, we feel that the medical profession of Boston
have also met with a severe loss.   To urbanity of
manners he united a devoted attention to the sick,
which gave him an increasing field of practice as
years sped their way.

Dr. McKean studied with Dr. Walker of Charlestown.   After receiving the degree of M. D., he visited Europe, passing considerable time in the hospitals
of Paris, and finally on his return to the United
States, established himself in business in this city,
about fourteen years ago.   Some ten or twelve years
since, soon after the organization of the Vermont
Medical College, then principally under the auspices
of Dr. Gallup, author of a valuable publication which
has just appeared, Dr. M. gave a course of lectures
on anatomy in that school.   He has been a counsellor
in the Mass. Medical Society, and a spirited promoter
of every plan for enlarging the sphere of medical
and surgical knowledge.

He was exceedingly tall and very slender, but with
the exception of occasional interruptions, arising from
a predisposition to a pulmonary disease, he enjoyed,
of late, very good health.   On the day of his decease, he had been as well apparently as in months
past, and manifested unabated activity in the routine
of professional visits, even till within an hour of the
arrival of the messenger of death.   On sending,
about 6 o'clock, to the room to which he had retired
for study, to call him to tea, he was found dead in

his chair. We have heard of no post mortem examination, and presume his death was occasioned by some affection of the heart.—*Bost. Med. and Surg. Jour. Ap.*, 1839.

Dr. LAUGHLIN MCLEAN was a native of Scotland, and emigrated to this country between the years 1735 and 1740. Dr. McLean, after arriving in America, first settled in Wethersfield, in Connecticut, where he continued for some time associated with his countryman, Dr. Norman Morrison. After residing in this town for a season, he moved to Hartford, and continued many years the ornament of his profession, extensively useful and greatly beloved by a numerous circle of friends and employers. Dr. McLean has always been spoken of as a man of refined education, great dignity and ease of manners, and of uncommon benevolence of heart. He died at an advanced age, and left behind him a family whose descendants are still living in Hartford or the vicinity.—*S. B. W., in Bost. Med. and Surg. Jour.*

Dr. THOMAS MINER. The following short notice of this distinguished physician is from the pen of his intimate friend, Dr. Woodward of the Worcester Insane Hospital, in a letter to Dr. Smith, editor of the Boston Medical and Surgical Journal, and is published in the 24th volume of that Journal. A few years ago, in connection with Dr. Tully, he published a most valuable and interesting work on typhus fever, which caused a great deal of controversy and hypercriticism at the time. Whatever may be the merits of the doctrines he advanced, whether they were true or false, it is not my intention to canvass them here. It is certain that the work was most severely criticised; from that time it obtained a greater celebrity than it ever before had, and the public, although divided on the subject of the real worth of the work, were generally satisfied that it was one of deep erudition and research. At any rate it was one that gave the author great notoriety as a writer, and great fame as a practitioner. It is often so with those who are most abused by caviling criticism. For some time after this he held the office of President of the Connecticut Medical Society, one of the most distinguished institutions of the kind in the Union.

'Dear Sir :—Our mutual friend, Thomas Miner, M. D., died at my residence this morning at half past 3 o'clock. The doctor, as you probably knew, had for twenty years or more, been affected with a disease of the heart, which had prevented his engaging in active business. During the last winter he suffered extremely with this disease. Early in March he came on to Worcester to see what could be done to alleviate his sufferings, and, as he said,—' If he could not be relieved, to die with his friend. Soon after he arrived here, we discovered œdema of his feet and ankles, which pointed too clearly to be mistaken, to the fatal mischief that was lurking within the chest. The symptoms of dropsy were rapidly developed. He was unable to lie down, and spent a large part of each night in his chair. Three weeks ago he took cold, which resulted in pneumonia. This disease was severe, and for some days threatened his life. Quite unexpectedly he got better, and for a week indulged hopes that he could return to his friends in Connecticut. He did not probably, from the first appearance of dropsy, expect to recover. The acute disease of the lungs was soon followed by great increase of the action of the heart and general dropsy, which terminated fatally this morning.

Dr. Miner was a remarkable man. He has left behind him few as ripe scholars, profound philosophers and philanthropists in the medical profession. Ill health having for some years precluded active engagement in professional duties, he has devoted his whole time to study and reflection. His mind was very active to the last. He was, perhaps, one of the most learned physicians in New England—not only in professional attainments, but in foreign languages and theology. He was acquainted with the French, Italian, Spanish, and German languages, and was often employed by publishers in the country to translate them. He was particularly fond of the German, and read works on medicine, theology and philosophy in that language with great pleasure.

You well know his estimable and moral qualities. His heart was benevolent, his feelings kind. In his life he exemplified the christian character; in sickness and death he bore testimony of unshaken confidence in the christian hope of a joyful resurrection. Dr. Miner was 64 years of age.—S. B. WOODWARD, *Worcester, April 23, 1841.*

An account of his last sickness and post mortem appearances may be found in the 24th vol. of the Bost. Med. and Surg. Jour. p. 207.

The principal incidents of the life of Dr. Miner are given in the following sketch from his own pen, addressed to his fellow townsman, Joseph Barrett, M. D. ; who has obligingly furnished us with a copy for publication.—*New Englander, Jan.* 1844.

Auto-biography of Dr. Miner.

MIDDLETOWN, CONN. *Feb. 9th*, 1837.

Dr. Joseph Barrett :—Dear Sir,—I thank you for the solicitude which you have been so obliging as, at various times, to express, to obtain a few memoranda of the principal events of my life. If you survive me it may, perhaps, be a satisfaction to have a record upon which you may depend for your own information, though it may be so barren as to contain little, if any thing, which may be of interest beyond the limited sphere of a few personal friends.

I am now fifty-nine years old, and in one respect may be considered as having lived but a small part of that time. I was originally a weakly child, so that a considerable part of the time, till I was fourteen years old, I was unable to go from home to school. In the years 1798 and 1799, I had the intermittent fever two seasons in succession, and in 1801, I was unable to walk for three months at a time, from rheumatism. Finally, about the year 1819, while fully employed in professional business, I suddenly broke down from a subacute inflammation of the lungs, attended with hectic fever, and a severe palpitation of the heart, arising probably from an organic lesion of that viscus. From this latter affection, I have never completely recovered, but have remained a valetudinarian the last eighteen or twenty years, a large portion of the time, being unfit for active exertion of body or mind.

On the whole, therefore, there have been but about twenty or twenty-five years in my life, which I have been able to employ much for the benefit of myself or others ; this is what I mean by saying, that I have lived but a small part of the time since I was born.

I was born in Westfield, the north-west parish of this town, where my father was the Congregational clergyman, Oct. 15, 1777. I received my elementary education principally at home from my father, till I was fourteen years of age, though about two years of the time I was able to attend a very excellent common school, kept by the late Rev. Joseph Washburn, who afterwards was the minister of Farmington. After having made some progress in Latin and Greek under my father, in the spring of 1792, I went to Chatham to complete fitting for college, under the tuition of the late Cyprian Strong, D. D., and joined Yale College in September of that year. In September, 1776, I took the degree of A. B., and within a month, being then nineteen years of age, I went to Goshen, Orange county, state of New York, to take charge of an Academy. After remaining in that county three years, and having my constitution much impaired by the two periods of intermittent, to which I have referred, I returned in December, 1799. In the course of the next year, I entered myself as a

law student in Judge Hosmer's office ; but within a
few weeks, remaining still at my father's, I had a
serious attack of rheumatism, which disabled me from
doing much during 1801.   However, in the autumn
of that year I took charge of an academy at Berlin,
which I kept about two years, till I was interrupted
by loss of health.   The school flourished very well
while I was able to attend to it, and Mrs. Emma
Willard of Troy, then Emma Hart of Berlin, and
Prof. E. A. Andrews, now teacher in Boston, were
among my most distinguished pupils.   I was then interrupted by ill health both in my attempt to study
law, and as a teacher.   However, when I was about
twenty-five years old, I commenced the study of
medicine with the late Dr. Osborne, of this city,
engaging a part of the time in instruction.   Here
William L. Storrs, Esq., was one of my most promising pupils.   At that time, Dr. Osborne had probably
much the best medical library in the State, and I
continued reading under his direction about three
years.   The winter of 1806 and 1807, I spent with
Dr. Smith Clark of Haddam, visiting his patients
with him, and seeing his practice.   In the spring of
1807, I returned to my father's and began practice ;
but in the autumn removed into the city and remained until the middle of the next summer.   After looking about me for a permanent residence, during
which time I spent a few weeks at Southington, in
August, 1808, I settled at Lynn.   There I continued
in full practice till May 8th, 1810.   I married Phebe
Mather, daughter of Samuel Mather, Esq.   She died
February 5th, 1811.   In this city and vicinity, I soon

had as much professional business as I could attend to, and more than my health would bear. In February, 1819, I was seized with an affection of the lungs and heart, which suddenly ended in a great degree my professional career, and left me a confirmed valetudinarian at the premature age of forty-one.

Since 1819, the little that I have done has been of a very various and desultory character, my infirm health preventing continued application to any thing of importance. For several years I practised some in consultation, and amused myself in reading two or three foreign languages, besides writing occasional medical and literary essays. For two or three years before the Medical Recorder of Philadelphia ceased, I made most of the selections, abridgments and translations from the French, which appeared in that work. In 1823, in connection with Dr. Tully, I published Essays on Fevers and other Medical subjects ; and in 1825 an account of Typhus Syncopalis. The latter has been several times republished entire, or abridged in other works, as in the Medical Recorder, Boston Medical Journal, Potter and Calhoun's edition of Gregory's Practice, and Thatcher's Modern Practice.

As there was no public medical school in Connecticut when I studied physic, of course I began to practice under a license from the Medical Society, and it was not till 1819 that I received the honorary degree of M. D. from Yale College. The following are the principal specimens of the attention with which I have been honored by my professional brethren. Since the organization of the Medical School

of Yale College, perhaps three tenths of the time I
have been one of the Censors or members of the
committee. I was a member of the committee for
devising ways and means, and forming the plan for
the Retreat for the Insane, as a colleague with Dr.
Todd, Dr. Woodward, Dr. Tully, Dr. Ives, and
others, and with the assistance of Dr. Tully wrote
the committee's address to the public, which preceded
our soliciting donations. My name was at the head
of the committee, and I was therefore chairman of
the body; not from any merit of mine, but from the
modesty of Dr. Todd, who did not wish to appear as
the official leader of an Institution, over which it was
expected he would soon preside. In 1832 I was
elected Vice President of the Medical Society of
Connecticut, and in 1834, President. Having held
the latter place three years, it is my intention to decline being a candidate at the ensuing meeting of the
medical convention, in May next. Many of my
fugitive Medical Essays, besides what I wrote for the
Medical Recorder, have been published under the
signature of Senex or Celsus, in the Boston Medical
Journal, or the United States Medical and Surgical
Journal, though a few others have sometimes appeared in different periodicals. The article on the vario-
loid and small pox, and on the moral effects of prevalent malignant diseases, in the Christian Spectator
for March, 1830, was written by me; and I have
translated a few articles from the French and from
the German, for Silliman's Journal.

A few farther particulars may perhaps be worth
stating. Like many other young men in early life,

I entered pretty ardently into politics, reading not only party productions, but treatises on the law of nations, and various things of the kind. But as early as 1800 I became heartily disgusted with the subject, and gradually got out of its reach, so that for more than twenty years I have not voted at a single election. In my religious views I am a Christian, and, as far as I understand the subject, I am nearer a Quaker in sentiment than any other sect. I am in favor of defensive war, and consider it as much a duty to arm against a band of robbers or pirates, as against a flock of wolves or tigers; and I do not consider it as a virtue to refuse customary titles to respect, or to use *thee* and *thou*, or to wear a broad-brimmed hat and a drab coat, or to number the months or the days of the week instead of naming them. With these exceptions, and perhaps a few others of the kind, I think I must be considered as in sentiment a Quaker. This may perhaps account satisfactorily to you, for some peculiarities in my habits, which you may have noticed. As to mental philosophy, though here my acquirements are rather limited, I am nearer a Kantian than any thing else. In medicine in general, I coincide with the views of the school of the Vitalists. My early medical reading was pretty extensive; but of late I have attended but little to the subject, and in fact have lost much of my taste for medicine. From the state of my health, being unable to attend closely to any one thing for a long time, a great portion of my information is but little more than smattering, scarcely going deeper than the surface. Perhaps it more nearly resembles the superfi-

cial knowledge which we occasionally meet with in
an old bookseller, who has picked up here and there
a little upon almost every thing, about which his cus-
tomers converse.

My father, in common with most country clergymen of his day, besides a slender salary, had a small
farm of his own, upon which he generally labored
more or less, every day through the summer. In the
winter he often had a small school composed of
twelve or fifteen young men who were the sons of
farmers, or young mechanics, who had just gone
through their apprenticeship. My mother was a woman of uncommonly good management in her domestic affairs. With the small salary, the little farm,
and the school, the family (which usually consisted of
my father and mother, three children, and a female
domestic, who in many particulars performed the
affairs of a boy and girl) lived very comfortably and
decently. My father had not many books, but he
had a share in a good public library in the city, and
we had access to a small library in the parish. The
family frequently spent their winter evenings in listening to some one who was reading a book of travels,
the Spectator, the history of our country and revolution, foreign history, or some interesting book of the
kind. Besides attending daily to the duties common
to religious families, Saturday evening was spent
principally in reading the Bible, and learning or re-
peating the catechism. After going to church twice
on Sunday, the rest of the time was spent in reading
the scriptures or such writers as Watts and Doddridge.
In the evening some of our neighbors generally call-

ed in, and the time passed in pleasant conversation upon the events of the past week, and other topics of the day.

Except that my father, from the difficulty of procuring sufficient assistance in the management of his little farm, had occasionally to labor rather too hard, in addition to his regular weekly preparation for the pulpit, our family may be considered during the first fourteen years of my life, while I remained at home, as living very comfortably, rationally, and pleasantly. My parents, in common with most of their day, knew very little of the nature and necessity of a proper physical education ; consequently, as I was always a feeble child, I was probably injured greatly, by ill-directed kindness. I was unable to go very much to the common school, and never became familiar with the common athletic sports of boys. I well recollect, when I was a large boy, I had been so much confined within doors, that my countenance was as pale and white as milk, resembling those plants which have vegetated in the cellar without the light of the sun. Some attempts were made to teach me to labor on the farm, but these were rather injudiciously managed. The common tools on the farm were too heavy and clumsy for one so feeble as I to use to advantage. My father seems never to have thought how easy it might have been to furnish me with a light hatchet, hoe, fork or rake. I believe this is rather a common oversight with farmers in their first attempts to teach their boys to labor. Those who are sturdy soon overcome the difficulty of using heavy instruments ; but they are a great embarrassment to the slender. As I kept tolerably busy within doors with my books, my deficiency in labor and other exercises that tend to strengthen and harden the constitution, was not much thought of. The consequence was, that I early contracted a tender and effeminate habit, which continues to this day, and has been the great burden of my life. Every boy in New England that is born and brought up in the country, ought to be early and habitually taught the use of the axe, the hoe, the spade and the rake, so that if occasion should require, it would be no great task for him to cut his own wood, and make his own garden, whatever might be his future condition, or profession, or situation in life. Such knowledge is often of great convenience, but its greatest benefit is in giving strength and firmness to the system.

In addition to the great and irremediable mistake which was made in my physical education, as great or a greater blunder was made in the literary and scientific department. I was sent to college before I was quite fifteen years old, which was one year at least, and probably two years too early for me to receive the full benefit of the institution. My miscellaneous information from reading history, travels, essays, and such books as are usually found in social libraries, together with a pretty familiar acquaintance with Salmon's and Guthrie's geographies, as well as with the early editions of Morse, was tolerably extensive for a lad of my age, but I was not very well grounded in Latin and Greek, and had no foundation laid in the mathematics. The consequence was, though I passed regularly through the course without a single public or private censure from any of the faculty, and with even some small tokens of approbation, yet I made no figure as a scholar. I had some standing from the amount of my former miscellaneous and general information ; but that was all for which I was in any way distinguished. Except learning the elementary parts of the mathematics so as to be able to teach surveying and navigation tolerably well for that day, I knew nothing further of that science.

My mind was not so closely disciplined, and my habits of attention were not so accurately formed, as to have enabled me to make much progress in mathematics during the rapid manner in which the science was studied by the class. I believe the same was the fact with all the younger part of my associates. They made but little progress in a study for which they either were not ripe, or were not previously prepared. My acquirements in the languages were merely decent, and not such as to merit any peculiar notice, either for eminence or defect. On the whole the four years of my college life, though they were far from being trifled away or lost, were spent under very great and permanent disadvantages, and I did not acquire half the solid learning that I might have done had I been two years older, and proportionably better prepared. Many with a real or affected modesty, blame themselves for their misimprovement of early advantages. I have very little of this lamentation to make. The error consisted principally in the mistaken judgment of my friends, in estimating my early acquirements greater than they actually were, and supposing me to have a ripeness of mind, to which I had not attained on entering college.

These are the common mistakes of parents, guardians and teachers. If the memory is capacious and tolerably stored with facts—as was the case with mine—the inquiry too often is made, to ascertain how far the other faculties of the mind are developed. The judgment may be still in embryo. But if the other faculties are tolerably developed, they have probably not been disciplined, so that they can be applied with facility and rapidity to the higher branches of education in the manner in which they are usually studied in a common academical course. This is a statement of facts rather than an apology.

The principal object in almost all my literary, philosophical, biblical and scientific pursuits has been my own amusement for the time being, taking but little pains to arrange it so as to be serviceable to others. The Rev. Henry Channing, now of New York, Prof. Tully, Dr. J. P. Kirtland, of Poland, Ohio, Dr. Comstock of Lebanon, Dr. Hooker of New Haven, Dr. Bronson of Waterbury, and Dr. Woodward of Worcester, have been among my principal correspondents. To these I might add Dr. McGregor of Rochester, Dr. Swann of Tennessee, Dr. Calhoun of Philadelphia, Dr. Cartwright of Natchez, and Dr. Fisk of Salisbury, as occasional correspondents. The venerable Noah Webster, LL. D., is among my most respected correspondents. He possesses letters from me upon criticism, etymology and other philosophical subjects. He also did me the honor, occasionally to send me his manuscripts, soliciting my remarks upon them previous to publication.

Among the physicians with whom I have been most intimate, are the names of Coggswell, Todd, Ives, Tully, Woodward, Hough, Ward, Hooker, Comstock, North, Bronson and various others. My friend, Chester Whittlesey, Esq., of Southington, possessed more of my letters than any other man. Judge Hosmer and the late Richard Alsop, Esq., were among my earliest and permanent friends in this city. Asahel H. Strong, Esq., Charles Denison, Esq., the Rev. Thomas Robbins and Prof. Silliman, are among my most distinguished college classmates.

The above is the outline of all that I recollect concerning myself, which you would probably feel much interest in knowing. I am conscious of having omitted several names of gentlemen to whom I have been under much obligation; others have undoubtedly slipped my memory. THOMAS MINER.

DR. SAMUEL LATHAM MITCHILL was born in North Hempstead, (Plandome,) Queens County, Long Island, N. Y., on the 20th of Aug., 1764. In this village his father, Robert Mitchill, of English descent, was an industrious farmer of the society of Friends. He died in 1789, leaving behind him six sons and two daughters, most of whom he lived to see respectably settled in life. Agricultural pursuits became, for the most part, their occupation, and industry and economy were the characteristics common to them all. In the subject of this memoir, who was the third son, were early remarkable those habits of observation and reflection which were destined to

51

elevate him to an enviable distinction among his cotemporaries. Fortunately for mankind, his talents and laudable ambition met a discerning and liberal patron in his maternal uncle, Dr. Samuel Latham, a skillful and intelligent medical practitioner in his native village. The resources of this medical gentleman happily enabled him to enter upon and complete that system of education which the limited income and numerous family of his parents of necessity denied. Of this uncle he always spoke with becoming gratitude and ardent affection. At an early age he was placed under the direction of Dr. Leonard Cutting, a graduated scholar of the University of Cambridge, England; whom an attachment to the principles of liberty had induced to visit our shores, and in whom the polished habits of the gentleman were happily blended with a profound and extensive erudition. With this excellent instructor he continued for several years, and with him acquired an intimate acquaintance with classical literature which constituted one of the favorite amusements of his leisure hours throughout his subsequent life. It is due to this kind preceptor to state, that he early predicted the future eminence of his pupil, and contributed by his praise and direction to its fulfilment. After acquiring a partial knowledge of the elementary principles of medicine with Dr. Latham, he removed to the city of New York in 1780, and became a pupil of Dr. Samuel Bard, with whom he continued about three years.

In the twentieth year of his age Mr. Mitchill was happily enabled to avail himself of the advantages held out by the University of Edinburgh, which at that time was adorned by the talents of Cullen, Black and Monro. Here students from all parts of the civilized world repaired, as the most able seat of medical learning then in Europe ; and of nearly a thousand youths, many of whom have risen to the first distinctions in science and letters, the talents and diligence of Mitchill acquired for him general applause, and an undivided esteem and regard. The late Sir James Mackintosh and Thomas Addis Emmet, who have since acquired such eminence in other pursuits, were among his friends and compeers ; and we have the testimony of the last named excellent individual that no student of the university exhibited greater tokens of promise. After a residence of about four years, at the end of which, in 1786, he received the honors of the profession, he made a short excursion into England and France, and returned to his native country, then rapidly recovering from the disastrous effects of the revolutionary contest.

On his return to his native state, Dr. Mitchill, with a constant interruption to his medical studies, devoted a portion of his time to acquire a knowledge of the laws and constitution of his country, under the direction of Robert Yates, at that time chief justice of the State of New York. The result was a fixed and unalterable attachment in him to those principles which triumphantly asserted at Saratoga and Yorktown, and since embodied in the constitution of the United States, became the corner stone of new institutions, sacred to the rights and best interests of mankind.

By the influence of the chief justice he was employed in the commission for holding a treaty with the Iroquois Indians, and was present at the adjustment made at Fort Stanwix, 1788, in which the right to a large portion of the western district was purchased for the benefit of the government. During this period he extensively explored the frontiers of New York and Canada, and seems also to have been engaged in various matters of a political character. His experiments on the mineral waters of Saratoga, which he subsequently reinvestigated, appear to have contributed to the extensive celebrity which those waters have since obtained.

His appointment to the chair of Chemistry in Columbia College, marks the confidence of his friends in his abilities; and from this school he first made known to his countrymen the new theory of chemistry recently matured by the genius of Lavoisier and his associates. The admirable nomenclature, the scientific arrangement of this system, together with its brilliant results, form an era in chemical philosophy, and an important chapter in the history of the human mind. The doctor was wont to repeat with much complacency this happy commencement of his professional career. He was, however, far from adopting all the principles of Lavoisier; and in a memoir published shortly after, he presented a modified system, which involved him in a controversy with the celebrated Priestley, then recently arrived on our shores. It is to the honor of these distinguished individuals that the disputation was conducted with mutual courtesy, and ended in a personal friendship, which terminated only with the life of the great founder of pneumatic chemistry.

From his connection with many of the chief officers of the State government, and particularly with Chancellor Livingston and Simeon Dewitt, originated the Society for the promotion of Agriculture, Manufactures and the Useful Arts. Before this body he delivered their first public address, which made its appearance in the first volume of their Transactions. This Society, which consisted of the members of both houses of the legislature, and of such other individuals as interested themselves in agricultural pursuits, was incorporated at his instance, and has proved by its various publications a valuable aid in unfolding the active resources of the commonwealth. His mineralogical survey of the State of New York, undertaken in 1796, under the direction of this institution, forms a memorable event in his career, and first laid the basis of his reputation with the philosophers of Europe, which continued from this time thenceforth to increase. This report was probably the first attempt in mineralogical study in America, and led the way to the more ample investigations of Maclure, Gordon, Cleaveland, Dana, Van Rensselaer and others. It has often been referred to by the savans of Europe, with approbation. He contributed, at times, local sketches of a like character of different parts of the country to various scientific journals; and it has furnished occasion of regret that so competent an observer had not more fully prosecuted these meritorious researches. Throughout his life he was a persistent believer in the Wernerian hypothesis, and contended that the most luminous evidences of its truth were found in the formations of the western hemisphere.

The New York Medical Repository originated in 1797, under the editorial career of Saml. L. Mitchill, Edward Miller and Elihu H. Smith. Of this journal he was the chief editor for more than sixteen years.

In 1807, the act of the legislature empowering the Regents of the University to establish a College of Physicians and Surgeons in the city of New York took effect ; and upon the organization of this school, Dr. Mitchill was appointed the Professor of Chemistry, which, however, his public duties obliged him to resign. In the following year he was elected to the chair of natural history, in the same institution. In this science so congenial to his taste, and in which he was acknowledged to be without a rival among his countrymen, he delivered courses of instruction for twelve successive years with eminent success. Of these lectures which embraced the extensive regions of mineralogical, botanical and zoological inquiry, he published an outline, which exhibited a compass of thought, and capacity for generalization for which he was little accredited by the censorious.

The reorganization of the college in 1820, occasioned a new disposition of the professorship, when Dr. Mitchill was commissioned by the Regents as professor of materia medica and botany. In this capacity he continued his professional labors until 1826, when, with his colleagues, he resigned all connection with an institution, the interests of which he had promoted nearly twenty years. It may be sufficient to observe that it opened in 1807 with fifty-three students; that for a while there existed in the city two other institutions, which at length yielded to its superiority; and that for several years it was attended by two hundred students. Difficulties having at length arisen between the trustees and professors, the latter withdrew in a body from an institution, which, under their exertions, had been elevated to rivalship with the oldest medical school in the country. In common with his colleagues, he received upon his resignation, the thanks of the Regents of the University for the faithful and able manner in which he had discharged his duties as instructor and lecturer in the college. In the new college, which was immediately thereafter formed, under the name of Rutgers Medical College, Dr. Mitchill was appointed to the office of Vice President.

It is with pleasure we record the name of Dr. Mitchill among those who first gave impulse and activity to that splendid system of internal improvement which has given renown to New York, and rendered her a brilliant example to her sister states. We refer to the statutes of her legislature of 1798, which conferred on Chancellor Livingston the exclusive right to navigate by steam the waters of New York. This bill owed much to the zeal and assiduity of Dr. Mitchill, arrayed against a host of scoffing and sneering opponents. The projected attempt was at this time unsuccessful, but by the united exertions of Livingston and Fulton, eventuated in those magnificent efforts in steam navigation which have changed the internal commerce of nations.

In the Congress of the United States, both as representative and senator, the bills for reducing the required term of residence for foreigners from fourteen to five years, on medical quarantine and health laws, on salt duties, were a few among the many subjects which called forth a happy display of his varied information and persuasive elocution. His knowledge of the political relations of the American confederation, and familiarity with the statistics, rendered him at all times a most useful member both in the house and in committee ; those who expected to see in him the mere abstract philosopher were delighted to find in him the highest social qualities, and a research which scarcely any subject of human inquiry had eluded.

In 1799 Dr. Mitchill was united in matrimony to the daughter of Samuel Akerly, Mrs. Catherine Cook, his amiable partner and lamenting survivor. In the domestic relations of life, as husband, brother and friend, his zeal and affection were exemplary and disinterested.

Dr. Mitchill derived from nature a hardy and robust constitution, but occasionally labored under a bronchial affection, to which he acquired a predisposition from an attack of inflammation in early life. He died after a short but severe illness in the 67th year of his age, on the 7th of September, 1831, at his residence in the city of New York. His funeral was honored by the attendance of a large and respectable body of his fellow citizens.

Dr. Mitchill was a member of innumerable scientific societies. Of the Lyceum of Natural History of New York, he was the founder, and for many years its President. He enriched its annals with many contributions, and still further displayed his zeal in behalf of his favorite pursuit, by a donation to them of a large portion of his valuable cabinet.

Of his numerous writings a large part relate to subjects of transient interest or of technical science. These we shall neither attempt to enumerate nor to characterize. Among his most elaborate productions are his addresses before the State Agricultural Societies, his correspondence with Priestley, his Chart of Chemical Nomenclature, his Introduction to Darwin's Zoonomia, his paper on the alkaline properties of the waters of the ocean in the American Philosophical Transactions, his Discourse before the New York Historical Society on the Botanical history of North and South America ; a paper on the Fishes that inhabit the waters of New York, in the Transactions of the Literary and Historical Society of New York ; his appendix to Cuvier's Theory of the Earth ; his biographical Discourses on Dr. Bard and on Thomas A. Emmet.

As a lecturer, simple, plain and didactic, he arrested the attention of his auditors by his ample and ready knowledge of his subject, and by a fund of apt and characteristic anecdotes. In his excursions through different sections of the United States, and during his residence at Washington, he had become intimately acquainted with many of the more interesting portions of our country, and with the various

characters of our countrymen ; and no small part of
the interest of his lectures consisted in reminiscences
connected with these circumstances of his life.

Reference has been already made to his early attainments in the literature of Greece and Rome ;
evidence, indeed, of classical taste were to be found
in almost all his compositions both written and oral ;
and he had been known and acknowledged as one of
our most eminent writers, had he not become still
more conspicuous as an adept in natural curiosities.
That vivacious and fertile imagination which was
usefully occupied with the bones of the mastodon and
Wernerian formation, might have illustrated and illu-
minated the paths of literature. We refer for the
evidence of this opinion to his admirable discourse
before the New York Horticultural Society, which
the scholar may consult for the beauty of its style,
and the agriculturalist for the useful lessons it imparts.

For about twenty years, Dr. Mitchill acted as one
of the physicians of the New York Hospital ; and
his diligence and attention to the duties this office
imposed, when not called from the city by other obligations, were marked and exemplary. Nor was he
deficient, notwithstanding his multifarious pursuits, in
the practical knowledge of disease. Those who were
accustomed to regard him as a mere theorist, by personal intercourse perceived in him the acute personal observer of the different phases of disease. Like
Darwin and Cullen, he judiciously, when at the bedside, rejected speculations and trusted to observation
and experience as the only safe guides.

In assigning to Dr. Mitchill an eminent rank

among the cultivators of natural science, we are fully warranted by the authority of those who have pre-eminently excelled in this branch of knowledge. The illustrious Cuvier, both in his lectures and in his printed writings, referred to him in terms of signal approbation. More recently the ornithologist, Audubon, has bestowed upon him the tribute of his applause. Let it be recollected that his knowledge was acquired not among the facilities of a royal or imperial cabinet, but amid the fatigues of travel, and while resident among a population little disposed to speculative investigation, or to regard his pursuits with favor or reward. Though justly deemed the Nestor of American science, he bore the honors which thickened around him meekly, if not unobtrusively, and ever showed himself ready to aid the diligent inquirer by counsel and encouragement. It happened to few men to pass through life with less of censure, or with a more fixed and unchanged approbation.—*Life written by his colleague, Dr. J. W. Francis.*

DR. NORMAN MORRISON, who, as a scholar and a man of science was in no way inferior to his distinguished countryman, Dr. McKean, of whom I have just spoken, was born in Scotland, about the year 1690. He received his education at the University of Edinburgh, under the instruction of the distinguished teachers who filled the professors' chair in the department of medicine in that celebrated University.

Dr. Morrison came to this country about the year

1740, and first settled in Wethersfield, Conn., where he remained about two years. He then moved to Hartford, and soon gained a high reputation for medical science and practical skill as a physician. Many pupils resorted to him and his distinguished countryman, Dr. McLean, as the fame of both was alike honorable and extensive. Like Elliot, Dr. Morrison was a thorough and diligent scholar, had a valuable library, and did much in that day to inspire his pupils with a taste for reading, and encourage systematic and regular practice. The benefit of his labors in instructing a class of pupils of unusual eminence, was widely diffused, and its influence can hardly be said to have ceased at the present time. Those of the present century who knew him, or knew of his fame, bear testimony to his great accomplishments as a man and a scholar, and to his superior eminence and judgment as a physician. Amongst his pupils were the celebrated Dr. Osborne of Middletown; Dr. Wolcott of Windsor; and Dr. Farnsworth of Wethersfield. The following anecdote is related of Dr. Morrison, with which he used to amuse his friends, although somewhat at his own expense. There lived in a neighboring parish a Dr. Andrus, a self-taught but shrewd, ingenious man, little acquainted with books, but who had picked up in various ways, considerable knowledge, particularly by his acquaintance with the Indians in the neighborhood, denominated the 'Farmington tribe.' He obtained from them their knowledge of roots and herbs, so as to have gained much reputation with the public, although he was hardly admitted into the pale of the regular profession. A respectable patient in Hartford under the care of Drs. Morrison and McLean, having heard of this modern Esculapius, desired much to see the renowned Doctor of Indian skill. Unwilling to meet Andrus, but yet not wishing to disoblige their patient they agreed to address a note to the Doctor to meet them at a certain time. Wishing to have a little sport with the Indian Doctor, and not at all unwilling to disconcert and mortify him, they wrote the note in the Latin language, which they knew he could not read, and dispatched a messenger with it to the Doctor's house. On the reception of the note the Doctor attempted to read it, but it was all 'Greek' to him, whichever side up he attempted it; but a shrewd Yankee was not easily to be entrapped, even by a crafty Scotchman. Andrus bade his messenger wait, and went with all speed to his minister, who was no less a man than Rector Williams, afterwards President of Yale College, who easily interpreted the mysteries of the note for him. Seeing the object his quick discernment and ready wit led him to retort in the answer they required. Understanding the dialect of the Indian tribe, with whom he was familiar, he immediately replied in the unknown tongue, and the messenger was dispatched in return. The Scotch Doctors took the note, but they did not understand the 'Latin of it,' neither could they find an interpreter; but at the appointed hour the hero of Indian skill and learning appeared. The Scotchmen were much interested in his ingenuity and simplicity of character. They friendly requested him to interpret his own billet-doux, acknowledging their ignorance of the *learned language* in which it was written, and had a hearty laugh over it, as they many times afterwards did in telling the story of their attempt to cheat a Yankee.

Dr. Morrison died in Wethersfield, of an epidemic pneumonia, at the house of his friend and pupil, Dr. Farnsworth, who was first severely sick under the care of his celebrated instructor. After Dr. Morrison was attacked with the disease, he predicted the recovery of his friend, unhesitatingly declared the certainty of his own death both of which events occurred in exact fulfillment, as to time and circumstances, as he had foretold. His death took place in 1791, at the age of 71.—S. B. W.

Dr. DANIEL OLIVER. I can learn but little in relation to the early history of this distinguished individual. He was born, I believe, in Salem, Essex county, Mass., about the year 1786. He was educated at Harvard College, and received the degree of Master of Arts there in the year 1805, and I believe the ad eundem degree of Master of Arts at Dartmouth College. After his graduation at Dartmouth, he studied the profession of medicine, and attended lectures and received the degree of Doctor of Medicine from the University of Pennsylvania. He also received the same degree from Dartmouth College. He was appointed lecturer on Chemistry in Dartmouth in 1815, and Professor of the Theory and Practice of Physic in that Institution in 1820, which office he held till the year 1836, when he resigned, and was appointed Professor, I believe, of the same branches in the Ohio Medical College at Cincinnati, and of the same, and perhaps of some other branches at Bowdoin College, Brunswick, Maine. He was also Professor of Moral and Intellectual Philosophy at Dartmouth College, and of Materia Medica and Botany. He was a Fellow of the American Academy of Arts and Sciences, and an Honorary Member of the Mass. Medical Society. Before his decease, which occurred in the year 1842, he received the degree of Doctor of Laws from some one of our colleges, I believe from Harvard, but not having the latest catalogue before me, I am not absolutely able to determine. Were I able to procure as many facts in relation to his private, as to his public history, I might fill a small volume. One thing is certain. So many honors could not have been conferred upon him by different learned institutions unless he was worthy of receiving them. I lament the paucity of materials for a more full biography of him, and shall avail myself of a few observations in relation to him by my friend Dr. J. V. C. Smith, in his Medical Journal of June 15th, 1842.

'Medical scholars throughout the United States, must necessarily be familiar with the name and distinguished attainments of the late Daniel Oliver, M. D., LL. D., who died at Cambridge, Mass., on the first of June. He was a man of mild deportment, gentlemanly in his intercourse, and remarkable for the purity and moral worth of his character. Dr. Oliver made no high pretensions—was never obtrusive nor was he ever known to deviate from the upright course of a Christian physician. He entertained correct views of the subjects of life, and, in all his movements with the world, seemed to act under a deep feeling of responsibility to a higher Power. In the character of a teacher of medical science, he was regarded in the light of a sound methodical philosopher, who reasoned from facts. A theory might entertain him, but until some tangible evidence of the truth of a proposition could be established, his understanding never readily assented to it. He was eminently correct in the chair: the students felt that they were guided by an honest man, who knew all that was known on the subject on which he discoursed. With indefatigable perseverance, authors of all epochs and of all languages too, of estimation in literature, contributed to enlarge the boundaries of his knowledge, and thus to enhance the value of his lectures. There was no meteoric display of learning in the lecture room—no attempt at brilliancy of expression, or untimely throes of wit. A calm, dignified manner, that commanded both respect and attention, characterized the public exercises of the Professor. That quiet manner which marked the habitually thoughtful man—evidencing the power and majesty of a cultivated intellect—was strikingly manifested in the good man whose death is now deplored. He was not one of those inapproachable literary giants, who maintain an ascendency over those less learned than himself, by keeping wholly out of sight. All who knew him loved him, and he loved all who loved God.

To strangers he sometimes had the appearance of coldness and reserve ; but this should be attributed to

his supposing that they could feel no particular interest in him, rather than to any want of kindness of
heart or philanthropy. He was a man of erudition,
delighted much in the perusal of the works of the
Greek and Latin poets, philosophers and historians,
in their original languages. Nor was his acquaintance less with German and French authors. He had
an exquisite taste in music, and was a tolerably good
performer on the piano. He delighted greatly in
metaphysical speculations, and his views were characteristic of great acuteness and vigor of perception,
subtlety of discrimination and original and unexpected deductions. As a member of society his dealings
with others were dictated by justice, religion and humanity. To preserve the *mens silic conscia recti* was
his principal aim in all things, and though easily persuaded and yielding to the requests or persuasions
of others, as to matters merely indifferent, in other
cases, especially where honor or conscience was concerned, he was known to be perfectly inflexible, and
a striking example of the *justum tenacem, propositi
virum.* A few days before his death, he assured a
friend sitting by his bedside, that in his situation ' he
found the consolations of religion unspeakable.'

Such were the prominent traits of this excellent
physician. Aside from a variety of scientific and
literary productions of which he was the known author, his large work on philosophy, widely circulated in this and other countries, will be a permanent
record of his fame. The science of life was studied
by Dr. Oliver with indefatigable industry. Life, however, was too short for the accomplishment of the

53

many benevolent designs of such a mind.   Conscious
of the approach of death, he looked forward with the
confidence of a Christian—believing that this was
only the commencement of a never ending existence.'

Dr. Joseph Parrish.   I am indebted for the memoir of the life and character of this distinguished
physician, to a discourse delivered by George B.
Wood, M. D. before the Medical Society of Philadelphia, October 23d, 1840, for a notice of him,
which I have taken the liberty to abridge.

Dr. Parrish was born on the 2d of September,
1779.   He received a good English education, and
was taught Latin at the Friends' school in Fourth
Street, at that time in considerable repute as a place
of instruction in the learned languages.   He afterwards paid some attention to French, and still later
in life to the Hebrew, which he cultivated exclusively
in reference to the study of the Bible.   He could
not, however, be said to have a decided literary turn ;
and, though he took care to qualify himself well as a
physician by a somewhat extensive course of medical
reading, and in the few leisure intervals of a very
active life occasionally perused works of general interest, yet he was indebted, as well for his professional skill as for his extensive knowledge of men and
things, less to books than to an extraordinary faculty
of observation and a memory unusually tenacious of
facts.   He nevertheless always attached great importance to mental culture, and in his last will, while
giving directions in relation to the education of his

children, he expresses the sentiment that he would rather a child of his should expend every cent of his inheritance in the acquisition of knowledge than that he should arrive at maturity in the possession of a large estate without the advantage of scientific attainments.

The moral and religious education of Dr. Parrish was of the most guarded kind. He was brought up in strict conformity with the principles and habits of the Society of Friends, and early in life received strong religious impressions, which preserved him in a remarkable degree from the temptations of a warm and lively temperament. From some notes which he left behind him, made about the commencement of his medical studies, it appears that even in youth he was under the habitual guidance of that inward principle, in which the Friends recognize the Divine Spirit operating upon the mind, and the reality of which is one of the prominent points of their religious faith.

But while thus moral according to the strictest rules of his self-denying sect, he indulged freely in the innocent sports and recreations of boyhood, and was distinguished among his companions by his skill in various athletic exercises. He was a swift runner, a good swimmer and an excellent skater. This accomplishment he carried with him into manhood ; and it is related of him when in middle age, and in full reputation as a physician, that having occasion to make an occasional visit during winter, on the opposite side of the river, he accepted from a friend the loan of a pair of skates, and astonished the spectators by some of those complicated and graceful evolutions which have now become almost an affair of tradition among us. His aversion to confinement and fondness for the fresh air never forsook him. Throughout the whole course of his life, he could not tolerate a close and heated apartment, slept always in summer with his windows up, and even during illness found a degree of coolness essential to his comfort which was almost hazardous to his attendants. There is no doubt that his personal predilection influenced greatly his course of practice; and long before the profession generally, in this place, were prepared to adopt the plan, he had introduced into the treatment of various diseases a system of exercise, exposure to cool air, and free indulgence in cool and refreshing drinks, which to the great comfort of the patient, and success of the physician, have at length, in many instances, superseded the old system of drugs, warm beverage and confinement.

His youthful partialities were strongly directed towards the study of medicine; and those among his early friends who afterwards witnessed his extraordinary professional success, took pleasure in recalling many evidences which he had exhibited, even in boyhood, of a natural turn and natural qualifications for this pursuit. He was fond of reading upon diseases, exhibited an instinctive disposition to visit and nurse the sick, and in the absence of other modes of indulging his propensity towards the healing art, is said to have exercised his skill upon the inferior animals, and to have exhibited some dexterity in the treatment of their fractured limbs. The fears of his parents,

singular panic at that time prevalent throughout the country. An individual was found dead in his bed, and a living worm along with him of that kind which frequents the Lombardy poplar, and is thence commonly called poplar worm. The public somewhat unphilosophically leaped to the conclusion that this worm and the sudden death were in the relation of cause and effect. Rumor speedily collected numerous confirmatory observations; in the hot bed of popular fear suspicions quickly ripened into facts; and the belief became to be very widely diffused that this species of worm was exceedingly venomous, and that a frightful death was lurking in every Lombardy poplar in the country. A war of extermination commenced both against the worm and the tree which sheltered it. The one was slaughtered without mercy, the other given every where to the axe and the flames; and our streets would soon have been left without shade but for the timely publication of the experiments alluded to, which conclusively proved that the worms were harmless and the Lombardy poplar as guiltless of any noxious influence as it was of any extraordinary beauty.

But the event, which in the early career of our late friend contributed most to make him favorably known to the public, was the delivery of a course of popular lectures on Chemistry, which he gave first in the winter of 1807–8, and repeated afterwards in successive years. Popular lectures on scientific subjects were then a novelty in Philadelphia. He endeavored to give his instructions a practical bearing upon the ordinary pursuits of life, mingled with chemical details,

various physiological observations, calculated to obviate the too natural tendency of the uninstructed
to empiricism, and took advantage of the numerous
opportunities offered by his subject to illustrate the
wisdom and goodness of Providence.

In the mean time he had been attending diligently
to practice, and was acquiring in the arduous labors
of the Philadelphia Dispensary, that experience of
disease which was necessary to confidence in himself,
and to inspire confidence in those who might from
other causes be disposed to favor him.   He was
chosen one of the physicians of the Institution in
1806, and continued to serve it zealously until the
increase of his private business compelled him to
withdraw.   Upon his resignation in 1812, he received
the thanks of the managers ' for the faithful discharge
of the duties of his office for six years and a half.'
In 1818 he was elected a Manager, and in 1835 was
appointed one of the consulting physicians of the
Institution ; and the latter station was sustained by
him to the time of his death.

In 1808, about three years after he had commenced
practice, having been so far successful as to feel justified in incurring the additional expenses of a family,
he married a young lady from Burlington, the daughter of John Cox, one of the most respectable citizens
of New Jersey, and then, as at present, a highly esteemed preacher in the Society of Friends.   This
connection was in every way happy for Dr. Parrish.
It threw an almost uninterrupted sunshine over the
course of his domestic life, and surrounded him at its
close with the consoling sympathies of a large and

most affectionate family, whose love and reverence he had earned by a cordial participation in their feelings, and an ever active yet well regulated interest in their welfare. His wife survived him, and he never had to mourn the loss of a child. Few men have been more exempt from the miseries which too frequently invade the domestic circle, and few have better deserved such exemption.

There has been, perhaps, no example in Philadelphia of more rapid professional success, than that which fell to the lot of Dr. Parrish. Various causes contributed to this result. One was the patronage of the Society of Friends; and the countenance of Dr. Wistar, who on frequent occasions, exhibited confidence in the skill of his former pupil, and took every opportunity of promoting his professional interests. But it was undoubtedly to his own qualifications and efforts that he was chiefly indebted. He had already acquired a large practice, and was growing rapidly in reputation, when, in the winter of 1812–13, the great typhus epidemic, which so long scourged this country, made its appearance in Philadelphia, and elevated him at once into the foremost rank in his profession. Physicians were not generally prepared to recognize a disease of debility associated with apparently violent inflammation, and were in the beginning too apt to overlook the tendency to prostration which lurked fatally beneath the show of excitement. The attention of Dr. Parrish was strongly directed to the subject by the perusal of a treatise by Dr. North, who had seen so much of the disease in New Eng-

54

land, and who strenuously advocated the stimulant treatment. His aversion to theory in medicine left him open to the evidence of facts, however opposed to prevailing opinions; and he was quite prepared to encounter the disease by methods which had stood the test of experience, rather than by those which analogy would alone appear to indicate. The epidemic approached Philadelphia through New Jersey, and hung for awhile over the opposite shore of the Delaware before it burst upon our city. The inhabitants were alarmed by reports of a terrible disease in the town of Camden, which appeared to bid defiance to medicine. Dr. Parrish was called in to the aid of the physicians of the neighborhood. At the period of his first visit several cases had occurred, and all proved fatal. He was told that the disease was of an inflammatory nature, and had been treated by the lancet and other depletory measures. Its malignant aspect at once struck his attention. He saw through the veil of inflammation which it had thrown over its ghastly features, and beheld the deadly weakness beneath it. He advised an immediate abandonment of the lancet, and the substitution of an actively stimulant treatment. The effects were most happy. Numbers now got well, where before, all had died. A disease supposed to be almost incurable was found to be, in the great majority of cases, under the control of medicine. The terrors of the first awful reports gave way before the happier intelligence which followed; and the newly inspired confidence was directed especially towards the author of the change.

When the epidemic reached the city he pursued the stimulant plan of treatment, and his success was unrivalled.

From the commencement of his professional life he had exhibited an inclination towards surgery, which he cultivated assiduously whenever opportunities were offered. Towards the close of the year 1806 he was elected Surgeon to the Philadelphia Almshouse, where he had an ample field for observation and experience, especially in that branch of the surgical art always highest in his esteem, which aims at repairing injuries by a judicious employment of the resources of the system, and so far from seeking occasion for painful or deforming operations, endeavors to render them unnecessary. His reputation as a surgeon was of slower growth, but scarcely less distinguished in the end than that which belonged to him as a medical practitioner. His skill in diagnosis and judgment in the choice of therapeutical measures were highly appreciated by his medical brethren by whom he was constantly called into consultation, not only in Philadelphia, but also in the country for many miles around it. As an operator also he took rank with the most prominent surgeons of the city, and at the period of life when his physical powers were at their height, was second only to Dr. Physick, either in the number and magnitude of the operations which he performed, or in the extent of his reputation.

In addition to his station in the Almshouse Institution, he was, in the year 1816, elected Surgeon to the Pennsylvania Hospital as successor to Dr. Physick, and continued to discharge the duties in the two

offices conjointly for about six years. His place in
the Pennsylvania Hospital he continued to retain till
1829, when the state of his health, which was at that
time feeble, and a disposition to relinquish the more
fatiguing and severe offices of surgery to younger
hands, induced him to withdraw entirely from his
professional connection with the public institutions.
He considered the decline of bodily strength in a
surgeon as an intimation from nature that the period
for active service had passed; and I have often heard
him say that the necessity of using spectacles was
regarded by him as a call of duty to shun operations
in which a jet of blood from a divided artery might
occasion temporary blindness.

It was in the Almshouse Infirmary that he first
attracted notice by his clinical lectures, and laid the
foundation of that reputation as a medical teacher
which he sustained. In his regular rounds among
the patients, both in this Institution and the Pennsylvania Hospital, he seldom omitted an opportunity
of giving useful practical lessons to the students who
attended him; and so attractive was his manner, and
so obvious the high motives by which he was actuated, that large numbers constantly followed him, who
afterwards carried home with them, into almost all
parts of the Union, a great and affectionate respect
for his virtues, talents and attainments.

A natural consequence of his growing reputation
as a practitioner and clinical lecturer, was a great
increase of private pupils. He was seldom without
one or more students, even from the commencement
of his practice; but it was not till the year 1814 or

1815 that this number became considerable. From this period they rapidly increased till they amounted at length to about thirty ; a number at that time quite unprecedented in this country among physicians not immediately connected with the great medical schools, and equalled, I believe, only in one instance when this advantage was possessed by the teacher. Young men came to study with him from the various parts of the Union ; but the greater number were from Philadelphia and its immediate neighborhood ; and as this was the place where he was best known, and no extraneous motives influenced the choice of the pupils, the fact speaks strongly in favor not only of his reputation, but also of his real merit. Among the present practitioners of this city, there are, I presume, more of his former pupils, than of those educated by any other physician. He was in the habit of lecturing to the young gentlemen in his office twice a week during almost the whole year, in the winter upon surgery, and in the summer on the practice of medicine ; giving in his lectures not so much that elementary knowledge which is to be derived from books, as the result of his own experience and reflection.

About the year 1818, he was induced by the great increase of his pupils, and by his own oppressive engagements, to procure assistance in the instruction of his class, especially in those elementary branches of medicine which, though apt in their minutiæ to escape the recollection of practitioners, are nevertheless indispensable to the student as the basis of all professional knowledge. The extent of this aid was gradually increased, till at length courses of lectures were delivered every year upon Chemistry, Anatomy and Materia Medica, to which Midwifery was afterwards added ; as he himself never cultivated this branch of our art, and did not feel himself competent to teach it. Besides lectures, a regular series of minute examinations upon all the different branches of our art was also instituted ; so that a complete system of private instruction sprung up under his hands, which, if not antecedent to others of a similar character, was certainly original with himself and those who assisted him. Dr. Parrish, therefore, may be looked upon as one of the founders of that combined and more thorough scheme of private medical tuition, which constitutes a distinguishing professional feature of our city and our times ; and upon this ground alone would have claims to a most favorable place in our relations.

He sustained this system of medical instruction with a number of pupils varying from ten to thirty, till the year 1830, when he yielded to the influence of an institution conducted upon a plan somewhat similar to his own, but combining the talent and professional weight of some of the most prominent physicians in this city, of whom, moreover, several had the advantage of being connected with the most flourishing medical school in the country.

But his peculiar abilities as a lecturer were not yet lost to the medical community. An association of physicians was formed called the ' Philadelphia Association for Medical Instruction,' at the head of which he allowed his name to be placed, and in which he continued to labor faithfully as long as it existed. The object of this association was not to compete with the public schools, but merely to afford· to the private pupils of the members those advantages which were enjoyed by others, and which it was not in the power of one individual to bestow. It continued in successful operation for about six years, when it was dissolved in consequence chiefly of the advancing age of its chief supporter, who began to feel that he had borne his share in the burthens of the day, and was justified in withdrawing from a portion, at least, of the labors, which, though they had not surpassed his energies or will in the prime of life, began now to press heavily upon him.

Though occupied as we have seen, Dr. Parrish found time to contribute various medical and surgical papers to the journals, all of which are characteristic of his practical tone of mind, and some highly valuable. They are contained chiefly in the Eclectic Repertory, of which he was one of the editors, and in the North American Medical and Surgical Journal. Among them may be mentioned, as worthy of special attention, ' Observations on a peculiar catarrhal complaint in children.' ' On infantile convulsions arising from intestinal spasm.' ' On mammæ liable to be mistaken for cancer.' ' On pulmonary consumption,' and, ' On the connection between external scrofula and pulmonary consumption.' His remarks on the last mentioned disease are highly interesting, not only from their intrinsic value, but also from the fact that his views in relation to its treatment, were justified by the result in his own case.

Attacked when a young man, by a complaint of the chest, which he believed to be of a consumptive character, instead of confining himself to his chamber, and going through a long course of medicine, as was then fatally common, he adopted the plan which he always recommended to his patients, of vigorous exercise in the pure air. Most of you recollect the unpretending vehicle in which he was accustomed to pay his daily professional visits. It was without springs, and its jolting movement over our rough pavements was any thing but comfortable to its occupants. This, however, was its recommendation with the Doctor, who thus imitated as nearly as possible, the effects of horseback exercise, and combined the pursuit of health with that of business. He entirely recovered from his pectoral affection. After his death, dissection revealed tuberculous cicatrices in the upper portion of each lung, and thus proved both the correctness of his diagnosis, and the efficacy of his plan of treatment. In addition to the above papers he republished Lawrence on Hernia with an Appendix, and, a few years before his death, put forth a work of his own upon Hernia and Diseases of the Urinary organs.

In the midst of his private engagements, he participated largely in the proceedings of those medical associations whose constitution and objects he could cordially approve. He was long an active member of the College of Physicians, in which he held successively the offices of Secretary, Censor and Vice President, and in all whose transactions he took a lively interest. Of the Medical Society of Philadelphia he was a zealous member, and at the time of life in which we are now considering him, was one of its most efficient speakers. They who are old enough to remember the highly animating scenes which took place in the Medical Society about twenty years since, cannot have forgotten the prominent share in the debates taken by Dr. Parrish, nor the life and vigor, yet perfect good nature and amiableness which characterized his style of speaking. His undaunted opposition to the assaults which the theory of Broussais was then making upon the old medical opinions, was fruitful in interest and results. It was on one of these occasions that he brought before the Society the stomachs of recently slaughtered animals, to show that those post mortem appearances which had been considered as proofs of pre-existing inflammation were often present in cases of violent death occurring in perfect health. He was for some time Vice President of the Medical Society. That he did not hold a higher station, was owing to an invincible repugnance on his own part to stand in the way of what might be considered the just and reasonable claims of others; and not only here, but in all other places, he would accept of no office, the access to which might be over the disappointed hopes or wounded feelings of a medical brother.

But his sympathies were not confined within the limits of his profession. In common with the Friends, he was opposed to the Institution of slavery, and he was averse to capital punishments for any crime. Whatever he engaged in he entered into it with all

55

his soul. He was a zealous elder in the church to which he belonged.

After having accumulated a sufficiency of this world's goods, he gradually curtailed his business. There was a short period after he had begun to contract his business, during which he again put forth all his energies and labored with the spirit and activity of youth. This was during the prevalence of the epidemic cholera in Philadelphia. At the approach of this disease he felt like the veteran warrior, who, while resting upon his laurels, hears the distant sounds of invasion, and rushes once more eagerly to the contest.

His life was at no time a life of idleness. Few things were more abhorrent to his nature than mental inactivity; and in his last illness he considered as among his greatest trials, that debility of mind which he felt to be stealing over him a few days before his close. Even in the intervals of business, his intellect was ever active. He has often told me that many of his peculiar views, both professional and otherwise, were the result of his reflection during his solitary rides from house to house, in pursuit of his business. His last years, therefore, though less cumbered by almost overwhelming engagements than those of his earlier life, were still fully and profitably occupied. Besides attending to his restricted practice, to his duties as the father of a large family, and a prominent member of the church, and the care of a not inconsiderable estate, he participated also in various public concerns of a useful or charitable character.

He was especially active in the organization and subsequent management of the Wills Hospital for the lame and blind ; and was President of the Board of Managers in this Institution from its commencement to the time of his death.

The practice of operative surgery occasioned him often great distress especially in children, upon whom he never inflicted pain without appearing to suffer it in his own person ; and operations in infantile cases at length became so distasteful to him, that he avoided them whenever he could do so with propriety.

Nor was the benevolence of Dr. Parrish merely of a passive character. It was, on the contrary, highly practical. When he had reason to suspect that his patients were poor, he would often endeavor to satisfy himself of the truth by the most delicate means in his power, and would then contrive, in a manner least offensive to their feelings, to avoid receiving compensation for his services, without leaving behind an oppressive sense of obligation. He never, on any occasion, exacted payment of a medical fee ; and so strong was his aversion to compulsory modes of collecting debts of this nature, that in his will he expressly and strictly enjoins on his executors to put no claim on his account of medical services into legal suit. He made it a point not to charge for attendance in cases of injury received by firemen in the discharge of their duty.

Cruelty, oppression, and every form of injustice were abhorrent to his nature. This same feeling was extended towards the brute creation. The animals which he had occasion to use were always treated with the greatest kindness ; and the provision made in his Will for the old age of a favorite horse which had served him long and faithfully, is generally known. Old Lyon was a remarkable brute, and almost as well known in Pennsylvania as his master. The dog-like docility with which he followed at the word of the Doctor, and the sagacity with which, when left to himself, he moved off with the vehicle to some shady spot in summer, or to some sheltered position in winter, were subjects of almost universal remark.

In all his pecuniary transactions, Dr. Parrish was scrupulously just. He did not feel himself authorized to take advantage of another in a bargain, and never incurred any responsibility which he was not fully able to meet. His conscientiousness also was exhibited in various other ways.

In his medical lectures he felt himself bound, in detailing his experience, not to conceal his mistakes, so that the pupil might have the benefit not only of his successes as an example, but also of his missteps as a warning. Few are capable of this magnanimity, the great majority being satisfied if they tell only the truth, without in all instances telling the whole truth. One of the most striking instances of the influence of a sense of duty over his conduct, was in his declining to take the office of Professor of Anatomy in the University of Pennsylvania, which he believed and I have no doubt upon the best grounds, to have been at one time within his reach.

To the practice of surgery he was happily adapted by the same qualities and in addition, by those essential physical requisites, a good eye, a steady hand, and general firmness of nerve.

Towards the sick the deportment of Dr. Parrish was most happy. The cheering smile with which he accosted his patients, his soothing kindness, his encouraging and confident manner while there was still ground for hope, and his affectionate sympathy and consolation when hope was over, remain indelibly impressed on the grateful recollection of thousands in this city. He was frequently consulted by his patients in the capacity of a friend and counsellor as well as physician, and thus became the confidant of many private concerns, which he always considered as a sacred trust committed to his honor. He was scrupulously careful never to violate professional confidence. Perhaps in no respect did Dr. Parrish appear to greater advantage than in his relations with his professional brethren. It was one of his maxims that no physician could have a satisfactory professional standing who disregarded the good will and good opinion of his fellow practitioners. He held in abhorrence that meanness of spirit which, for a little apparent profit, would insinuate evil of a brother, or even assent by silence to a mistaken estimate of his worth. No medical man could long remain in a hostile attitude towards Dr. Parrish.

From a regard for his fellow practitioners it may be inferred that he had pleasure in meeting them in consultation. He had none of the jealousy which fears a rival in every person with whom he may be associated in attendance, nor of the overweening and arrogant self-esteem which owns no fallibility of judgment. It was his custom, whenever he supposed his patient or his friends might derive additional aid, or when the case was one of a doubtful or embarrassing nature, to offer a consultation; and when a suggestion to this effect came from the patient himself, he always promptly gave his assent, however inferior in age and standing might be his proposed associate.

Another trait which favorably distinguished his intercourse with the profession, was an extraordinary punctuality in the fulfillment of his engagements. In consultations he very rarely failed to meet at the time appointed; and so jealous was he of his character in this respect, that it was a habit with him to present his watch when he was second in entering the house, in order to prove that he was not after his time.

Towards the younger members of the profession he conducted himself in a manner calculated to win their affection as well as respect. It was a fine trait in his character, and one which has endeared him to many now present, that when any of his young friends, through accident or other cause, acquired a footing in families which he had been in the habit of attending, instead of feeling unkindly, or endeavoring in any way to interfere with their interests, he seemed to enjoy their success, and took pains to strengthen the impressions in their favor through the influence which his long professional intercourse with the families naturally gave him.

As a teacher, without having cultivated either rhetoric or oratory as an art, he was a fluent and by no means inaccurate speaker, and when under the impulse of high principles or strong feeling, was often truly eloquent, attracting the fixed attention of the audience, and carrying their whole sympathies along with him. His instructions did not consist of labored treatises upon disease, presenting in a regular and compact arrangement all that was known upon the subject. They were rather vivid pictures of experience, in which the pupil was enabled to see the very events as they passed, and to see them too with the trained eyes of their preceptor. They were made to enter into the very case, to share in the reflections, hopes and fears of the speaker, and thus to take an almost personal interest in the progress and termination of the disease. His lessons became, in fact, to his pupils, a sort of experience of their own.

It now remains to consider Dr. Parrish in the closing scenes of life. This is the touchstone which tries the value of the past, and distinguishes what was sterling worth, from the false glitter of profession and the deception of self-esteem. He can only be said to have been truly happy in life whose end is happy. To the friends of Dr. Parrish it is a source of the purest satisfaction, that he passed successfully through the last and severest trial, and that the close of his career was in harmony with its whole course. He was attacked in the summer of 1839 by the disease which ultimately proved fatal, but continued to attend to his various avocations, though somewhat irregularly, till about the beginning of the present year (1840) when he confined himself to his house on account of a severe bronchial affection, superadded to his former complaint. From this he partially recovered, so as to be able to ride out occasionally, and even visit patients; but he suddenly became worse, about the close of February, and taking to his bed, continued to sink gradually for nearly three weeks, and died on the 18th of March, in the sixty-first year of his age. Though somewhat lethargic towards the conclusion of the disease, he was capable, when roused, of thinking with perfect clearness, and of fully appreciating his condition, till a day or two before death. In the midst of much bodily distress, and great derangement of his nervous system, he preserved unimpaired those amiable traits of character by which he was distinguished in health, frequently expressing a grateful sense of the kindness of those who administered to him, and carefully avoiding any expression which could wound their feelings. With the full conviction of the fatal character of his disease, and with the near prospect of its termination he was perfectly calm and self-possessed, made all the necessary arrangements in his affairs, spoke to his family as a tender husband and father solicitous for their present and eternal welfare might be expected to speak, and uniformly expressed his reliance upon the goodness and mercy of Providence, and his hope of a happy hereafter. Under the feeling of his utter bodily prostration, he used to say to his physicians that he was like a log of wood on the Delaware, floating about at the discretion of the winds and waves. At one of their latest visits, when hearing and sight were failing, and the power of articulation were almost gone, he repeated this expressive figure, and could just be heard

to say in addition, 'but even the log on the Delaware has its care taker.' Thus the reliance upon a superintending Providence, which was one of the governing principles of his life, did not fail him in death.

The almost unprecedented array of his fellow citizens of all classes who attended his remains to the grave, the general expression of regret for his loss, and the measures taken by the various bodies to which he belonged, to procure some public commemoration of his worth and services, are evidences of a general esteem and affection such as seldom fall to the lot of individuals unconnected with public life. Perhaps no one was personally known more extensively in the city, or had connected himself by a greater variety of beneficent services with every ramification of society. It is true that no marble has been erected over his remains, and that the very spot where they are laid will soon be undistinguishable to every eye save that of conjugal or filial love; yet the remembrance which he has left behind him, the only monument which the rules of his unostentatious sect allow, is far more precious than the praises of carved stone, which gold may purchase or power command. Should this humble tribute to his worth add in the least to the brightness or the direction of that remembrance, the author will feel the sweet reward of having paid a double debt to gratitude and to truth.

Dr. PHILIP SYNG PHYSICK. I am indebted to a memoir of this distinguished American Surgeon, by J. Randolph, M. D., of Philadelphia, read before the

56

Philadelphia Medical Society, and somewhat abridged by Dr. Hays, and published in the American Medical Journal for May, 1839, for the data and facts on which this biography is founded, and principally for the language also.

Philip Syng Physick was born in Philadelphia, on the 7th of July, 1768. His father, Mr. Edward Physick, was an Englishman, and was characterized for possessing strong mental powers, with which were united strict integrity and considerable knowledge of the world. Previously to the separation of the United States from Great Britain, he held the office of keeper of the Great Seal of the Colony of Pennsylvania, and subsequently to the Revolution, he took charge of the estates belonging to the Penn family, and served as their confidential agent. Dr. Physick's mother was a most estimable, pious woman, who was blessed with a strong intellect, and evinced throughout her life, great judgment and decision of character. The Doctor never ceased to feel and express the greatest filial love and reverence for those honored parents. He frequently declared that he was convinced that whatever was most useful and excellent in his character, was attributable to the early lessons and impressions which he imbibed from them.

By such parents as these, the greatest care and attention would naturally be bestowed upon their children. Fortunately, his father had succeeded by great industry and attention to business, in accumulating a property, which in those days was looked upon as considerable, and being thus in possession of ample means, he was enabled to carry out fully the plan of education which he designed for his son.

In doing so, Dr. Physick informed me that his father was influenced by a degree of liberality very unusual in that, or indeed, in any other age. Double fees, which he uniformly transmitted to the teacher, testified the great importance which he attached to a liberal education, and the value which he thought should be set upon the sources from which it emanated. This was not only intended for an encouragement to the instructor to use his best endeavors on behalf of his pupil, but because the donor believed the charges for tuition at that day were not a fair equivalent for the services rendered.

Mr. Physick placed his son, when eleven years of age, in the Academy belonging to the Society of Friends, in South Fourth Street, under the tuition of Robert Proud. At this period, Mr. Physick resided in the country, on the banks of the Schuylkill, several miles from the city, at an estate belonging to the Penn family. To facilitate the education of his son, he boarded him in the city, in the family of the late Mr. John Todd, the father-in-law of the present venerable Mrs. Madison. Even at that early age the subject of our memoir exhibited strong indications of those well regulated habits of order and method which adhered to him so closely through life.

Young Mr. Physick remained at this academy until he entered the collegiate department of the University of Pennsylvania. He then passed through the usual course of studies prescribed in that institution, and took the degree of Bachelor of Arts in

May, 1785. In June, 1785, he commenced the study of medicine under the superintendence of the late Dr. Adam Kuhn, well known as the pupil of Linnæus, and a most distinguished and successful practitioner, and then Professor of the Theory and Practice of Medicine in the University of Pennsylvania. Of the particular motives which influenced young Mr. Physick in the choice of this profession, I am unable to speak. It does not appear that he at that period evinced any strong predilection for this department of science. Probably he was in a great degree governed by the wishes of his father; and so strong were his feelings of filial obedience that I am very certain that he would at any time readily have yielded his own wishes to those of his parents. The following anecdote is traditionary in the family. His father while handling a knife, had the misfortune to cut one of his fingers; and the wound proved to be so severe that he was obliged to engage the services of a medical friend. Upon one occasion his son begged of him to be permitted to apply the necessary dressings and bandage to the finger; his father consented, and was so much surprised at the great skill and dexterity which his son displayed in making the applications, that he determined to make him a surgeon.

If it be true that we are indebted so exclusively to Mr. Physick for directing his son's attention to the study of medicine, to what an immeasurable extent does it not increase the amount of obligation and gratitude that we owe him?

Dr. Physick was remarkable through life for feelings of the most acute and susceptible nature. It may be truly said of him that he possessed a soul feelingly alive to the miseries and sufferings of others. He could not himself support pain·with an ordinary degree of fortitude, and it is undeniable, that he was extremely unwilling to inflict it upon others. This tenderness of feeling, which existed strongly in the days of his youth, continued in full force as long as he lived. He used frequently to declare at this period of his life, that he could never be a surgeon. Little was he aware that he was destined to afford a complete illustration of the position, that the practice of medicine and surgery, so far from hardening and rendering callous the feelings, has a direct contrary tendency, and serves pre-eminently to soften and refine them. His example, as well as the result of our whole experience upon this subject, demonstrates that for a man to become a great and good surgeon, it is absolutely necessary for him to possess to the fullest extent, the best and kindest feelings of our nature.

The following incident, which occurred to Dr. Physick, and which was in fact characteristic, may not be deemed uninteresting. Soon after he commenced the study of medicine, it was announced that an amputation would be performed upon a certain day, at the Pennsylvania Hospital. His preceptor, Professor Kuhn, wished him to witness this operation, but understanding perfectly well the peculiar temperament of his pupil, he advised his father to accompany him ; and fortunately too, inasmuch as Dr. Physick became so sick during the operation, that it was

necessary that he should be led from the amphitheatre
before it was concluded.

Dr. Physick continued his medical studies under
the superintendence of Professor Kuhn, for three
years. In those days it was customary for the student
of medicine, previously to obtaining the honors of
the doctorate, to go through a much more extensive
course of reading than is now deemed necessary.
By the direction of his preceptor, Dr. Physick read
through most diligently and faithfully many voluminous works of the older medical writers, some of
which, if not absolutely obsolete at the present day,
are only used as works of reference. We have abundance of evidence, that even at that early period of
life, Dr. Physick evinced the most resolute determination to qualify himself by every possible means, for
assuming a most useful and honorable standing in his
profession; and there cannot be a question but that
he must have gleaned from amidst this great mass of
laborious reading, much valuable information, which
he subsequently applied to a most valuable purpose.

Dr. Physick's whole deportment during his pupilage,
was so perfectly correct and satisfactory, as to merit
the entire approbation of Professor Kuhn; and it is
well known that Dr. Physick always cherished feelings of the warmest affection and regard for his venerable instructor.

In addition to the instruction which Dr. Physick
received from Professor Kuhn, he attended, at this period, the medical lectures delivered in the University
of Pennsylvania. He did not, however, graduate in
medicine in that institution. The opportunities for

the acquisition of medical knowledge offered by the schools and hospitals of this country, then in its infancy, were too limited to satisfy either his conscience or his ambition. He could not convince his mind that his knowledge of medicine was sufficiently enlarged to warrant him in assuming the deep and important responsibilities attendant upon the practice of a profession which involved the lives and happiness of his fellow creatures. For the completion of his education, he entertained an ardent desire to visit Great Britain, and to avail himself of the advantages which were afforded by the great schools and hospitals of London and Edinburgh. His father happily coincided with these views and determined upon accompanying his son to Europe. Accordingly they embarked in November, 1788, and arrived in London in January, 1789.

Dr. Physick's sole object in going abroad was to acquire medical information. He had no desire to partake of the gaieties and amusements of an European capital. Fortunately for Dr. Physick, his father's connexions in London were such, that he was enabled to introduce his son to some of the most learned and polished society of that great metropolis. An intercourse of this kind created for him an influence and gave him opportunities by means of which his cherished views were considerably promoted. All who ever saw Dr. Physick must have been struck with the exceeding dignity and courteousness of his manner. For this no doubt he was principally indebted to nature, though it must have been improved and confirmed by his association with the elevated society which he enjoyed whilst abroad. By means of this same influence, Mr. Physick succeeded in securing the consent of Mr. John Hunter, then one of the most celebrated anatomists and surgeons of the age, to receive the subject of our memoir under his immediate care and tuition.

Dr. Physick considered this the most important era in his professional life. He early became convinced of the extraordinary advantages which he might derive from this connection with Mr. Hunter, and proceeded accordingly to devote himself with the most ardent zeal to the study of practical anatomy and surgery. By dint of constant and unwearied application to his studies, aided, also, by a course of unceasing and untiring dissections, he soon made rapid advancement in the attainment of his objects, and what was also of much consequence, secured to himself the approbation and esteem of his great master. Mr. Hunter in fact was so well pleased with the zeal, industry and correct deportment of Dr. Physick, that he took pleasure in acknowledging him as a favorite pupil, and bestowed upon him, with the most unreserved confidence, the full benefit of his advice and experience. During this period Dr. Physick attended regularly the lectures delivered by Mr. John Clarke, and Dr. William Osborne on Midwifery.

Among the manuscript papers left by Dr. Physick, is a note book kept by him during his stay in England, in which he recorded such facts and incidents as came under his observation, which he supposed might be of service to him subsequently.

Dr. Physick continued to prosecute his studies with

the most exemplary perseverance and industry, under the immediate superintendence of Mr. Hunter, throughout the year 1789. On the first of Jan. 1790, he was appointed House Surgeon to St. George's Hospital for one year, the usual period of that service in the institution. This appointment he owed exclusively to the patronage and influence of Dr. Hunter. The advantages of such a situation to the student of medicine, in facilitating the acquisition of practical knowledge and skill, were of the utmost importance, and were so well known as to cause the place to be sought after by numerous applicants, most of whom, from the circumstance of their English birth alone, it might be supposed, could have had an influence which would have rendered them successful competitors against a foreigner for the place. Here were exemplified in the most happy manner the important advantages which Dr. Physick derived from the favorable impression which Mr. Hunter had imbibed respecting his general worth, his talents, and his acquirements. These considerations induced Mr. Hunter unhesitatingly to exert the whole of his influence in behalf of Dr. Physick, with what effect has been stated.

A few months after this period Dr. Physick had so severe an indisposition, that Mr. Hunter became alarmed about him, and was on the eve of insisting upon his return to America. This attack, no doubt, was principally owing to the laborious life which he led, and the close confinement to which he subjected himself. Providence, however, for its own wise and beneficent purposes, thought proper to restore him

57

to health, to the great delight and gratitude of his
parents and friends.

It was during the period of his remaining at St.
George's Hospital, that Dr. Physick acquired a vast
deal of that surgical skill and dexterity which laid the
foundation of his subsequent greatness. Having his
whole time occupied in administering to the wants
of such unhappy objects as were suffering from the
effects of accidents or disease ; continually engaged
in applying the necessary bandages and dressings to
fractured bones, dislocations, wounds and injuries of
every description, and seizing hold, as was his invari-
able custom, of every such opportunity of making
himself minutely acquainted with the most perfect
manner of performing these services, he soon became
remarkably expert in all his manipulations, and acquired a degree of experience which greatly increased his stock of practical knowledge. He indeed exhibited a degree of neatness and dexterity in the application of bandages and dressings never excelled
probably by any other surgeon.

During the period of his services in this institution,
he learned also the manner of constructing and con-
triving several kinds of instruments and apparatus
which he subsequently was the first to introduce into
this country, to the great benefit of our art.

An anecdote frequently related to me by Dr. Physick, connected with his early appointment to St.
George's Hospital, I may be pardoned for mentioning here, notwithstanding it has already been promulgated from another source. His success in obtaining this situation caused some slight degree of dis-

satisfaction on the part of some of the disappointed
applicants, who conceived that their claims for the
situation were stronger than his. In consequence of
this, Dr. Physick perceived that they evinced uncommon curiosity respecting his manner of discharging
his duties, and were disposed to scrutinize his actions with the greatest strictness. A short period after commencing his services, a patient was admitted into the hospital with dislocation of his shoulder,
the head of the humerus being lodged in the axilla.
Fortunately the accident was quite recent. It so
happened that at the time the man was admitted, the
whole class were in attendance at the house. They,
of course, were exceedingly anxious to witness the
manner in which the reduction could be effected, and
Dr. Physick was well aware that his method of restoring the bone to its natural position would be severely criticised. He directed the patient to be
seated on a high chair, and then proceeded to examine the injured shoulder, questioning the man as to
the manner in which the accident had occurred.
Whilst making these inquiries, he placed his left
hand in the axilla, and taking hold of the lower end of
the humerus with his right hand, he made all the extension in his power, then suddenly depressing the
elbow of the patient, he dislodged the head of the
bone, which glided instantaneously into the glenoid
cavity.

In relating this incident, Dr. Physick never assumed to himself much merit for his success, but rather
ascribed it, in a great degree, at least, to the favorable
nature of the case. His characteristic modesty, how-

ever, induced him to underrate his services; his success was doubtless principally owing to that unrivalled address and dexterity of which he subsequently proved himself so complete a master. The treatment of this case produced the most happy influence in promoting the interest and comfort of the Doctor during his stay in the Hospital. He stated that from that time forward he always enjoyed the uninterrupted regard and respect of the medical class.

In January, 1791, the period for which he had been elected to St. George's Hospital having expired, he quitted the institution, carrying with him the warmest testimonials from its proper authorities, of his medical qualifications, and also of his general good conduct. They went so far as to declare, that instead of considering him to lie under any obligations to the institution, they considered the institution indebted to him for the many benefits he had conferred upon its unhappy inmates, and for the useful results which had been produced by his singular zeal and abilities. He now received his diploma from the Royal College of Surgeons in London.

Soon after leaving St. George's Hospital, Dr. Physick received from Dr. Hunter a mark of respect and esteem, which was in the highest degree gratifying to him, and more particularly as it furnished conclusive evidence of Dr. Hunter's entire confidence in his professional skill and attainments. Mr. Hunter invited him to take up his residence with him, to become an inmate of his house, and to assist him in his professional business; he also held out inducements to him to establish himself permanently in London.

Notwithstanding the tempting nature of these offers, and the great advantages which Dr. Physick might have derived from accepting, it did not comport with either his own designs or those of his father, that he should exile himself from his native country. In accordance with the plan previously laid down for the completion of his medical education, he was to visit Edinburgh, in order to graduate in medicine in the University of that city. He, however, gratefully accepted Mr. Hunter's invitation to reside with him until this period should arrive; and accordingly he remained with Mr. Hunter, and assisted him, not only in his professional business, but also in the prosecution of his physiological experiments, and the making of anatomical preparations, until May, 1791, when he took his final leave of London. I may notice that his father had, previously to this period, returned to America.

The parting between Mr. Hunter and Dr. Physick was painful to the latter to an extreme degree, and certainly the most distressing event which occurred to him during his stay in London. The ties which bound him to Mr. Hunter were of no ordinary description. Mr. Hunter had not only extended towards him the warmest friendship and regard, but had also conferred invaluable benefits upon him by giving him the advantages of his powerful aid and influence, and by promoting, by all the means in his power, his medical researches. These obligations could only be acknowledged on the part of Dr. Physick, by the most sincere and ardent devotion to his beloved preceptor; and in fact the admiration felt for Mr. John Hunter by Dr. Physick, amounted to a species of veneration; he never ceased to consider him as the greatest man that ever adorned the medical profession. Could his honored master have been permitted to witness the closing career of his pupil, he would have felt himself amply recompensed by the rich harvest of fame and usefulness which the latter had gathered, in consequence of his valuable aid and instructions.

Immediately after his arrival in Edinburgh, Dr. Physick entered with his usual ardor upon the prosecution of his studies. He attended very diligently the medical lectures delivered in the University, visited constantly the Royal Infirmary, was a careful observer of the practice pursued in that Institution, and witnessed all the operations there performed. In May, 1792, having complied with all the requisitions demanded by the University, he obtained the degree of M. D. The subject of his thesis was apoplexy; and in compliance with the established regulations, it was written in the Latin language. The original manuscript of this essay which he first wrote in English, is now in my possession, and bears the most satisfactory evidence of having been prepared with a vast deal of careful attention.

To show the familiar knowledge of the Latin language which Dr. Physick possessed, I may relate the following anecdote. It is well known that the examinations for a medical degree in Edinburgh are conducted in Latin; and that there are many applicants for the honor who from not possessing a sufficient knowledge of that language, are compelled to have recourse to the aid of a class of men termed *grinders*, whose occupation consisted in preparing students, by a system of drilling which should render them competent to reply to such questions as were likely to be put to them. It so happened that, a short time previous to the examination, Dr. Physick was in company with a fellow student from this city, and in reply to some allusion made by his companion to these grinders, the Doctor stated that he should not seek their aid, but that he was determined to rely upon his own knowledge of the language to carry him safely through. His companion expressed much surprise at this statement, seeming to consider it as a vain boast on the part of Dr. Physick; and he intimated his doubts of the Doctor's capabilities, inquiring whether he meant to say that he possessed a sufficient knowledge of the Latin to enable him to carry on a conversation in that language, Dr. Physick satisfied him completely by instantly addressing him in the Latin, and continuing some time to converse with him in that language.

Dr. Physick returned to his native country in September, 1792, and commenced the practice of his profession in Philadelphia. His office was situated in Mulberry Street near Third. That Dr. Physick entered upon his practical career under the most favorable circumstances will, I think, be readily admitted. I have already shown that in addition to his own extraordinary qualifications, he had enjoyed the most ample opportunities of acquiring knowledge from sources distinguished alike for their exalted character and superior excellence. Nature also rendered her best aid for fitting him pre-eminently, by all external advantages, for the successful accomplishment of his objects. His personal appearance was commanding in the extreme. He was of a medium height; his countenance was noble and expressive; he had a large Roman nose; a mouth beautifully formed, the lips somewhat thin; a high forehead, and a fine penetrating hazel eye. The expression of his countenance was grave and dignified, yet often inclined to melancholy, more especially when he was engaged in deep thought, or in performing an important and critical operation. Dr. Physick rarely indulged in excessive mirth; he was, however, far from being insensible to playful humor, and on such occasions his countenance would be lighted up by a benign smile, which altered entirely the whole expression of his features. His manner and address were exceedingly dignified, yet polished and affable in the extreme, and when he was engaged in attendance upon a critical case, or a surgical operation, there was a degree of tenderness, and at the same time a confidence, in his manner, which could not fail to soothe the feelings and allay the fears of the most timid and sensitive.

During a period of general distress, the yellow fever being prevalent, history has at all times shown that the minds of the people are very apt to become excited and inflamed, and some threatening indications of riotous conduct having been exhibited, while Dr. Physick was serving in the Bush Hill Hospital, he was created an Alderman by the Governor of Pennsylvania, for the purpose of enabling him to quell disturbances.

The publicity which Dr. Physick obtained, together with the favorable impression which he produced during his residence in the hospital, led to acquaintances which subsequently assisted in promoting his professional success. Among others whose lasting friendship he then secured, was that of our late fellow citizen, Stephen Girard, at that melancholy epoch a member of the Board of Health, and who rendered the most important services throughout the epidemic, in alleviating the miseries and providing for the wants of the unhappy sufferers; services which should never be forgotten.

After leaving the hospital he removed to the city and gave his undivided attention to his professional engagements. In the year 1794, Dr. Physick was elected by the managers of the Pennsylvania Hospital, one of the surgeons to that institution. This period was the dawn of his great surgical fame and usefulness. The reputation sustained by the Pennsylvania Hospital for a long series of years, not only for the amount of benefits which it has conferred, but also on account of its excellent administration, are so well known as to render superfluous any encomiastic notice of it on my part. That Dr. Physick contributed largely to the support of its character and reputation, can be readily shown by a record of his services. It must be admitted, however, that his appointment to the hospital had a considerable influence in promoting his success, and leading to an extension of his business. The situation enabled him to add greatly to his stock of experience, and afforded him ample opportunities of perfecting himself in the operative department of his profession. I have already stated that in his manual procedures he exhibited the utmost degree of neatness and dexterity. Dr. Physick possessed pre-eminently all the qualifications requisite for a bold and successful operator. His sight was remarkably good; his nerves when braced for an operation, were firm and immovable; his judgment was clear and comprehensive, and his resolutions once formed, were rarely swerved from. In addition to these he owed much to his thoughtful and contemplative cast of character, which induced him to deliberate and reflect intensely upon all the circumstances of his case, and to make elaborately before hand every preparation which might become needful in the performance of his task.

In order to appreciate fully and correctly the amount of contributions made by Dr. Physick to the department of surgery, it is important to call to mind the imperfect condition of the art in this country, at the period of his commencing his professional career. It is well known that the principles of science which should govern the treatment of many disorders were at that day very imperfectly understood. It is true that there were some members of the profession, possessed of great merit and learning, who devoted themselves especially to the cultivation of surgery. These gentlemen were quite competent to the performance of what were then considered the capital operations in surgery; still it must be confessed that none of them ever acquired the necessary degree of skill and pre-eminence to create an unlimited confidence in his abilities. In consequence of this there was no head, no rallying point in surgery, an appeal to which, when once made, would be regarded as decisive. We cannot feel surprised at the comparatively insignificant position which the science of surgery then held, when we reflect, that prior to the appointment of Dr. Physick, surgery was not taught in this city as a separate and distinct department. The professorship of anatomy and surgery were combined in the University of Pennsylvania, and the duty of teaching both branches devolved upon one individual. Under these circumstances it would have been extremely unreasonable to expect an efficient course of instruction when it is well known that the usual period allotted to a course of lectures upon either department, as now separated, is confessedly too limited.

Soon after Dr. Physick's appointment to the Pennsylvania Hospital, his mind became engaged in the consideration of a class of disorders of which that institution then had, and continues to have its full proportion, namely, ulcers. The treatment of these affections was at that day but little understood by surgeons, and was for the most part exclusively empirical; consequently it was notoriously unsuccessful; and I am sorry to say, that there are good reasons for believing that limbs affected with ulcers were not unfrequently amputated, which, by a judicious and skillful treatment, might have been preserved.

Dr. Physick during the period of his services in the Pennsylvania Hospital made several valuable improvements in the treatment of fractures. Without entering minutely into the consideration of these, I may refer to his modification of Desault's apparatus for the treatment of fractures of the thigh. By increasing the length of Desault's splint, Dr. Physick accomplished a most important object, causing the counter-extension to be made more nearly in the direction of the axis of the limb, and also in keeping the patient more strictly at rest. This apparatus of Desault, thus modified by Dr. Physick, and with the blocks attached to the lower extremity of the splint by Dr. Hutchinson, for the purpose of making the extension in the direction of the limb, has been used in the Hospital for a long series of years with the happiest results. Dr. Physick never ceased to regard it as the most complete and successful method of treating fractures of the thigh.

Fractures of the humerus occurring at or near the condyles, are exceedingly apt to be followed by a projection of the elbow. In some instances the deformity is so great as to give rise to most disagreeable consequences, more especially where the accident happens to a young female. To Dr. Physick is due the credit of having invented a method of treatment which has succeeded, in many instances, in effecting a complete cure, without the occurrence of any deformity. This treatment consists in applying to the injured limb two angular splints, which should extend from near the shoulder down to the extremities of the fingers. In addition to this, he directs the patient to be kept in bed, ' with the arm flexed at the elbow, and lying on its outside with the angular splints supported by a pillow.'

In case of fractures of the lower end of the fibula,

where the accident is accompanied with a dislocation of the foot outward, Dr. Physick was in the habit, many years since, of treating the fractures upon a plan precisely similar to that recommended by Baron Dupuytren. To which of these gentlemen is due the priority of this invention, I am not able to say.

In the treatment of dislocations, the highest commendation is due to Dr. Physick for being the first to carry into full effect a plan of treatment, which, although originally suggested by Dr. Alexander Monro, of Edinburgh, was never put into execution, so far as I can learn, prior to its employment by Dr. Physick. I allude to the use of copious blood-letting, carried, when necessary, even *ad deliquium animi*, in order to produce a complete relaxation of the muscular system, and thereby facilitate the reduction of the dislocated bone. By this method of treatment, in very many instances, old and difficult dislocations have been reduced, which otherwise would have been irremediable, and limbs thus restored to usefulness.

In the year 1794, Dr. Physick was elected one of the Physicians to the Philadelphia Dispensary ; and during the period he held this appointment, he performed his duties with the strictest fidelity. He subsequently was appointed one of the consulting surgeons to this institution, and retained the situation till the time of his death.

From a reference to Dr. Physick's papers, it appears that his professional engagements increased very considerably in the year 1795. About this period his prospects of establishing himself in practice became exceedingly flattering. During the year 1795, he commenced keeping a journal of the most remarkable and interesting cases which occurred in his practice, more especially those of a surgical character. This Journal he continued up to the year 1810, although in consequence of the multiplicity of his engagements about this period, we have to regret the number of cases inserted is very considerably lessened. The first case recorded in the note book, is that of a lady affected with blindness from cataract. In this case he performed the operation of extraction of the opaque chrystalline lens, with complete success, and restored his patient to sight.

I may mention here that Dr. Physick's favorite operation for cataract, was that of extraction, and he always performed it whenever the condition of the eye was favorable. He acquired such a perfect degree of skill in extracting the lens, that his operations were almost invariably followed by success. I am of opinion that his operations upon the eye, in conjunction with those of stone in the bladder, did as much in establishing his great surgical character as any others which he performed. Operations of this nature, when successfully executed, in that day, were widely known. His first operation of lithotomy was not performed, however, until the year 1797. He subsequently performed it, as is well known, in numerous instances, with extraordinary facility and success. In performing his first operation of lithotomy, he accidentally divided with his gorget, the internal pudic artery. The hemorrhage from the wounded artery was exceedingly profuse. He immediately compressed the trunk of the artery with the fore finger of his left hand, next passed the tenaculum under it, and a ligature was then cast round it, and finally tied. This of course arrested the hemorrhage, but the ligature included along with the artery a considerable portion of the adjacent flesh. To obviate this inconvenience, Dr. Physick subsequently contrived his celebrated forceps and needle for carrying a ligature under the pudic artery. Since that period this instrument has been in general use for securing deep seated vessels. It has twice been successfully employed in the operation of tying the external iliac artery; in the first instance by the late lamented Dr. Dorsey, a favorite nephew of Dr. Physick, and one to whom he was ardently attached, and in the second instance by myself. No higher commendation could be bestowed upon this instrument than may be inferred from the numerous modifications which have since been made of it. I must be permitted to declare that, in my opinion, the original instrument, as designed by Dr. Physick, has never been equalled, either in point of ingenuity or utility.

During the years 1797, 1798 and 1799, the yellow fever reappeared in our city, and Dr. Physick was again found in the foremost rank of those who had to contend against its ravages. Whilst engaged in the performance of his duties in the year 1799, he was attacked himself for the second time with the fever, and his illness was so severe that for some time but slight hopes were entertained of his recovery. His convalescence was exceedingly slow, and he was left in such an enfeebled state that he was advised by his medical friends to make an excursion into the country, in order to recruit his strength. He accordingly took this opportunity of paying a visit to his brother, who was living upon a beautiful farm situated upon the banks of the Susquehanna, in Cecil county, Maryland. He was somewhat amused, whilst performing this journey, at being informed by an innkeeper on the road, that Dr. Physick of Philadelphia was dead. His health was greatly benefited during the period of his sojourn with his brother, and it appears that he conceived a warm attachment to the place, inasmuch, as after the death of his brother, many years subsequently, he became the purchaser of the estate, and during the latter years of his life he was accustomed to spend a part of every summer upon it.

During the prevalence of yellow fever in 1798, Dr. Physick was again resident physician at the Bush Hill Hospital, and upon leaving the institution, after the subsidence of the epidemic, he was presented in a flattering manner by the board of managers, with some valuable silver plate as an acknowledgment of their 'respectful approbation of his voluntary and inestimable services.'

The year 1800 formed a most eventful one in the life of Dr. Physick. During this year he formed a matrimonial alliance with Miss Elizabeth Emlen, a highly gifted and talented lady, and daughter of one of the most distinguished ministers of the Society of Friends. By this marriage he had four children, two sons and two daughters, all of whom are now living.

In the year 1800, a request was made to Dr. Physick, in writing, by a number of gentlemen engaged in attending the medical lectures delivered in the University' of Pennsylvania, that he would lecture to them on surgery. No man could feel more deeply the solemn responsibilities attendant upon such an enterprise than Dr. Physick. After mature deliberation, however, he determined to accede to their request, and this may be considered as the commencement of his labors as a lecturer.

The following anecdote will exemplify the ardor and zeal with which he entered upon the performance of his duties, and it illustrates also most happily the great advantages which may be derived from a word of encouragement and approbation, coming from a source in which entire confidence is reposed.

After preparing the lecture introductory to his course, he committed it to memory. Among the persons invited to be present, was his valued friend, Dr. Rush. The scene was a trying one to Dr. Physick. It was the first time he had ever publicly addressed an audience. I have been informed, however, that he acquitted himself extremely well. At the close of the lecture, Dr. Rush stepped up to him, gave him his hand, and congratulated him upon his success, saying to him emphatically, ' Doctor, that will do, that will do, you need not be apprehensive as to the result of your lecturing. I am sure you will succeed.' Dr. Physick never forgot Dr. Rush's kind manner to him on this occasion. He assured me that it exerted a considerable influence in strengthening and confirming his resolutions to persevere. It is needless for me to say that Dr. Rush's predictions respecting Dr. Physick's ultimate success in lecturing, were ful-

59

filled to the utmost. Five years subsequently to that
period, the Professorship of Surgery was created in
the University of Pennsylvania, and Dr. Physick was
elected to the chair.

In the year 1801, Dr. Physick was appointed *'Surgeon Extraordinary,'* and also one of the physicians to
the Philadelphia Almshouse Infirmary. In 1802 he
published in the New York Medical Repository, a
case of hydrophobia. In this communication he
gives an account of the appearances observed on
dissection ; and as a means of affording relief in
similar cases, he suggests, in conjunction with other
remedies, the propriety of performing the operation
of tracheotomy. I am not informed that he ever had
an opportunity of testing the value of the foregoing
suggestion, by the performance of the operation.

About this period it may be said that the talents
and acquirements of Dr. Physick began to be extensively known and appreciated, not only by the members of his own profession, but also by others. I may
mention that in 1802 he was elected a member of the
American Philosophical Society, a well merited tribute due to his rising greatness.

This year Dr. Physick devised and executed an
operation which forms one of the most brilliant
achievements in modern surgery, and has been productive of the most beneficial results to suffering
humanity. On the 18th of December, he performed
in the Pennsylvania hospital, his celebrated operation
of passing a seton between the ends of an ununited
fractured humerus, for the purpose of causing a
deposition of callus, and thereby producing the con-

solidation of the broken bone. The patient was a seaman who had had the misfortune to fracture his left arm, eighteen months previously, whilst at sea, and in consequence of the bones not having united, the limb was rendered nearly useless. At the expiration of five months after the performance of the operation, he was discharged from the hospital perfectly cured. Dr. Physick published an account of this case in the Medical Repository of New York, vol. I., 1804, and it was republished in the Medico-Chirurgical Transactions of London, 1819. Twenty-eight years after that the Doctor was accidentally called to see this same man, who was sick with intermittent fever. Upon questioning him he informed him that the arm which had been broken was quite as strong as the other arm, and that he had never sustained any inconvenience from the operation. The man died, and having obtained permission to make a post mortem examination, I procured his humerus which I still have in my possession, and regard it as one of the most interesting and valuable pathological specimens extant. At the place of fracture the two ends of the bone are perfectly consolidated by a mass of osseous matter, in the centre of which there is a hole, through which the seton had passed.

Dr. Physick's private journal, and also a book of cases kept by his nephew, Dr. Dorsey, clearly evince that at this period, Dr. Physick was occupied in attending to a most extensive and laborious practice. In Dr. Dorsey's note book are recorded the most interesting cases and operations occurring in the practice of Dr. Physick, to which he was a witness.

It has always been a subject of deep regret with the profession, that Dr. Physick should have evinced throughout the whole of his life such an extreme reluctance to the publication of the results of his valuable observations and experience. What a fund of knowledge has in this manner been permitted to pass away, which might have been happily applied to ameliorating the miseries of humanity? Strange as it may appear, I unhesitatingly assert that posthumous fame was not sought after by Dr. Physick. I am well convinced, however, that in the latter years of his life, he regretted very much himself that he had not published more for the benefit of his fellow beings; but at this period his disinclination and habits had become so confirmed that it was impossible for him to change them.

From the paucity of Dr. Physick's communications, and their considerable value, I make no apology for briefly noticing them. It has been necessary to collect them from various journals. I consider it unnecessary to enlarge upon them, however, inasmuch as my friend, Dr. Benjamin Horner Coates, is engaged in preparing an edition of Dr. Physick's works, with commentaries on his doctrines and practice.

In Dr. Coxe's Medical Museum, vol. I., for the years 1804–5, there are published by Dr. Physick three papers communicating cases occurring in his practice, together with practical suggestions, and by Mr. Bishop too, giving an account of improvements and modifications upon instruments made after the directions of Dr. Physick.

In the first paper, Dr. Physick communicates the particulars of a case of varicose aneurism, occurring at the bend of the elbow, in consequence of the artery being wounded in the operation of venesection, the lancet being pushed into the vessel, through the vein. He performed an operation, tied the artery above and below, and cured the patient. (See an account of the case, with a plate, in the Museum above referred to.)

The second publication was a description by R. R. Bishop, surgeons' instrument maker, of the gorget, as constructed according to Dr. Physick's plan. This has already been spoken of in this memoir. (See a plate of this gorget in vol. I. of the Med. Museum.)

The third publication in the Medical Museum was exceedingly valuable and interesting, being the first annunciation of a new method of treatment, suggested by Dr. Physick, for the relief of a formidable disease, and one which had previously baffled the skill of the most experienced physicians. In this communication, Dr. Physick recommends the use of blisters for the purpose of arresting the progress of mortification. In this paper Dr. Physick gives an account of two cases of mortification which came under his own notice, in which he applied blisters to the mortified parts, with the most beneficial effects. Since that period, blisters have been frequently employed for the purpose of arresting the progress of gangrene and mortification, with the most successful results.

The fourth publication consists of a description by

R. R. Bishop, of the curved bistoury, as improved by Dr. Physick for the operation of fistula in ano, with a plate. (See Med. Mus. vol. I.) This well known instrument, thus modified by Dr. Physick, combines the advantages of both the blunt and sharp pointed bistoury. Since the period of its invention it has been in general use.

In the fifth communication Dr. Physick describes the history of a case of luxation of the thigh bone forward, and the method which he employed for its reduction; and the paper is accompanied by a plate. (See Med. Mus. vol. I.)

In the year 1805 the chair of Surgery was made distinct from that of Anatomy, and Dr. Physick was elected, I believe unanimously, Professor of Surgery. I presume it will not be denied, that however great the advantages might have been which accrued to Dr. Physick in consequence of his being appointed Professor of Surgery in the University of Pennsylvania, the institution itself derived equal advantages from his connection with its medical faculty. It is certain, that soon after his appointment, the number of students who resorted to this city to attend the medical lectures greatly increased. Although the University at this time contained men of the most resplendent talents, who undoubtedly did much towards establishing the fame of that school, still it is worthy of record, that the zenith of Dr. Physick's fame and usefulness was the period at which the University of Pennsylvania obtained the acme of its reputation.

It is almost impossible to conceive of the great amount of labor he was in the habit of performing daily during this period of his life. He has frequently told me that it was his custom, throughout the winter months, to rise at four o'clock in the morning. This hour being too early to disturb a servant, he was obliged to arrange his own fire. He would then sit down to his desk and prepare his lecture for the day; after which he would dress himself, and then take his breakfast, and leave his house between eight and nine o'clock to attend an extensive and laborious practice. In addition to all this, he discharged his duties as Surgeon to the Pennsylvania Hospital, and to the Almshouse Infirmary. He used often to remark, that in order to obtain entire success as a practitioner of medicine, it was necessary to work hard. He told me that in London this idea was conveyed by the emphatic expression, Mr. ——, or Mr. ——, is *working* his way into business.' It will be conceded that no portion of his success ever came to him gratuitously; on the contrary, he made laborious exertions to obtain it.

Dr. Physick's manner as a public lecturer was extremely grave, dignified and impressive. His style was clear, ample, and chaste. He was uniformly careful not to say too much. His choice of language was remarkably good, and he possessed the happy faculty of communicating knowledge agreeably and clearly to a degree which I have never known surpassed. Perhaps one great reason for this was that he never undertook to instruct others upon subjects which he did not clearly comprehend himself. He attempted no display of oratory; neither did he permit his reason and imagination to run wild in the regions of theory and fancy. He found much better employment for his mind in constantly studying the realities of life, and in reflecting upon the best methods of promoting the welfare of his fellow creatures.

His lectures were carefully prepared and written out. He did not at all approve of extemporaneous lecturing ; as he thought that in lecturing upon scientific subjects, and more especially such as involved the lives of our fellow beings, no man had a right to place so much confidence in the strength of his memory as is implied in that practice. (In this sentiment I perfectly agree with him.—S. W. W.)

Dr. Physick's course of lectures on surgery was eminently valuable from being founded principally upon his own practical knowledge and experience, and also from his discarding all mean hypotheses ; besides which his lectures derived an additional attraction and importance from the circumstance that his reputation for stern integrity and strict veracity was so well known and established, that whenever he asserted facts to be true, they were implicitly believed.

As a letter writer he was exceedingly exemplary and peculiar. In general his letters were remarkably brief and pithy. He was excessively annoyed at being obliged to read letters of an unmeaning and unnecessary length. It was the same with respect to books. I have often heard him complain of the hardship of being obliged to read through a volume of two or three hundred pages, to get at ideas which might have been embodied in ten or twenty.

In the third volume of the Eclectic Repository, for

October, 1812, Dr. Physick published an account of a new method which he had employed for the purpose of extracting poisonous substances from the stomach, by means of a stomach pump or syringe. Physicians are now so well acquainted with this method, that I shall not here attempt to describe it.

In the winter of 1813–14, Dr. Physick suffered from an attack of typhus fever. On this occasion his illness was so extreme, that his medical friends despaired of his life for some time. He gradually convalesced, but his constitution did not entirely recover from the shock which it then received. From this period he never enjoyed what might be called uninterrupted health.

About the period to which we are alluding, he begun to experience certain unpleasant symptoms, indicative of a diseased condition of the heart, and which eventually terminated in organic affection of that organ, and doubtless laid the foundation for the hydropic complaint of which he died.

Among the complicated forms of diseases to which he was subjected must also be enumerated a nephritic disorder, with calculous concretions in the kidney. It is impossible for language to describe the pain and agony which he frequently endured from passing of the small calculi through the water into his bladder. Upon one occasion, about ten years previous to his death, I knew him to be for near two hours without any pulse perceptible at the wrist, in consequence of intense suffering, caused by the lodgment of a small calculus in the bladder. It remained fixed in this situation for some days, and grew to the size of a small

60

pea; it finally passed into the bladder, and was discharged a few minutes subsequently through the urethra.

Among the improvements suggested by Dr. Physick, I should mention that in the Eclectic Repository, vol. VI. for the year 1816, he published an account of a method which he had proposed for forming ligatures out of animal fibre. The medical world is now familiar with his observations on the subject.

It is my opinion that the period which we are now commemorating may be considered as that at which his professional engagements had acquired their greatest extent. His pre-eminence both as a physician and a surgeon, was at that time so generally conceded in this city, as to lead to the greatest demand for his professional services. In addition to this, his surpassing fame and reputation were so completely established, and so widely disseminated, as to induce strangers from all parts of our country to resort to Philadelphia, in order to be benefited by his skill and experience.

It follows, also, as a natural consequence of his exalted position, that many persons who could not make it convenient to leave their homes, would apply to him for his advice and opinions in writing; so that in addition to his other labors, much of his time was occupied in keeping up an extensive correspondence.

In consequence of his infirm health, he resigned his situation as a surgeon in the Pennsylvania Hospital in 1816, after having held the office twenty-two years. A short time before, he had resigned his situations in the Philadelphia Dispensary, and Philadelphia Almshouse Infirmary.

In the year 1819, Dr. Physick resigned his chair of Surgery in the University of Pennsylvania, and was transferred to that of Anatomy, which had become vacant the preceding session by the death of his nephew, Dr. John Syng Dorsey. It was always a source of deep regret with Dr. Physick's immediate family and friends, that his comforts in the evening of his days, and whilst laboring under physical infirmities, should be so greatly interrupted by translating him from the chair of Surgery to that of Anatomy. We had positive assurances from himself that the change was contrary to his own wishes and inclination; how far the interests of the institution to which he belonged may have been promoted by it, I do not mean to inquire. My own impression is, however, and I believe I am not singular in the opinion, that if he had continued in the chair of Surgery up to the period when he retired from the University, it would have numbered in its catalogue of students many more than it has ever shown.

In the Philadelphia Journal of the Medical and Physical Sciences, vol. I. for the year 1820, Dr. Physick gave an account of the method which he employed for the removal of scirrous tonsils and hemorrhoidal tumors. This consisted in strangulating the tumors completely by means of a soft wire ligature passed through a double canula, and removing the wire at the expiration of twenty-four hours; instead of allowing the instrument to remain applied, as was formerly the custom, and the parts separated and the wire thrown off, a process requiring a week or ten days. Experience has shown this to be a valuable improvement on the old way.

A few years subsequently he became convinced that the best method of removing scirrous tonsils was by excision. He contrived a very ingenious instrument for this purpose, and also for excising the uvula ; a full description of which, accompanied with a plate, was published by Dr. Hays, in the American Journal of the Medical Sciences, vol. I. In vol. II. of the same Journal, Dr. Hays, its editor, published the description and plate of a process, invented by Dr. Physick, and employed in certain cases to facilitate the extirpation of the tonsils by means of this instrument. The forceps is so constructed, that the tonsil may be seized and drawn through the aperture to any distance that may be deemed proper ; when its extirpation may be immediately effected.

The last paper written by Dr. Physick, is one which he published in vol. III. of the Philadelphia Journal of the Medical and Physical Sciences, in which he communicated the particulars of a case of carbuncle, with some remarks on the use of the common caustic vegetable alkali in the treatment of this disease.

In the year 1821, Dr. Physick was appointed Consulting Surgeon to the Institution for the Blind. In 1822 the Phrenological Society of Philadelphia elected him its President. In 1814 he was chosen President of the Philadelphia Medical Society. He held this situation until the time of his death. In 1825, Jan. 6, he was appointed a member of the Royal Academy of Medicine of France ; so far as I know, the first American who ever received that honor. In 1831, in consequence of his declining health, he felt it incumbent on him to retire from the active duties of the University; and accordingly he resigned his situation as Professor of Anatomy. In acknowledgment of the extraordinary services which he had rendered in elevating the character of the school, and in promoting the cause of medical science, the institution, upon accepting his resignation, conferred upon him the highest honor in its power, by electing him unanimously, 'Emeritus Professor of Surgery and Anatomy.'

Not the least among the improvements effected by Dr. Physick in the methods of treating diseases, may be considered his management of affections of the joints; and more especially that condition of the hip joint known by the name of 'morbus coxarius,' or hip disease. I may mention generally that his practice consisted in the application of a carved splint, to keep the limb strictly at rest, and prevent the least possible motion of the joint, and a course of active and long continued purging.

In the American Journal of the Medical Sciences, No. 14, Feb., 1831, I published a detailed account of Dr. Physick's method of treating morbus coxarius, accompanied by a plate, exhibiting the application of the carved splint. The superiority of this method of treatment is now so completely established in this country, as to lead to its adoption by the profession generally.

In October, 1831, Dr. Physick performed the operation of lithotomy on Chief Justice Marshall. The particulars of this most interesting operation have been given in the periodicals of the day.

In November, 1836, he was elected an honorary fellow of the Royal Medical and Chirurgical Society of London. The conferring of this honor was a full acknowledgment of his exalted merits, and justly acquired reputation, and he did not affect to conceal the high gratification which he derived from it.

It may be interesting to mention that the first and the last capital surgical operation which he performed, was the extraction of the chrystalline lens for cataract. The operation was performed on the 13th of August, 1837. I was present, and watched him with the most intense anxiety. He was quite collected and firm, and his hand was steady, though he was laboring under great mental and physical suffering. Whilst witnessing this effort in the cause of afflicted humanity, I felt a melancholy conviction that it would be the final act of his professional life.

From this period his complaint went on increasing in intensity and violence. The symptoms of hydrothorax became developed to a most painful extent, and he suffered extreme agony from oppression at his chest and difficulty of breathing; so much so, that sometimes he became unable to lie down in his bed for whole nights together, but was obliged to stand upon the floor, supported by assistants. His malady became uncontrollable, and it resisted the most strenuous efforts that professional skill and affectionate attendance could exert.

Some time previously to his death, anasarca took place; and in consequence of his remaining so much in the erect position his lower extremities became enormously swollen and distended with serum. The integuments at length gave way, and openings formed, which finally ulcerated and became gangrenous. The father of American Surgery expired without a struggle on the morning of the 15th of December, 1837, at twenty minutes past eight o'clock.

> ' He gave his honors to the world again,
> ' His blessed part to heaven, and slept in peace.'

It must be admitted that by the community at large, Dr. Physick's private character was but imperfectly understood. This was owing to the habits of perfect seclusion which he contracted, and to the slight intercourse, other than professional, which he permitted himself to enjoy with his fellow citizens. It must not be supposed, however, that this insulation arose from moroseness of character, or want of inclination to mingle with society. A satisfactory explanation may be afforded by the entire self-abandonment with which he devoted himself to his professional engagements. This formed one of the most striking and remarkable points in Dr. Physick's character. History probably cannot show an example of a more pure and absolute devotion to professional pursuits than he exhibited.

Previously to performing important surgical operations, his feelings were so harrowed up, and he experienced so much anxiety, that it was the custom of his family to endeavor to prevail upon him to execute such operations as speedily as possible, in order to relieve his mind.

To those who only saw Dr. Physick as the bold and unflinching operator in surgery, his character might have appeared cold and unfeeling, but to the few who knew him in his private circle, the veil was well drawn. It was in the gentle charities of domestic life, as the tender and affectionate parent, or the sympathizing friend, that his true character became revealed; and his heart was felt to be keenly alive to the kindest and softest emotions of which human nature is susceptible. He never appeared to be so happy as when surrounded by his children and his family; and indeed I feel assured that this formed one of the greatest consolations to him in the midst of protracted sufferings.

In his intercourse with his professional brethren, Dr. Physick's conduct was regulated by the strictest principles of honor and integrity. Whenever he was called in consultation with other physicians, without inquiring how exalted or humble their position might be, he was scrupulously careful to avoid saying or doing any thing which could wound their feelings, or prejudice them in the least in the estimation of their patients. He invariably stated his own opinions in a frank and manly manner, and was ever willing to pay due deference to the opinions of others. Upon all occasions he was happy and ready to confer upon his fellow practitioners the benefit of his advice and experience, whether the information desired had special relation to themselves, or those under their charge. He was far removed above the meanness of interfering with the patients of others; and whenever he had it in his power to render a service to a younger member of the profession, by a word of encouragement or commendation, it was cheerfully bestowed.

It was impossible that a man possessed of a mind of so reflective and contemplative a character as his, should not turn with anxious solicitude to the doctrines of religion, and the contemplation of a future state. Religion constituted, in fact, the most engrossing subject of attention during the latter years of his life. How far he derived comfort and consolation from his religious studies, it is not for me to say. I am very certain, however, that a more pure and ardent seeker after divine truth I never knew. As an observer of the principles of strict integrity and morality, I believe it will be conceded that he was exemplary to a remarkable degree. He, however, arrogated nothing to himself from this source. He expressed to me but a short period previous to his death, that he possessed no merits of his own to give him a claim to salvation. His humility and self-abasement upon the subject of religion were extreme; and he was always willing and ready to apply to any source, however humble it might be, provided he thought he could be enlightened and instructed by it.

His course of reading upon theology was very extensive; and unfortunately for him, he read many works of a conflicting and contradictory nature. The effect of this upon one who had, during all his life, been in search of indisputable evidences, was to create at times gloomy and desponding views. Yet for many years of his life he was in the uniform habit of perusing every morning a portion of the

61

New Testament; and when, in consequence of his
illness and increasing infirmities, he was incapable of
so doing, his children were constantly employed in
reading this and other works of devotion to him.
During his last illness he derived great pleasure and
satisfaction from the visits of his friend and pastor,
Dr. Delancy, whose kind attentions towards him
were unremitting. I feel assured that the hopes and
promises of the Christian religion were the greatest
sources of consolation to him in the closing hours of
his life, and smoothed his passage to the tomb.

DR. JAMES HENRY PIERREPONT of Portsmouth,
New Hampshire, was born at Springfield, Mass. I
am sorry that I am not able to obtain more facts in
relation to his early history. He was, for many years,
one of the most distinguished physicians in Portsmouth, where he died in the year 1839. Dr. Smith
in the 23d vol. of his Journal observes:—'Were it
not for a most appropriate and beautiful memoir of
the late lamented Dr. Pierrepont of Portsmouth, N.
H., by the Rev. Dr. Burroughs of that town, whose
eulogy on his life and character exhibits the distinguished moral worth and high professional attainments of the subject of an excellent discourse, we
could not have sympathized, as we now do, in the
great loss sustained by those who have gathered together to mourn over the lifeless remains of one
whom they had delighted to honor. At the special
request of the medical faculty of the place, Dr. Burroughs was requested to deliver the eulogy to which

these observations refer, on the 28th of Jan., 1839. It commences thus—' *Colossians, chap. 4, verse* 13. The beloved physician,'—and the author shows most clearly that the subject upon which he was called to speak gave elevation to his own thoughts, and thus he was better qualified to impress the listening multitude with a profound sentiment of respect for the memory of a good man, whose existence had been a blessing in his day and generation—one in whom there was no guile, and whose firm reliance on the Divine promises enabled him to exclaim in the last agony of expiring nature—' O what delightful tranquillity.'

By carefully studying the pages of this performance, we perceive that Dr. Pierrepont was not sufficiently appreciated in early life. It was a misfortune not to have reached the meridian of professional eminence, till age in some measure disqualified him for assuming that commanding position which youthful ambition prompts most men to obtain. He became distinguished too late. This was not his fault, but a misfortune ; the loss was to a community which might have had much of his services, had the constitution of his mind and its various powers been seasonably discovered.

Such integrity, parental kindness, universal philanthropy and practical usefulness, as Dr. Pierrepont is represented to have possessed, appear to have resulted from a deep conviction of the urgent necessity of conforming to the requisitions of that Divine system of faith which a benevolent Governor of the universe has revealed to man in the gospel. Feeling that this

is but the beginning of an endless existence—a preparatory state in which the faculties of the soul are only
indicating their latent powers, to be unfolded in the
ceaseless duration of eternity. Dr. Pierrepont was
too conscientious to waste the precious privileges
and opportunities of the age to acquire knowledge;
thus each succeeding year gave him higher and
stronger claims upon the confidence and admiration
of society.

Peculiar habits of study and untiring devotion to
the learning of others, prevented him from embody-
ing his own thoughts and experience; posterity,
therefore, will be but partially benefited by his profound acquirements. Physicians, engaged in the active and generally distracting pursuits of practice,
have less opportunity than almost any other class of
persons for constructing finished, permanent, literary
or scientific records in a country like this, where all
is bustle, activity and restless enterprise. Much as it
is to be lamented that the vast amount he had stored
in a well disciplined mind is lost now to the world,
the moral excellence which such an unblemished
reputation as that of the ' beloved physician' is calculated to exert, must and will have the happiest
influence on that wide circle of which he was the
friend and counsellor.

Being prepossessed neither in favor of the eulogist,
or of the eulogized, both of whom were unknown to
us before taking up the pamphlet which called forth
the foregoing expressions, we cannot conclude without cordially recommending this singularly captivating, eulogistic biography to all young physicians. It

WRIGHT POST, M..D.

W.C. Sharp's Lith.Boston.

points the way to usefulness, teaches the responsibilities and relations of the profession, individually as well as collectively, and lastly, but most triumphantly, shows the glorious prospects connected with a well spent life.'—(*See Burroughs' Discourse.*)

DR. WRIGHT POST. I am indebted to the Biographical Memoir of Dr. Post, delivered as an introductory lecture before the students in Rutgers Medical College, New York, Nov. 4th, 1828, by my excellent friend, Dr. Valentine Mott, Professor of Surgery in that Institution, for the following facts in relation to Dr. Post. The Doctor says:

' Dr. Post was born at North Hempstead, Queens county, Long Island, on the 19th of February, Anno Domini, 1766. Of his juvenile habits, I have received but little information. It is very possible that if some of his early and more intelligent associates could now be found, some anecdotes might be obtained, indicative of his physical temperament, and the character of his mind, during the early stages of his education. Such traits are by no means uninteresting or unimportant in the delineation of character ; and it is much to be regretted that there is not a more general care among parents, teachers and friends, to leave behind them such memorials of infantile dispositions and boyish propensities, as might serve as starting points in biography, and valuable hints to those who are interested in the science of education. But few there are who in these respects possess the discrimination of an Edgeworth, or who in comprehensiveness of observation, and vividness of description, approximate to the talents of Scott.

The subject of our memoir possessed, as we are informed by one of his relatives, a remarkably quiet, amiable and accommodating disposition, but was resolute and firm in his purposes, and industrious and active, both bodily and mentally. His morals during his boyhood, are said to have been very correct. He was never known to engage in the mischievous sports, or dangerous intrigues, too common at country schools, and his mother has been heard to remark, that his conduct was never such as to afford her occasion for uneasiness or trouble on his account. He was placed under the tuition of David Bailey, a teacher of respectability in the neighborhood of his parents' residence, from whom it is believed he received a portion of classical instruction, and from whom it may be presumed he derived a rather more than ordinary taste for learning; for it was probably from some evidences of this kind, that his parents were induced to place him, at the early age of fifteen, as a student with Dr. Richard Bailey, at that time one of the most celebrated and skillful surgeons in the city of New York. With that gentleman he entered with becoming diligence on his professional studies; and although we are not furnished with any special account of his progress, there can be no doubt, that there were, both in his early scientific attainments and in the general stability of his character, decisive evidence of great respectability.

After remaining about four years with Dr. Bailey, he was judged, at the age of nineteen, to be a suitable candidate for the advantages of a more enlarged sphere of instruction. He accordingly proceeded to London and became the house pupil of Mr. Sheldon, whose reputation as a teacher of Anatomy and Surgery were at that time deservedly celebrated.

The acute and playful mind of his London teacher, gave interest to the study, and induced the American youth to estimate more highly the lessons and opportunities which he enjoyed. Those of you who have heard the admirable lectures which Dr. Post was in the habit of delivering for successive years, on the important subject of diseased Spine, and fractures of the Patella, may remember the frankness of his acknowledgments to Mr. Sheldon. They were among the master copies of his preceptor's lectures. The Monograph of Mr. Sheldon on the last disorder, is universally known and appreciated.

The zeal of the master was soon imparted to the pupil. The latter became quickly imbued with the love of Anatomy, and it was here that he learned those lessons which in time were matured into the most masterly use of the scalpel, in the tedious and frequently disgusting duties of practical and laborious dissection.

His teacher possessed in an eminent degree the requisite qualifications for making his pupils excellent Anatomists. He would often throw aside the reserve and formality of a preceptor, and become himself the pupil, working with his students with the greatest diligence, and mingling his cares and wants with theirs. With such advantages, few young men, it may be presumed, with any taste for science, would fail to become enamored with his pursuit, and to catch a portion of the zeal of a master thus ardent and accomplished.

Such advantages were not lost upon the subject of our memoir. He united with great industry and patient perseverance, that peculiar readiness in the use of the scalpel, which is seldom known to fail in producing a consummate Anatomist.

His first visit to London was in the spring of 1784, and he returned in the fall of 1786, having been absent about two years and a half; which time he spent in attendance upon the Lectures and Hospitals of this great metropolis, most of the time residing with his preceptor, the illustrious Sheldon. Mr. Sheldon on taking leave of his American pupil, presented him several beautiful Anatomical preparations, made by himself, as tokens of his affectionate regard.

It does not appear that he resorted to any other school or means of instruction, than those which he enjoyed in London. As a school of Anatomy and Surgery, there were no others in Great Britain which could come into competition with it, or afford inducements to one whose object was mainly a perfection in the fundamental part of a medical education.

Immediately after his return from Europe he commenced the practice of his profession in this city. As early as 1787, the year after his return from Europe, Dr. Post delivered his Lectures on Anatomy in the unappropriated apartments of the New York Hospital, while the Surgical Lectures were delivered by Dr. Bailey. But these efforts were entirely interrupted by the occurrence of the *Doctor's Mob*, as it has been called. Owing to an imprudent exposure of an anatomical specimen by some students, the populace broke into the building, and destroyed almost every thing. In 1790, having been four years engaged in practice, he married the daughter of his preceptor, the distinguished Dr. Bailey, with whom he soon after (in 1791,) became associated in the practice of Physic and Surgery.

Dr. Bailey now held the Professorship of Anatomy and Surgery in Columbia College ; and as was natural to one thus circumstanced, who was anticipating a release from those active and onerous duties, he looked around him for a successor, and doubtless discovered in his son-in-law the qualities which afforded a most rational promise of success in this important and responsible station. Fully aware, however, of the great advantages of ample preparation, and with a noble view to the future elevation of his youthful relative, Dr. Bailey advised his return to London.

Two years after his marriage, viz., in 1792, he was appointed Professor of *Surgery* in Columbia College, at the time that Dr. Bailey was appointed to the Anatomical chair.

His appointment to the Chair of Surgery took place in the spring of 1792, and immediately thereafter he sailed again for Europe ; and in addition to the further extension of his knowledge, it was a *desideratum* with our traveler to lay the foundation of a Museum, which might be rendered subservient to the purposes of instruction, when he should afterwards assume the business of a teacher.

In this interesting object he was eminently success-

62

ful. The collection which he brought out with him on his return, in the autumn of 1793, was then, and we believe is still, the largest and rarest in this country.

It was during this visit to London, that he enlisted as a pupil under the learned and distinguished Cruickshank; and while attending to his instructions, he also availed himself of the lessons of his then assistant and director, the late celebrated Dr. Bailey of London.

In this great school, and under these great masters it was, that Dr. Post prepared some of the finest and most beautiful injections of the absorbent system, which we have ever seen. His specimen of the lacteals of the large turtle filled with mercury, and the delicate and complicated structure of the *Testis* in all its multifarious parts, possess a finish and beauty, which are rarely, if ever, surpassed.

It was at this period that Cruickshank was prosecuting with great zeal, his researches into the hidden structure of the absorbent system, and in which the merit of his discoveries will be as imperishable as the science itself.

Having again accomplished his visit, and gained what appears to have been the exclusive object of his ambition, a thorough knowledge of Anatomy and operative Surgery, as taught and practised in the greatest school in Europe, Dr. Post returned home, and entered with great devotedness upon the duties of practical life.

Such accomplishments in the scientific part of his profession could not remain long inefficient. His

practice as a physician was sought after, and his surgical skill very soon exhibited itself in characters so
unequivocal as to gain the highest confidence, not
only of the public, but of his medical brethren, who
in due time assigned to him, with universal assent,
the most elevated station in the circle of *Operative
Surgeons* in this region of our country. His early
operations were marked with that freedom of thought
and action, which could arise only from a thorough
knowledge of the principles upon which he was proceeding—principles essentially dependent upon a minute acquaintance with the Anatomy of the parts,
and of the best modes then known or practised, of
conducting an operation.

One of his early performances gained for him no
inconsiderable share of celebrity both at home and
abroad. It was the case of a false Aneurism of the
femoral artery near the ham, from the wound of a
bayonet. The patient was a respectable farmer of
West Chester county, a member of the Society of
Friends, who confiding in the skill and judgment of
Surgeon Post, resolved to submit to an operation
which had never been performed in America; and
at that time but very seldom in Europe. For this
purpose he came to the city in the summer of 1796,
and placed himself at the disposal of the operator.
It was a triumphant case, as it fully established by its
successful termination the important principle of the
immortal John Hunter, the pride and ornament of
British Surgery.

The femoral artery was in this case tied, agreeably
to Hunter's plan, below the middle of the thigh, a

place sufficiently remote from the disease for the artery to unite by kindly adhesion. It has subsequently been common among surgeons, to select the lower part of the upper third of the thigh for the application of the ligature ; not that the place chosen by Hunter was not remote enough from the aneurism, but because the artery is there not accessible, and the operator interferes less with the surrounding parts.

The patient rapidly and perfectly recovered, and survived the operation about thirty years. The gratitude and friendship which he felt for his surgeon, he believed it his duty to testify, by paying him at least an annual visit ever afterwards. On one of these occasions, he found his benefactor at dinner with a company of his friends. He entered the room and was urged to take a seat with them, but perceiving it was not a convenient time he remarked, ' I have come to pay my annual visit, but I will not now interrupt thee, thou knowest the rest,' and departed. What feelings is a communication of such simple but pathetic energy not calculated to excite ? Here is the proudest triumph of philosophy. It is at such a moment, that virtue receives the highest boon which this world can bestow. Compared with mere pecuniary gratification, such a testimonial of the ' memory of the heart' is like ' a spot of azure in a cloudy sky.'

Dr. Post's surgical fame continued to increase with his age and experience. His knowledge of the powers of art, or more properly, of the remedial powers of nature, when its ordinary course is interrupted within the limits which science may prescribe, taught him to foresee to what lengths a surgeon might attempt to go, without incurring the hazards of a too fearful responsibility, or of a criminal temerity.

Long before the distinguished British Surgeon, Sir Astley Cooper, established the safety and propriety of tying the carotid artery for Aneurism, we have heard Dr. Post assert in his lectures, that he believed that not only one might be tied for Aneurism, but that both might be interrupted by ligatures, and the patient recover. This opinion he lived to see confirmed by example ; and in two cases did he himself contribute to the small stock of facts which the history of Surgery at that time afforded. In two cases did he operate for Carotid Aneurism upon the plan laid down by Sir Astley Cooper, and in both did the patients recover.

Our late esteemed friend, Dr. Dorsey of Philadelphia, was the first person in the United States, who performed the great surgical operation of tying the external iliac for inguinal Aneurism. Dr. Post was the second ; but the case of the latter was much the more formidable, as the situation of the tumor and the attachment of the peritoneum rendered it necessary for him to divide the latter membrane to get at the artery, thereby opening the peritoneal cavity ; a circumstance which greatly augmented the danger and difficulty of the operation.

In this case he adopted the plan of Abernethy and Freer, of making the incision nearly parallel with the linea alba and little to the outside of a middle line between it and the spinous process of the ileum. In

this way the incision through the parietes is made
directly upon the peritoneum, and may endanger its
division.   We think the operation has since been
greatly improved by going through the internal abdominal ring, by which the surgeon gets readily under the peritoneum, and the danger of cutting this
membrane is thereby avoided.

But the master stroke of Dr. Post in Surgery, remains yet to be mentioned.   It is certainly for the
honor of our time, for the credit of America, and for
the pride of our city, that the first successful operation of tying the subclavian artery above the clavicle
on the scapular side of the scaleni muscles, for bra-
chial aneurism situated so high in the axilla as to make
it expedient to tie this artery, was first successfully
performed by him, whose skill and science we are
now endeavoring to commemorate.   To succeed in
an operation of such delicacy and danger, and which
had failed in the hands of such master spirits in surgery as Ramsden, Abernethy and Cooper, was a triumph reserved for our friend; and it was certainly an
achievement, which, if nothing more had been done
in this country, must have removed the imputation of
inferiority in one of the most important arts of civilization and humanity, and furnish the most complete
rebuke to the taunting inquiry, 'What have your
American Physicians and Surgeons ever accomplished?'   We esteem it our good fortune to have had the
honor of being selected to assist at this memorable
and great performance in Operative Surgery.

We believe we may also claim for our friend the
exhibition of opiates in large doses in inflammatory

diseases, long before the publication of Dr. Armstrong's Treatise on Fevers.

The diligence and success with which Dr. Post had availed himself of the opportunities he had enjoyed in the study of Anatomy, had fully qualified him for assuming the station which had been designed him by his friends at home; and accordingly soon after his second return from London, in 1793, an exchange of Professorships took place between him and Dr. Bailey, who during Dr. Post's absence had lectured on both subjects. By this arrangement Dr. Bailey taught Surgery, and Dr. Post delivered the Anatomical course, executing for a long time, all his own dissections, acting as demonstrator and lecturing on the art of making and preserving anatomical specimens, and daily adding to his cabinet.

From this time till 1813, he discharged the duties of Professor of Anatomy and Physiology, with what success we shall presently give our opinion. During this long period of more than twenty years, he was sustained in the Medical School of Columbia College by several eminent coadjutors. For a while in conjunction with his preceptor, Bailey, on Surgery, Mitchill on Chemistry, Hamersley on the Theory and Practice of Medicine, and Hosack in the chair of Materia Medica and Botany.

Upon the union of the Medical Faculty of Columbia College with the College of Physicians and Surgeons in 1813, Dr. Post was appointed to the chair of Anatomy and Physiology, in the now concentrated Medical School of New York, in conjunction with Professor John Augustine Smith. Since this memorable confederacy of Medical and Surgical talents, which also included Macneven and Francis, death has summoned away from us the illustrious subject of our eulogy, the venerable President Bard, and his associate Vice President De Witt, and Professors Stringham and Osborne.

The station of Professor and Teacher of Anatomy, our friend continued to fill through the various modifications which the Medical School of this city had undergone during a period of forty years—and it may perhaps be asserted safely, that the distinction which he acquired as a teacher of Anatomy has not been excelled in this country.

For perspicuity and accuracy in unfolding the complicated structure of the human frame, he was peculiarly happy. His habits of patient and persevering attention laid the foundation for his perspicuity, so essential to the qualifications of a good instructor. Multiplied as are the evidences of Dr. Post's extensive and accurate knowledge of Anatomy, I am happy to add the following fact favored me by a friend.

During Dr. Post's last visit on the continent of Europe, he visited with much interest the anatomical collections and museums of the renowned medical schools of France. At his visit to that of Paris, he was deeply engaged in a close examination of the great cabinet at that place. In looking at some valuable preparations in anatomy, he was struck with one which betrayed in his opinion a wrong disposition in minute structure. He noticed this to his learned friend who accompanied him. The preparation was submitted to examination ; Dr. Post was found to be correct, and the preparation was removed.

We are not sensible of ever having listened, during the course of our studies, to any teacher, either in this country or in Europe, whose lessons were better calculated than his to furnish accurate information. His elocution, though plain and simple, was easy and natural. He rarely, if ever, aimed at the graces and elegancies of diction, or soared into the regions of imagination. But his delivery, if it had not the power of the mountain torrent, or the rapidity of the tempest, possessed in general the attractiveness of the velvet lawn,

'Shorn by the scythe and levelled by the roller.'

The literary acquirements of Dr. Post were not very extensive. He entered at so early an age upon the special duties of his profession, and pursued its avocations with such unremitting industry, but a very small portion of his time, beyond that which the cares of his family demanded, could have been left for literary indulgence or the cultivation of science, out of the immediate sphere of his professional obligations.

His constitution was feeble ; and although he kept so careful a guard over himself, as rarely in his life to be laid up for many days together, yet the fatigues of a very extensive practice were beginning so imperceptibly to undermine the remaining portion of his physical powers, that he deemed it prudent and

63

necessary, about thirteen years before his death, to relinquish his duties altogether for a season and travel for health.

He now made a third voyage to Europe in 1815, and after traveling for a few months in several countries, but especially in France, visiting the celebrated Schools and Hospitals of Paris and Montpelier, he returned home with greatly renovated health, and resumed, but with more caution and selection, his attentions to the calls that were soon accumulated upon him.

It is our belief that few professional men in any country ever enjoyed a larger share of the public confidence and esteem than Dr. Post; and certainly no man among his professional brethren was ever consulted with a more general willingness than he. In his intercourse with his fellow practitioners his deportment was uniformly correct. He was remarkable for great punctuality in his engagements, and for a scrupulous exactness and delicacy in his deportment, in all cases in which private advantage is too apt to interfere with mutual interests and the rights of individuals. He was never on those occasions officious or overbearing in his views or opinions, but took pleasure in increasing the confidence of patients and their friends in the judgment of their physician and surgeon, and appeared gratified by the opportunity of thus promoting the respectability of the young practitioner. He was therefore emphatically the friend of the junior members of the profession. He never trampled upon their rights, nor intentionally on their feelings.

It will hence be naturally inferred that the moral character of Dr. Post was of an elevated order. Such we believe was emphatically the fact; and that his moral principles were founded, not upon the mere speculations of worldly convenience, but upon the essential basis of all sound morality—religious conviction. He was a member of the Episcopal Church, and amidst the engagements of an anxious profession he was strict in his attendance upon public worship; thus giving the weight of his example in support of the important duty of social and religious exercise, while in his general intercourse with the world he exhibited the fruits of practical christianity.

He was for many years one of the vestry of the church to which he belonged, and at the time of his death the senior warden.

At the annual commencement of the University held in April, 1814, the honorary degree of Doctor of Medicine was conferred on Dr. Post by the Regents; a well merited honor for his varied professional talents. The recommendation for the testimonial in his behalf was unanimously concurred in by all his colleagues. In 1816 he was chosen by the Board of Trustees of Columbia College one of their body, which honor he held till death. Upon the organization of the Literary and Philosophical Society of N. York, he was one of their members by charter—he held the office of one of the board of Counsellors for several years. He was also a member of the New York Historical Society. He was for more than thirty-five years one of the Surgeons, and a Consulting Surgeon, of the New York Hospital. He was for several years an active officer of the Medical Society of the county of New York.

In 1821, upon the decease of President Bard, he was appointed his successor as President of the College of Physicians and Surgeons, which station he retained until his resignation of all the offices he held in the College, in the spring of 1826.

The only foreign distinction I have learned was conferred upon him, was that of an Associate of the Medical Faculty of Stockholm.

Among his most active and personal friends abroad we may enumerate as best known to fame, Percival Pott, Esq., Dr. Fordyce, Sir Astley Cooper, Charles Bell, John Abernethy, Sir Everard Home, the late Henry Cline, sen., Matthew Bailey, and Sir William Blizard.

Such in general was the professional, moral and religious character of Dr. Post. As an Anatomist, his knowledge was *minute, thorough* and *comprehensive;* as a Surgeon he was *acute, dextrous, elegant* and *masterly;* as a Physician, *discerning, practical* and *judicious;* as a citizen *moral* and *exemplary;* as a husband and parent, *kind* and *affectionate.*

To say that he was faultless, would be to claim for him more than belongs to any of the descendants of Adam. It is not our intention, in commemorating the merits of our departed friend, to indulge in the strain of fulsome panegyric.

It is our opinion, even, that the often repeated advice,

'De mortuis nil nisi bonum,'

is too restrictive in its adaptation to the object of a just
delineation of character, how pure and exalted soever
the personage whose worth we celebrate. As the
great end of biography is the instruction of the living, it should with all needful fidelity exhibit whatever may have been prominent in its subject, which
can aid the cause of virtue or shed a useful light
upon the principles of our common nature.

It has been our object in this brief memorial of
our late venerable colleague to exhibit those traits of
excellence to which we trust all will allow him to
have been justly entitled. That with other advantages in early life, and a more decided taste for literary
acquisition, he might have shone with greater brilliancy, we do not pretend to doubt. Dr. Post was
not, either from education or from his natural or
acquired habits of reflection, qualified to distinguish
himself in the ranks of medical literature. Excepting a very few papers descriptive of some of the
most interesting surgical cases, he has left nothing
behind him as an evidence of literary talent. There
is reason to believe that he was greatly averse to the
exercise of writing. His introductory lectures seldom exhibited proofs of originality of thought—nor
did his anatomical and physiological lectures evince
any great research beyond the plain and obvious track
which duty and decency prescribed.

With far more judgment than imagination, his
mind was well fitted for the demonstration of truths
attainable only by patient industry. With more
learning he would have been more attractive and
amusing, even among his bones and muscles; but

it is questionable whether he would have been equally plain and intelligible in his illustrations. With
more erudition he would have descanted more wisely upon the history of Anatomy, and animadverted
with more authority upon the blunders of his predecessors; but it is doubtful whether the light which
beamed from his scalpel would have been less brilliant, or the appropriate and practical instruction
which issued from his lips less edifying and impressive. With more extensive reading he would doubtless have been a more able Physiologist. His acquaintance with Chemistry was very much confined to the general principles of that very imperfect
science which was taught in his youth, and of course
the modern doctrines of Physiology were not much
attended to by him.

His devotedness to his patients and the extent
of his practice would necessarily lead him to a frequent examination of the changes of Materia Medica; while his thorough acquaintance with the
varying features of diseases and of the power of
all the well known medicaments were guarantees
against any obvious, and perhaps we may add, any
important defect, in the practice of his latter years.

After his health became too feeble for the exercise
of his accustomed skill in Surgery and attention to
his patients, he felt his hold of the world to be loosened; and he waited with the calmness of a Christian for the moment which should separate him from
it. He informed me some time before his death,
that if his life was spared he should never more

attend to the duties of his profession, or if it pleased God to take it, *he was satisfied.*

Having removed to his country residence at Throgsneck, about fourteen miles from the city, he remained about three weeks very much detached from society, but in the full possession of his mental faculties. His bodily strength, always feeble, had been for several months rapidly wasting, and at the period we now allude to, decay and debility appeared to have arrived at an extremity barely sufficient to support the connection between the immortal mind and its feeble tenement. On the morning of the 14th of June, 1828, perceiving a change in his own symptoms, he called his servant, and uttering a few words indicative of great tenderness and kindness, he yielded his breath like a taper wasting to a point, and expiring in its socket.'

—————————' Exhausted by the storm,
' A fatal trance hung o'er his pallid form,
' His closing eye a living lustre fired,
' 'Twas life's last spark, it flutter'd and expired.'

DR. EDWARD POST, member of the Royal College of Surgeons, London, &c. &c. The subject of the present biographical notice was the eldest son of Dr. Wright Post, and grandson of the late Dr. Richard Bailey; and was born in New York on the 15th of March, 1791. At an early age he was placed under the care of the Right Reverend Richard C. Moore, then a resident of Staten Island, by whom he was initiated into the rudiments of mathematical and classical learning. At his eleventh year he was removed to Columbia College, where he continued till the age of eighteen. He remained two years with each of the junior classes; during which period he made great proficiency, particularly in the French language, geography and history. His protracted pupilage in this seminary was in accordance with the plan of education prescribed by his father, who deemed it improper to invest him with academic honors at the early age his talents would have enabled him to graduate with credit.

In 1811, with a mind amply stored with the elements of medical science, derived from private study and public instruction, he embarked for Europe. In the schools of England and France he acquired large accessions of medical knowledge. He diligently attended the Infirmaries, in order to improve himself in anatomy and practical surgery; and for a time acted as dresser in Guy's hospital. The copious collection of manuscript notes which he has left, taken from the lectures of the most eminent professors of the different branches of medical science, bear respectful testimony that his transatlantic advantages were not unimproved.

During his residence on the continent he traveled through France, Italy, Switzerland, visiting every thing worthy of observation, and improving himself in the languages of those countries; in the two former of which he conversed with great accuracy and fluency.

In London his health became impaired from intense application; and during the prosecution of his studies at Montpelier, whilst on an excursion, he was attacked at Avignon with rheumatism, with which he had been much afflicted when a boy. It now principally affected his head and breast, and with such violence as to confine him for two months, and rendered his recovery extremely doubtful.

On his return to his native city in 1814, he appeared perfectly restored, and promised to relieve his anxious father from the burden of his professional duties, by being associated with him in his private practice, and also in consequence of being appointed Lecturer on Anatomy by the Trustees of the College of Physicians and Surgeons.

He was, however, soon obliged to relinquish all thoughts of practising his profession. An accumulation of cares in consequence of the necessary absence of his father, (whose ill health rendered a voyage across the Atlantic desirable,) with the disquietude occasioned by the malignant aspersions of invidious competitors, brought on a variety of troublesome symptoms, which were followed by a partial return of his former disorder. Conceiving that the milder climate of the South would conduce to his recovery, he embarked for Charleston, S. C., but on the passage he was attacked with hemiplegia, which, after a distressing confinement of five weeks, terminated his existence on the 26th of January, 1816.— *Dr. G. C. Bailey in Transact. Phys. Med. Soc., N. Y.*

Dr. Nathaniel Potter. I have in vain endeavored to procure a more extended notice of this distinguished man, and am obliged to accept the following notice of him from the Maryland Medical and Surgical Journal for March, 1843.

Professor Nathaniel Potter, M. D., departed this life in Baltimore on the morning of the 2d of January, 1843, after a sudden and very brief illness, in the 74th year of his age.

Dr. Potter was a native of Caroline county, on the Eastern shore of Maryland. The greater part of his long and useful life was passed in Baltimore, where he early achieved the eminent position in the medical profession which he retained to the last, and to which he was justly entitled by his natural abilities and by his literary and scientific acquirements. Soon after settling in this city he exerted himself, in association with the late Dr. Davidge and others, as one of the most active agents in establishing the medical department of the University of Maryland. In this institution he filled with distinguished honor for more than thirty years, and up to the time of his death, the chair of the Theory and Practice of Physic. In private and domestic life, Dr. Potter manifested many amiable virtues, which will be remembered with affectionate fondness by his family and friends. As a practitioner of medicine he was remarkable for promptitude and integrity of judgment, and for the boldness and energy of his remedial measures. As a teacher he was perspicuous and impressive, displaying in his lectures extensive knowledge and great practical good sense, rendering his subject pleasing and attractive by his native power of wit, and illustrating and enforcing his doctrines by the ample resources of a profound and elegant erudition.

DR. SAMUEL PRENTISS. I am indebted to the Hon. Samuel Prentiss of Montpelier, Vermont, Senator in the United States Congress, and son to the subject of this notice, for the principal part of the facts which I now present. He regrets exceedingly that the death of his mother, at the age of eighty-four, which happened two days before his arrival at Montpelier from Washington, has prevented him from giving the precise information which he could have wished.

Dr. Prentiss was born in Stonington, New London county, Conn., in the year 1759. He was son of Col. Samuel Prentiss, who was first a Major and then a Colonel in the American revolutionary army, received a good academical education, and studied the profession of medicine with Dr. Philip Turner, of Norwich, Connecticut, one of the very best American surgeons of the age in which he lived. He entered the army of the revolution while quite young, and acted for a time as military waiter to his father, but soon after this he returned to civil life. After studying his profession he once more engaged in the public service, in the capacity of assistant surgeon in the army, where he acquired a great deal of practical knowledge in his profession. After the close of the war he married a daughter of Capt.

Holmes, of Stonington, Connecticut, and soon removed to Worcester, in Massachusetts, where he resided several years. Not far from the breaking out
of Shays' rebellion, he removed to Northfield, Mass.,
then in the old county of Hampshire, and during the
insurrection was zealous and active on the side of
the government. His practice as a surgeon, while
at Northfield, was very extensive; and for many
years he was the principal operator in this part of
the country. His ride extended throughout the
western counties of Massachusetts, and far into the
States of Vermont and New Hampshire. In fact,
he was almost the only operating surgeon in this
section of the country for more than twenty years,
which sufficiently attests the estimation in which his
professional services were held by his professional
brethren and the public. I regret that I am not able
to give the number, or even an abstract, of his
capital operations. If he ever kept such an abstract
or numeration, I have never been able to find it.
His capital operations must have been numerous,
for the profession was not then crowded with operators as it is at present, when we have two or three,
and perhaps more, professed surgeons in almost every
county.

He was admitted a Fellow of the Massachusetts
Medical Society in the year 1810, when he resided
at Bernardston. He continued his fellowship till
the time of his death, which occurred at his residence in Northfield in 1818, at the age of fifty-nine.
Out of a numerous family, four sons survive him.
Samuel has twice been elected to the Senate in Con-

gress by the Legislature of Vermont, and is now one of the principal Judges in the Supreme Court of that State. John H. resides at Cooperstown, in the State of New York, and has twice been elected to the House of Representatives in Congress from that State. William, the youngest of the family, resides at Milwaukie in Wisconsin, and has been a member and President of the Legislative Council of the Territory, showing that Dr. Prentiss has not been unmindful of the education of his children.—*My Address before the Mass. Med. Society.*

DR. VALENTINE SEAMAN. This eminent physician was the fourth son of Willet Seaman, a native of North Hempstead, L. I., and a distinguished merchant of New York. He was the son of Samuel, grandson of Nathaniel, and great grandson of Capt. John Seaman, who arrived from England and settled at Hempstead about the year 1660.

The subject of this notice was born April 2d, 1770, and like his father adhered through life to the Society of Friends. Having received the elements of an ordinary education, he commenced his medical studies under the care of Dr. Nicholas Romeyn, at that time conspicuous as an able teacher of several branches of the healing art, and who, by his connection with Queen's College, New Jersey, was enabled, with his collaborators, to impart to his scholars an entire system in medicine and surgery. The city Almshouse was at that time the only institution in New York in which medical instruction was imparted, and in this young Seaman entered as resident physician, the duties of which he discharged most worthily, aided by the practical acumen of his preceptor.

In 1791, he repaired to the University of Pennsylvania, and attended the lectures of Shippen, Rush, Kuhn and others, where he was honored with the degree of M. D. Like almost all other candidates for popular favor in professional life, he encountered many difficulties at the commencement of his medical career, and it was not till the appearance of the malignant yellow fever in the city of New York, in 1795, that his merits became better known and more widely appreciated. He entered with great zeal into an examination of the nature of the pestilence, and drew up a paper of some extent on the character of the disease as it had prevailed in the city in 1791, and other succeeding years. He came to the conclusion that the disease might have been imported, and that it required a combination of local causes to give it potency.

About this time he commenced a course of lectures on midwifery in the city Almshouse, for female practitioners, and published a syllabus of his instructions. His account of the epidemic disease which occurred in 1800 was published in the 'Medical Repository,' which may be referred to for other contributions to medical science, made by him during his professional life.

Interested in inquiries of a physical nature he was not indifferent to the mineralogical society of New York, which was organized about this time, and having made personal examination on the subject, he printed a small volume on the mineral waters of Ballston and Saratoga, a performance not without its use, at that early stage of philosophical research into the native products of the United States.

His appointment in 1796, as one of the surgeons of the New York Hospital, in connection with Post, Kissam and Bayley, he held until his death, and the better to render it advantageous to the medical student, he projected, in 1811, a course of clinical surgery, while his friend, Dr. Edward Miller, assumed clinical medicine. This plan was soon after interrupted by the lamented death of Dr. Miller in the spring of 1812. The personal intimacy and friendship of these individuals was of the most cordial and confidential nature. Upon the death of his associate, Dr. Seaman paid a feeling tribute to his private character and professional worth, in a special discourse delivered in the surgical theatre of the hospital.

Dr. Seaman was conspicuously active in introducing the practice of vaccination in New York. The vaccine virus had been forwarded to the city some time before, by George Pearson of London; but Seaman, who had enjoyed a personal acquaintance with Jenner during his visit to Europe for the benefit of his health, feeling the deepest interest in the inquiry, obtained matter from a patient who had been vaccinated by Dr. Waterhouse of Boston, and who arrived here at a proper period to take the infection. With this matter he vaccinated his own son and a number of citizens. The disorder assumed precisely the description given of it by Jenner. In 1816 he published a discourse on the subject, which he had delivered before his clinical class.

In 1810–11, Dr. Seaman united with several other professional gentlemen and formed a new medical institution, which was associated with Queen's College, New Brunswick, then under the presidency of the Rev. Dr. Livingstone, which new organization lasted about three years.

His philanthropic labors were not limited to the profession. He was a member of the Manumission Society, for the liberation of slaves and the protection of those manumitted; and for many years he was an officer of the society, which he deemed an efficient means of meliorating the condition of the African race; and with C. P. Colden, Thomas Eddy, John Mussey and others, he had reason to be gratified with the benefits resulting from his efforts.

In the winter of 1815–16 his health was much disturbed by an inflammation of the lungs, from which he was never relieved, and which ultimately terminated in pulmonary consumption, of which he died in June, 1817, in the 48th year of his age. He was married in early life to the second daughter of John Ferris, of Westchester, by whom he had a family of nine children. Dr. Seaman was a laborious practitioner in the healing art; as a clinical physician he was most assiduous, and his benevolence and humanity were worthy of himself and the respectable society of Friends to which he belonged. Among the list of his medical pupils was Dr. Valentine Mott of New York.—*J. W. Francis, M. D.*

DR. THOMAS SEMMES was born in Prince George's county, Maryland, Aug. 13, 1779. He prosecuted his professional studies at Alexandria, Virginia, under the direction of the late Dr. Elisha Cullen Dick, and graduated at the University of Pennsylvania in the year 1801. His inaugural dissertation on the general effects of lead, and on the nature and properties of the *saccharum saturni*, presented many striking and original observations concerning the character of that substance, and was distinguished by a depth of reflection and solidity of judgment which gave evidence of future eminence in his profession.

After having visited France, Spain, and several other countries in Europe, Dr. Semmes returned to Alexandria, where he continued to reside and to pursue the practice of medicine until the period of his death.

An indisposition to appear before the public as an author, great diffidence, and a love of retirement, were the causes why talent and learning of no ordinary degree, remained in comparative obscurity. He preferred the secluded path of duty, benefiting his fellow men by the personal application of his great skill and knowledge, to stations which he could easily have attained, but in which, though his abilities might have appeared more conspicuous, his usefulness might have been more questioned.

The theoretical views of Dr. Semmes were clear, profound, and often bold and original. His practical success was almost unprecedented, and the pub-

65

lic confidence was never, at any moment, or under any circumstances, withheld from him. That confidence was amply repaid by his energy, zeal and untiring assiduity in his practice generally ; but more especially during the epidemics which raged in Alexandria in 1803, and 1821, and more recently during the prevalence of the Asiatic cholera, so called, in the summer of 1832.

The acquirements of Dr. Semmes were not confined to medical knowledge. He was an excellent scholar, and well read in general literature. His personal virtues and accomplishments are recorded in the hearts of all who knew him. Well may the remark of Horace, concerning his friend, be applied to him. He was ' *homo ad unguem factus.*'

(*From the Am. Med. Jour.* 1833.)

Dr. Erastus Sergeant was the oldest son of the Rev. Erastus Sergeant, the first minister of Stockbridge, Berkshire county, Massachusetts, the missionary to the Housatonnuc Indians at that place. And not only the first minister of Stockbridge, but one of the very first white settlers of that town. It is believed that Erastus, the subject of this memoir, was the first male white child ever born in Stockbridge. He was born in the year 1742. I know little of his early life, having lost the notes containing a memorial of him by his brother-in-law, the venerable Dr. Oliver Partridge of Stockbridge, now living (1843) in the 92d year of his age.

Dr. Sergeant was fitted for college, I believe, under

the superintendence of his father, and entered Princeton College in New Jersey, where he remained two
or three years, I believe, a classmate of the celebrated
Dr. Benjamin Rush of Philadelphia, but I think he
did not graduate there. When he left college he
commenced the study of medicine with my grandfather, Dr. Thomas Williams of Deerfield, who was
then one of the most distinguished physicians and
surgeons in western Massachusetts. He remained
with Dr. Williams two years, the usual period of medical pupilage in those days, and then returned and
commenced the practice of physic and surgery in
Stockbridge, his native place, not far from the year
1764. He was immediately introduced to a good
run of business, thus reversing the doctrine that 'a
prophet is not without honor save in his own country.'

So long ago as the year 1774, when Dr. Partridge,
from whom I have the subsequent information, commenced the practice of medicine in Stockbridge, the
medical men who were engaged in the practice in
Berkshire, were Drs. Barnard of Sheffield, Whiting
of Bennington, Sergeant of Stockbridge, Childs of
Pittsfield, Guiteau of Lanesboro', and Lewis of Lee.
These were all good and respectable physicians, who
often met together in consultations. In difficult cases
Dr. Sergeant was the last resort. He was a most
excellent practical surgeon, and he performed nearly
all the capital surgical operations in his circle of
practice, which extended over a diameter of thirty
miles in extent, and he was considered to be very
successful in his operations, even in cases which
were considered to be desperate. He educated se-

veral students in the profession of medicine, who afterwards proved to be eminent men and successful practitioners. His library was large and well filled with the standard medical literature of the day.

He was elected a Fellow of the Massachusetts Medical Society in the year 1785. He continued a member till the year 1814, a period of twenty-nine years, when he died at the age of 72 years. During this period the Society often honored him with the office of Counsellor.

Dr. Sergeant was tall, erect and spare in flesh. In the latter part of his life he was threatened with pulmonary consumption. While sitting at his dinner table in November, 1814, he suddenly began to cough. He arose from the table and went to the fire, and was immediately attacked with hæmoptysis in so violent a manner as almost instantaneously to extinguish life. His friends rushed to his assistance, but the vital spark was forever extinguished.

Dr. Partridge in concluding his remarks upon his character observes—'He was endowed with a sound judgment and skill in his profession, was sedate, with a large share of Christian grace, and he was truly the 'beloved physician.' It was said of him that no one ever spoke ill of him from his youth up.' This is a brief but true account of this most excellent and worthy man.

Dr. DANIEL SHELDON, who practised medicine with great reputation and success, in Litchfield, Connecticut, for more than half a century, was born in the city of Hartford, October 19th, 1750, O. Style. His early education was received at the long known and celebrated 'Hartford Grammar School,' then, no less than now, appreciated as one of the best literary institutions of the kind in New England.

After leaving this school, and when quite young, he placed himself under the tuition of the eccentric and celebrated Dr. Seth Bird of Litchfield, one of the most prominent medical men of his time in the State, who was his relative by marriage, and a most suitable instructor for a young man of Sheldon's age and abilities. He continued with Dr. Bird some years. When at the early age of twenty-one he commenced the practice of medicine in that part of Woodbury, Conn., now incorporated into a separate town by the name of Washington. His practice soon became so extensive that he took as a partner in business Dr. Seth Hastings, father of the celebrated musician of that name, a gentleman who afterwards gained great celebrity in his profession.

While Dr. Sheldon remained in Woodbury he married Miss Charlotte Judson, by whom he had two children, one a daughter who was insane for a long period, and died at the Retreat in Hartford. The other, Daniel Sheldon, Esq., who was for many years Clerk in the Treasury Department at Washington with Secretaries Wolcott and Gallatin, and afterwards went to France with Mr. Gallatin as Secretary of Legation and charge of affairs. When Dr. Lemuel Hopkins left Litchfield for the city of Hartford in 1784, Dr. Sheldon removed to Litchfield, and continued there till his death. In this new location his practice became more respectable and extensive, and he established a reputation which was not surpassed by any medical practitioner in the State. Dr. Sheldon married for his second wife Miss Huldah Stone, sister of Mrs. Hopkins. From this time a friendship commenced between these two eminent medical men which, continued till the death of Dr. Hopkins in 1800.

In person Dr. Sheldon was small, slender and delicate. He was predisposed by the conformation of his chest to pulmonary complaints, and while young had an abscess formed in his lungs, which burst and discharged an immense quantity of pus so fetid that for months after it was disagreeable to be in the room with him, or even to ride by his side on the highway. Dr. Sheldon gave the writer a particular account of the illness which preceded this great abscess. He was sick two weeks with what was considered a mild remittent fever, in which he had chills, exacerbations of heat, and finally free sweating. He was attended by Dr. Bird and Hopkins, who were esteemed the best physicians in the State, and who were not inferior to any others. On the fourteenth day of the fever, Dr. Bird visited his patient, and found him in a free perspiration, and encouraged him that as the time for a crisis had arrived, and the perspiration indicated its commencement, he might expect that the disease would soon yield and he would be again convalescent. Before Dr. Bird left the room the abscess burst, and established beyond controversy the true nature of the disease. This ulcer did not wholly heal for two years. During its discharge he took an immense quantity of Peruvian bark in infusion or decoction, and contracted a habit of taking opium, which continued till old age, when it was abandoned. Dr. Sheldon informed the writer that such was the quantity of bark taken in the course of his illness that the grounds rejected amounted to more than *two bushels.* He took from two to four drachms of opium daily for nearly or quite forty years. In old age he left it off without detriment gradually diminishing it for two or three years. His usual pill was a drachm which he swallowed without difficulty.

In a very short time after the discharge of this abscess of the lungs, Dr. Sheldon resumed his practice which had been interrupted for a few weeks only, and rode on a bleak and rough country more than half a century, always on horseback, performing an immense amount of business, while his emaciated and extremely delicate frame, drawn over almost to a curve, would indicate such a feeble state as entirely to forbid any active employment. Dr. Sheldon lived to the extreme age of 89 years and a half, and towards the close of life became corpulent and bulky. He died April 10th, 1840.

Dr. Sheldon was endowed by nature with a vigorous and well balanced mind; he was quick to discover and ready to apply all his knowledge in the practice of his profession. He had the tact which led him at once to the indication of disease, and boldness in his prescriptions which only comes properly from a thorough knowledge of the case. He was also a learned man, fond of books, and a thorough, diligent student. He had a faculty of gleaning from authors whatever was valuable in their works by a hasty perusal of their pages. His memory was retentive, he profited greatly by his own experience, and was enabled to have analogies by which that experience was of great value to him. In the treatment of pulmonary consumption he had great and desired celebrity. Many persons affected with symptoms of that disease, flocked to him from a great distance, and his success sustained his reputation, till from age and infirmity he ceased to practice his profession. The writer met him repeatedly in such cases. There was no quackery about his practice, but plain, open, common sense views of what changes might be wrought by perseverance and suitable remedies.

Accustomed as he was to the use of opium in his own case, he was not afraid to prescribe it for others. His remedies were simple, but effective. Substantial diet, narcotic and tonic remedies, and riding on horseback, which he considered superior to all other means of restoration, and quite superior to all other modes of exercise. He was a successful physician in this and other chronic cases, and his counsel was sought by many respectable individuals near and remote. It was my good fortune to meet him occasionally, and at our last interview he spent some days with me at my residence. His conversation was most instructive and his kindness and courtesy made a deep impression on my feelings. In investigating a case of pulmonary consumption, he paid great attention to the nature of the secretions from the lungs. If the pus was benign, he gave, in many cases, a favorable prognosis, and many cases with symptoms very alarming, recovered under his prescriptions, in which other physicians predicted unfavorably. In a case under my care in which low diet, and antiphlogistics had been prescribed by a physician high in the confidence of the patient, he recommended animal food, and a generous diet of vegetables and fruits, myrrh, iron and opium. The patient gained strength, flesh and courage under this treatment, but finally fell a victim to the disease.

The evening of Dr. Sheldon's days were spent in tranquillity and ease. To a competency saved from the earnings of his professional life, a good fortune was added by a legacy from a son, who died in France some years before his father.

Dr. Sheldon was an ardent friend of medical improvement. He was one of the original petitioners for the establishment of a State Medical Society, and for many years was an active member of the Society, and its Secretary.

The honorary degree of Doctor of 'Medicine was conferred upon him by the corporation of Yale College.

Dr. Siccary of Virginia. I introduce the name of this physician in this place, in connection with the use of the Tomato plant, which is now so generally employed both in medicine and as an article of diet. It is believed that he was a Portuguese Jew. Mr. Jefferson states that we are indebted to him for the introduction of that admirable vegetable, the Tomato.

66

' He was of opinion that a person who should eat a
sufficient abundance of these apples would never die.
Whether he followed his own prescription is not
known; but he certainly attained to a very old age,
and particularly for the climate in which he lived.
The tomato is raised in abundance in Virginia and
the adjoining states, and is regarded as a great luxury, and by some is considered a preservative against
bilious diseases.'—*Dr. J. A. Smith, in Sewall's discourse.*

DR. ISAAC SMITH was a native of Easthampton
Society, where he spent his early days in acquiring
the elements of that education which was the foundation of, and prepared the way for, the usefulness so
manifest in his after life. He commenced medical
practice after completing his course of studies with
reference to that pursuit, at North Killingworth, where
he resided a few years, and there became familiar
with that description of typhus fever which has prevailed to some extent the present season; and afterwards established himself in his profession at Chatham, where he continued to practice until his death,
a period of 39 years.

In his deportment and intercourse with the members of his profession, he was always open, candid,
frank and hospitable. With the sick, upright, beloved, kind, attentive and sympathizing, always ready to
sacrifice his comfort, ease and happiness for the good
of his patient. His practice was plain and well
adapted to the case, and his native judgment and

long experience gave him a claim to confidence which was rarely disappointed. He was a regular attendant upon divine service, and a communicant of the Congregational Church, always appearing to rejoice in christian privileges and duties.

Though the friends of the deceased wish not for the 'language of panegyric,' nor do we claim for him the more distinguished talents, or that he was pre-eminently skillful in *all* the diseases to which a community is incident, yet he possessed, in an eminent degree, the key to the fine sensibilities of the soul, and knew the sympathies and idiosyncrasies of his subjects, and could more readily address his conversation, and adapt his prescriptions, in their case, than now can any other.

The disease which caused his death was a fever, mild in its attack, and he was enabled to attend to his professional duties, with few exceptions, until about a week before he died. He appeared unaware of the lurking mischief which was undermining his constitution. Retching and vomiting, with a redundant secretion of vitiated bile, and distressing hiccough, with tympanites, were the most urgent symptoms in the last stage, which continued until the system gave way. In his sickness he was seldom heard to complain, though during the last week his sufferings were great. The calmness and composure with which he met death, evinced most clearly the character of the man. With a strong reliance upon a Savior, and his soul firmly stayed upon his God, he bade adieu to his family, his friends and the world, on the night of the 19th of December, 1839, aged 67 years, in the full hope of an immortality beyond the grave.—*T. M. 2nd, in Bost. Med. Jour.*

Dr. Nathan Smith. Perhaps a more perfect instance of persevering industry rendering a man eminent and useful, cannot be found in the annals of our profession, than that of the great New England surgeon, the subject of the present notice. The late eminent Dr. Dwight, President of Yale College, who was intimately acquainted with Dr. Smith, and was his personal friend, used to hold up his character to the senior classes in that institution, as a pattern of indomitable industry under difficulties, by giving them a brief sketch of his life. And a better one could not have been selected. In proof of this we need only to give a brief outline of his life. This must be peculiarly interesting to the profession in New England, for it is believed that no physician either before, during, or since his time, had so wide a sphere of popularity; and he was as well known in almost all our towns as their resident physicians and clergymen are.

Dr. Nathan Smith was the son of respectable parents, whose circumstances as to property were limited. He was born at Rehoboth, Massachusetts, September 13th, 1762. His father removed to Chester, in Vermont, while the subject of our memoir was quite a youth. His early education was extremely limited, having only the advantages of a common school, in a comparatively newly settled country. His summers, too, like those of most of the sons of far-

mers, who are not fitting themselves for professional
pursuits, and perhaps many of his winters, were spent
in the employment of farming.

While he was quite a youth, towards the close of
the revolutionary war, he enlisted in the Vermont militia, stationed on the frontier, for the purpose of re-
sisting the incursions of the savages, who were prowl-
ing in that section of the country. It is not exactly
known how long he remained in the army. He has
often entertained his friends with a history of his privations and sufferings, while encamped in the wilderness with scarcely any of the necessaries or even con-
veniences of civil life. While in this campaign he
was shot at by an Indian, and the ball narrowly
missed striking him. He did not suffer alone in these
privations and trials. His fellow citizens generally, and the pioneers of the forest were subjected to
the same hardships and dangers in repelling the assaults of an implacable and blood-thirsty savage foe.
Young Smith had learnt the use of the musket in the
occupation of hunting and securing game, and driv-
ing the ferocious predatory beasts of the forest from
the habitations of the first settlers. These are the
common employments of the first settlers of any portion of our extended country. It was no uncommon
thing in those days for the young hunters to be absent
from their homes for several days. On one of these
hunting excursions, he was left by his associates, in
the depth of winter, at a considerable distance from
home, and with a very scanty stock of provisions.
Even this short supply was exhausted, while he was
looking for the return of his companions, and unfor-

tunately for him a sudden thaw occurred which softened the snow, which was then several feet deep on
the ground so much as to render it impossible to travel far. He remained here in this situation for several days, and lived entirely upon the flesh of some
game which he had killed, without bread or salt.
By the time that traveling became practicable he was
attacked, in consequence of innutritious food and exposure with afflicting disease. He, however, reached
the nearest house with great difficulty, and he was
confined here and at his father's house for many
months, in consequence of this sickness. He continued this kind of active and laborious life until the age
of twenty-four. We are not informed of his acquirements in knowledge during this time, but probably
they must have been small. Still they must have
been somewhat respectable, for during some of the
winter months he was employed as a teacher of a
common school in the neighborhood, which must have
required some talents.

A trifling event occurred about this period, which
directed him in the course of the employment in
which he was to be engaged during his future life.
He was accidentally present at a surgical operation
which was performed by Dr. Josiah Goodhue, then,
and for a long while afterwards, the most successful
and eminent surgeon in that section of the country.
He was deeply interested in the operation, and after
this he devoted his thoughts to the structure of the
human frame, and was ambitious to learn more concerning the wonderful formation of the human body.
He soon after consulted Dr. Goodhue upon the sub-

ject, and desired to become a medical pupil in his
office. They were then unacquainted with each
other. The Doctor inquired of him his qualifications. He was informed that till this period he had
only labored with his hands during his life. Dr.
Goodhue kindly informed him that he could not take
students who had not received a preparatory education ; and gave as a reason that the profession was
in a low state in that part of the country, and that
the only way to elevate it in the estimation of the
public, was for young men with the proper qualifications only to be advised to pursue the study of the
profession. He told him, likewise, that if he would
place himself under the tuition of a person competent to instruct him, and would obtain as much literary information as would enable him to enter the
Freshman class of Harvard College, he would accept
him as a student. The advice was cheerfully adopted. He placed himself under the instruction of the
Rev. Mr. Whiting of Rockingham, Vermont, where
he remained till he was qualified to enter the office
of his medical preceptor. He studied his profession
for three full years with Dr. Goodhue, who now resided in Putney, Vermont. His preceptor always
attested to his great assiduity and industry in his
professional studies, and he always regarded him with
that esteem and even love, which is always elicited
in the mind of a preceptor when they are drawn forth
by diligence and good habits on the part of the student. Dr. Smith always reciprocated these kind
feelings, and always spoke of his instructor in the
highest terms of approbation and applause, as well

for the information which he gave him while a pupil, as for the good advice and instruction which he communicated to him in after life.

Dr. Smith commenced the practice of his profession in Cornish, N. H., where he continued for two or three years, when he suspended his practice for a while and attended the medical and philosophical lectures in Harvard University. Here he received the degree of Doctor of Medicine, after having read an inaugural dissertation on the circulation of the blood. He then returned to Cornish, and re-commenced the practice of his profession.

At that time the country was new, and in fact almost a wilderness, with here and there a flourishing town and little village. The practice of medicine there, at that time, was at an extremely low ebb. A great portion of the physicians there were poorly educated, and of course unskillful. The same remark applies to almost the whole of the states of Vermont and New Hampshire, except, perhaps, the town of Portsmouth, and a few in the immediate vicinity of it. To be sure there were some eminent physicians and surgeons settled throughout various parts of these states, whose talents were highly respectable, but they were few in comparison with the numbers at present. He viewed this state of things with regret and painful forebodings, and instead of profiting himself merely, by taking advantage of the ignorance of others, by striving to elevate himself, he zealously engaged in the endeavor to correct the evil, by furnishing to others the means and opportunities of procuring an enlarged and competent medical education. To effect this purpose he proposed the establishment of a Medical Institution in connection with Dartmouth College, at Hanover, N. H. This proposition was soon acceded to, and the appointment of Professor of Medicine was conferred upon Dr. Smith.

For many years he taught all, or nearly all the branches of the profession, which are now taught in our most celebrated medical schools, unaided and alone. He was not satisfied with this arrangement, and he wished to qualify himself more thoroughly for the employment as a teacher of medicine, and he was determined to avail himself of the advantages which were then presented at the great medical school of Edinburgh, then in the zenith of its glory, and considered to be the best medical school in the world. His practice at this time had become profitable, but he was willing to relinquish it for a while for the purpose of obtaining more information on the branches which it had now become his duty to teach. He went to Great Britain and remained there about a year attending medical lectures in Edinburgh under the instruction of those luminaries in medical science, the illustrious Monro and Dr. Black, who were then zealously engaged in teaching the most important branches in that celebrated school, and attending the practice of the unrivalled medical hospital. His visit to Europe was attended with the most beneficial results. He was at an age in his profession when he could receive the most advantage from it. He had practised long enough to know what he ought further to learn, and practising upon what he then learnt, on

67

his return, his course was one of unsurpassed success. The medical school at Hanover, under his auspices and co-operation, now flourished in a very flattering degree. Other professors were associated with him, and medical students now flocked to this school from various parts of the country. It commenced with twenty students, but that was a period when medical students did not, as they now do, consider it necessary to attend courses of medical lectures for the completion of their medical pupilage, and long before he left the school, the average number was not less than sixty. These students generally resided in various parts of the New England States. As death gradually encroached upon the older members of the profession in these places, these students occupied their places, and in this way that portion of the country became filled with an enterprising race of young physicians who looked to Dr. Smith for counsel and advice in those difficult cases which are continually occurring in the practice of our profession. This, of course, gave him a great amount of business, and in this way he became known throughout New England as one of the very best of physicians and surgeons in the country.

Few men in less extensive business than Dr. Smith can estimate the labor which he endured in traveling over such an extent of country, a considerable part of which was a wilderness, and the territory more rough and mountainous than any part of our country. Nor can we calculate the immense good and happiness which he accomplished by affording professional counsel, advice and instruction to the younger members of the profession, as well as immense benefit which he gave the sick and distressed.

He continued these laborious exertions in instruction and practice while he remained in Hanover, which was until the autumn of 1813. He was now invited to accept the chair as a Professor, in the Medical Institution of Yale College, then just established at New Haven, which he accepted. From this period to the time of his death he lectured upon the Theory and Practice of Physic and Surgery to the various classes of medical students which attended that Institution. He also, since that time, delivered a course of lectures on the same branches in the Medical School at Dartmouth, and one at the Vermont University at Burlington; and also two courses at the Medical Institution of Brunswick College in Maine. His career as an instructor as well as of a practitioner of Physic and Surgery, since his removal to New Haven, was equally great, as while at Hanover. From seventy to ninety students at least, a term, have resorted to New Haven for the benefit of his instruction, and without detracting from the merits of his associates it is no injustice to say, that a great object of their attending this institution in preference to others, was to learn from his kindness and experience the practical part of the profession of medicine. Invalids either from medical or surgical cases, have been in the habit of resorting to New Haven, during his sojourn there, from all parts of the country, for the purpose of receiving the benefit of his skill. He not only did a great amount of business in the neighborhood, but he was frequently called into every county, and into almost every town in the State of Connecticut, and frequently into the neighboring States.

So active, so useful and so honored has been his life, that it was fondly hoped that his years and his usefulness might be prolonged for a long succession of years. But the final mandate of Jehovah must be obeyed by all. It summoned our beloved and faithful friend to a higher sphere of action, and left his mourning family and friends to bewail their irreparable loss. He was attacked about the middle of July, 1828, with a severe sickness, which continued but a short time, but it left him in a very enfeebled state, from which his friends perceived with deep regret that he did not entirely recover. This weakness continued through the summer and autumnal months, but his mind, notwithstanding, was firm and elastic, and did not partake of the debility of the body. He was unwilling to yield to what he supposed to be a trifling complaint, and, with the exception of a few days, he continued the laborious practice of his profession. Without any material alteration in his health for four weeks from this period, he was attacked suddenly with a severe influenza, which was accompanied and followed with a violent pain in the head attended with vertigo. These symptoms, however, were palliated by the use of remedies. On Thursday evening the 13th inst., he noticed a trifling numbness of one of his hands, and there was a slight indistinctness in his speech. The paralytic symptoms gained ground until the morning of the 26th, when life became extinct at 6 o'clock in the evening. He died in the 67th year of his age.

The above facts were principally obtained from the eulogium pronounced upon Dr. Smith, by Professor J. Knight of Yale College, one of his intimate friends. I cannot do better at the conclusion of this memoir than to give the closing remarks of Dr. Knight upon the subject.

' That our deceased friend was no ordinary man, the brief story of his life, already told, most conclusively proves. In early life he was a poor boy, in a comparatively small village, with a limited education, and still more limited means of advancing it. Thus he remained until past the period when most men are fixed in their situation for life. At this time his mind received a new impulse. He was resolved to render himself useful and distinguished. Having chosen his profession, he entered at once, with the decision which marked his character through life, upon the work of preparing himself for it. The means of acquiring an education were furnished almost entirely by his own exertions. He appears for many years, to have labored to acquire property, only to extend it in advancing his knowledge of literature and medicine. Following this purpose with untiring zeal, he obtained a medical education, such as then was almost entirely unknown in New England. With the same zeal, activity and intelligence, he entered upon the practice of his profession, and subsequently upon the business of instruction. By

pursuing this course his reputation gradually increased, until he became more extensively known than
any other medical man in New England. Indeed it
is doubted whether any other man in New England,
of any profession, possessed so large a number of
acquaintances and friends.

His acquaintance was not only extensive, but
reached to every rank in society. The poor knew
him as their benefactor; the sick, as their skillful
and attentive physician; the rich were honored by
his society; and the wise and good received him as
their friend and companion.

At the same time his influence over medical literature was equally extensive. This influence was
exerted through his large acquaintance among medical men, by his advice and example, as well as more
directly through the medium of the various medical
schools, which were favored with his instructions.
By means of his influence thus exerted, he effected,
over a large extent of country, a great and salutary
change in the medical profession. The assertion that
he has done more for the improvement of Physic and
Surgery in New England than any other man, will
by no one be deemed invidious. If the accomplishment of objects so important, with means so limited;
raising and sustaining so high a reputation from so
low an origin; the advancing in such a degree one
of the liberal professions, over so a large a country, be
not marks of strong native talents, fostered by industry, I know not where indications of such talents can
be found.

To form a correct opinion of the character of Dr. Smith, it will be proper to view him in the various relations which he sustained.

As a physician and surgeon, he early attained a high rank; a rank which he held through life. The present is neither the place, nor the occasion to inquire into his opinions upon medical and surgical subjects, nor upon his mode of practice. It may, however, be proper, as illustrative of his character, to investigate those qualities of his mind and habits of life, which raised him to this elevated station.

The first faculty of his mind which I mention, was a keen, discriminating inquisitiveness in every thing submitted to his inspection. Nothing passed before him unseen or unheeded. This quality, which in a weak mind is mere inquisitiveness, exercised to gratify an idle curiosity, is in a strong mind, a principle of rational inquiry, seeking in every direction for information to be applied to some valuable purpose. By the continual exercise of this quality, ripened into a habit of steady, fixed observation, he collected in his mind, not only the outlines of the diseases with which man is afflicted, but all the minute circumstances relative to their causes, progress and termination; and the effect of remedies upon them in their various stages.

Another faculty of his mind was a memory highly retentive. This is so nearly allied to the habit of observation just mentioned, and so certain is it that whatever we observe minutely is long remembered, that we are not surprised to find them so often associated in the same person. With him every fact which he observed, every truth which he heard stated, appeared to be indelibly impressed upon his mind. In the last year of his life, he would relate with wonderful accuracy, not only the great, but also the minute events which he had witnessed. Especially he remembered the diseases which he had seen, in all their varieties; the surgical operations which he had performed, and the causes requiring their performance, with all the attendant circumstances of person, time and place. By the aid of this faculty his mind became a storehouse well filled with facts suited to his necessities. From it he could, at will, draw forth materials to guide him in his practice; to confirm and illustrate his opinions.

Another faculty, which contributed more than either of the foregoing to his eminence, was the power of rendering all the knowledge which he acquired, whether from reading or observation, to some useful practical purpose. This is opposed to mere speculation. It does not inquire into matters which have no practical bearing upon the happiness of man; but it observes all things as they now exist, in the present age, and in this country. It looks upon the evils now to be remedied, and the blessings now to be enjoyed. It leads the physician to view diseases and accidents as they present themselves to his own eyes; and to summon together all the information and every fact which he possesses, to bear upon the case immediately before him. This faculty is familiarly called plain common sense. It was possessed in a high degree by Dr. Smith, in relation to all subjects connected with his profession. The same faculty was illustriously displayed in the lives of Washington, Franklin, Sherman, Dwight and Whitney.

Another faculty possessed by the deceased, and which aided him much in his successful career, was an undaunted moral courage. The physician often feels it to be his duty to apply a powerful remedy, and the surgeon to perform a painful and hazardous operation, in cases where he can give no positive assurances of their success. The timid man shrinks from such high responsibility, and suffers his patient to be destroyed by disease. Such was not Dr. Smith. Having satisfied himself what course was best for his patient, he honestly advised, and fearlessly pursued it; regardless of the censure that might follow, should it prove unsuccessful. With him there was no hesitation, no wavering between duty and expediency; between the welfare of his patient and his own reputation. This conduct, in one who valued reputation so highly, is the strongest proof of the existence of that courage of the mind, so much more noble, and so much more rarely found, than mere physical valor.

To these intellectual qualities were added others of a moral nature, which facilitated his progress, and rendered it more successful. I allude to the kindness, assiduity and delicacy with which he treated his patients. In him kindness was a natural feeling, springing out directly from the benevolence of his disposition. This feeling he doubtless cultivated from a knowledge of the effects which its expression produces in alleviating the distress as well of the body as the mind. In all his intercourse with the sick, the kindness of his heart beamed upon his countenance, and flowed forth

68

from his lips. Their faces brightened, and their spirits were roused at his approach, not more by the relief which they expected, than by the kindness with
which it was afforded.

The assiduity of his attention to his patients dangerously sick, was unremitted. He watched at their
bed side by day and by night, administering to all
their wants, and performing the offices of a kind
friend as well as of a skillful physician.

The esteem and respect which he entertained for
the virtuous female character, and the purity and delicacy of his conduct towards those who possessed it,
rendered him acceptable to all such as their physician.
The continual exercise of these feelings gained for
him at once their confidence and esteem.

As an instructor, the reputation of Dr. Smith was
high from the time he began the business of instruction. Of the method which he adopted in relation
to this subject, in the earlier part of his life, I have
little information. The facts, however, that for many
years, he gave instruction in all the branches of Medical and Surgical Science ; that this instruction was
acceptable to classes of intelligent young men ; and
that many who were thus instructed have become
eminent in their profession, prove not only versatility
of talent, but variety and extent of information, with
a happy method of communicating it. His mode of
communicating instruction, since his connection with
the institution in this place, has been simple, natural
and unaffected. He sought no aid from an artificial
style, but merely poured forth, in the plain language
of enlightened conversation, the treasures of his wis-

dom and experience. He occupied but little time with the theories and opinions of other men, referring to books only for the facts they contain; nor did he often indulge in theoretic speculations of his own; but gave principally the results of his practice and experience. His object was to instill into the minds of his pupils the leading principles of their profession; not entering fully into the details of the practice, but leaving it for them to apply these principles to individual cases as they should present themselves. These principles he would illustrate by appropriate cases, furnished by a long course of practice; related always in an impressive, and often in a playful manner, so as at once to gain the attention, and impress the truth illustrated upon the mind. He often urged upon them the necessity of correct moral deportment, of industrious habits, and especially of forming a judgment for themselves, concerning the cases which were presented to them.

He endeavored to inspire them, both by precept and example, with a love of their profession, with activity in the practice of it, and a zeal for the promotion of its best interests.

At the same time that he communicated to his pupils instruction, he gained their affection by the suavity of his manners, and by a course of conduct towards them, by which they were satisfied that he ardently desired their best interests. Of all who have been instructed by him, the number is small of those who were not his personal friends.

The various relations of life were sustained by Dr.

Smith in an exemplary manner. As a citizen, the same spirit which prompted him to enlist in the service of his country, when engaged in war, led him to support by his influence, her free institutions in time of peace; as a lover of good order, he rejoiced in the enaction and execution of wholesome laws and regulations; and as a friend of morality, he discountenanced vice in every form. The purity of his life, it is believed, arose not so much from the restraints of society, as from a purity of mind which remained unsullied. So far as personal observation enables me to speak, he regarded the institutions and ministers of religion with highest reverence. With regard to subjects of this nature, it is believed that his last days were his best days.

In his relations to his fellow men, there are particular traits of his character which ought not to pass unnoticed. He possessed strong social feelings and habits. Accustomed from early life to the society of men in every station, he entered readily into free and unreserved intercourse with all. In companies of every kind, learned or unlearned, polished or otherwise, his free conversation, his fund of anecdotes, and the acuteness of his remarks upon all subjects, whether relating to the common affairs of life, or the more important concerns of morality and literature, rendered him a welcome guest. His manners, which were free, yet unpresuming and unshackled by the forms of ceremonial observances, were such as to impose no inconvenient restraints upon others or upon himself. No one delighted

more in social intercourse with his friends, and in
a free interchange of feelings and opinions with
them. This was one of the pleasures of his life,
and this endeared him to those with whom he associated.

Dr. Smith was eminently a benevolent man. He
regarded man as his brother, and when in distress,
as a brother he afforded him relief. No one, it is
presumed, ever heard him say to the poor and destitute, ' Be ye warmed and be ye clothed,' without at
the same time furnishing the means of relieving their
necessities. That his charity was always discriminating is not probably true. It was the charity of
the heart, and not of calculation ; and often his most
valuable benefactions were rendered in the course of
professional exertions.

Although it would have been obviously improper
to enter in the body of this discourse, upon a consideration of the medical opinions and modes of
practice of Dr. Smith, a few remarks upon them
may not in this place be unacceptable. Upon these
subjects I have no means of information at hand,
previous to his removal to this city. The few remarks which are made, must therefore be considered as confined to the last thirteen years of his life.

All who have witnessed the practice of Dr. Smith,
must have remarked the rapidity and decision, and
at the same time the general accuracy with which he
formed an opinion on the cases of dieases submitted
to him. He appeared to strip diseases of all their
adventitious attendants, and to seize at once upon

their important and essential phenomena. This process was often so rapid as to resemble more the effect of intuition, than the regular deductions from a train of reasoning.

With the same rapidity, he saw, as it were with a glance, the course proper to be pursued, and with equal promptness, applied the appropriate remedies. This course of practice can by no means be held out as an example to the young and inexperienced ; nor is it perhaps the best mode to be pursued by any one. It is justifiable only in those whose habits of observation and discrimination have been matured by a long course of enlightened experience. Even such would escape occasional errors, by more careful deliberation.

The practice of Dr. Smith in the treatment of acute diseases was essentially the same as that of the other respectable physicians of New England ; varied somewhat perhaps by his notions of the nature of typhus, the prevailing fever of the country. What these notions were, and what his practice founded on them was, he has fully explained in his treatise upon typhus fever, published a few years since. If he had any peculiarities in the treatment of other diseases than pure typhus, they consisted in discarding the use of remedies comparatively inert, and in employing those which are more powerful and effective. He often asserted that the use of medicines, which, in common language, if they do no good, will do no harm, is usually the result of timidity or ignorance ; and that the physician who knows not when and how to apply or to withhold the more powerful articles of the materia medica, was unfit for his profession.

In the treatment of chronic diseases, energetic remedies, especially such as acted powerfully upon the stomach and the other organs of digestion, were more especially resorted to by him. To this course he appears to have been led, partly by his own reflections upon the nature and causes of most chronic diseases, and partly, by the situation in which he was placed, with respect to patients of this class.

Many of them consulted him after they had employed all the ordinary means of medication. Others still consulted him from such a distance as precluded him from watching over the tardy effects of ordinary remedies. Both these circumstances combined, led him to the administration of full doses of the more effective medicines, with the view of producing speedy and great changes in the organs diseased.

For the duties of a practical surgeon, Dr. Smith was eminently qualified, and upon the manner in which he performed these duties, his reputation must, in a great measure, ultimately rest. To these he brought a mind enterprising, but not rash; anxious, yet calm in deliberation; bold, yet cautious in operation. His first object was, to save his patients if possible, from the necessity of an operation; and when this could be no longer avoided, to enter upon its performance without reluctance or hesitation. In his operations he was calm, collected and cautious.

He manifested no desire to gain the reputation of a rapid operator, a reputation so ardently, and it is to

be feared so unfortunately sought for by many surgeons of the present day. He who commences an
important operation, with his eye upon the minute
hand of a watch, starts in a race against time, in
which the life of his patient is the stake, and often
the forfeit. The time only for the surgeon is *sat cito
si sat bene.* Neither did he make any display in the
course of his operations to gain the applause of bystanders. Hence there was no formidable array of
instruments ; no ostentatious preparation, so well calculated to excite the wonder of the ignorant, and to
strike a dread into the mind of the patient. Every
thing necessary was prepared, while all useless parade
was avoided. When engaged in an operation, his
whole mind was bent upon its proper performance.
Every step was carefully examined, every occurrence
carefully watched ; and if any thing unusual appeared, he would ask the advice of those present, in
whom he had confidence. In such cases his promptness and decision joined to what Cheselden calls ' a
mind that was never ruffled nor disconcerted,' were
of singular utility. By the aid of these he could look
with a steady eye upon the varying features of the
case, as they rose to his view, and adapt his measures,
at once, to every emergency. By this cautious mode
of proceeding, calculated to gain, not the applause of
those who were present on a single occasion, but the
enduring reputation of a judicious, skillful surgeon, he
performed with great success the most important operations. That his success was great, is fully attested by the facts, that of about thirty cases of Lithotomy, only three proved fatal ; and that in the course of

his practice, he lost no patient of hemorrhage in consequence of an operation, either direct or secondary.

His son, Nathan R. Smith, M. D., of Baltimore, says in the conclusion of this memoir that, 'In the practice of surgery, Professor Smith displayed an original and inventive mind. His friends claim for him the establishment of scientific principles, and the invention of resources in practice, which will stand as lasting monuments of a mind fertile in expedients, and unshackled by the dogmas of the schools. It is believed that he was the first in this country to perform the bold operation of extirpating the ovarian tumor. With him the operation was altogether original, for although it had been at that time once or twice performed in Germany, he was then unacquainted with the fact. He was also the first to perform the operation of staphyloraphy. Important scientific principles were developed by him in relation to the pathology of necrosis, on which he founded a new and successful mode of practice. He also devised and introduced a mode of amputating the thigh, which, although resembling methods for some time in use, is sufficiently original to bear his name.

The apparatus which he invented for the treatment of fractures is altogether new, and has been adopted by some of the best surgeons in every part of our country as decidedly preferable to any in use. His mode of reducing dislocations of the hip is new, philosophical and ingenious.'

69

DR. THADDEUS SPAULDING, who died suddenly of inflammation of the lungs, at South Reading, on the 14th of April last, (1844), was born in Townsend, Mass., Nov. 1st, 1791. Possessing naturally a great thirst for knowledge, he was not satisfied with the pursuits of agriculture, to which his father was devoted, and in which he wished his only son to engage for life. He therefore determined to prepare himself for one of the learned professions, and in the midst of many obstacles and discouragements he entered upon a regular course of study. He pursued a part of his medical studies under the instruction of the distinguished Dr. Matthias Spaulding of Amherst, N. H., and attended lectures at Dartmouth College. In the year 1815, he established himself in practice in South Reading, and soon after became connected in marriage with the family of the late Dr. John Hart, who was celebrated as a surgeon and physician in that place and vicinity for more than half a century.

Dr. Spaulding resided nearly thirty years in South Reading, and for most of the time, had an extensive practice. While there was nothing peculiarly striking, either in his medical acquisitions or character, yet he was always regarded as a very skillful and successful practitioner of medicine. In his knowledge and treatment of diseases generally, he relied more on observation and experience than any information derived from books. In the department of Obstetrics, he had extensive experience, and proved himself a very successful accoucheur. In all his intercourse with his patients, he was remarkably kind and attentive ; and such was the blandness of his manners, the dignity of his deportment and the tenor of his remarks, that they were peculiarly calculated to inspire confidence and command respect. But it was in the capacity of a business man, and in the relations which he sustained to the public, for which Dr. Spaulding was mainly distinguished.

For more than twenty years he held a commission of justice of the peace and performed a great deal of business connected with this office. He was always looked to by his fellow townsmen and citizens as a faithful counsellor and able adviser in adjusting all difficulties, and carrying into effect all the public enterprises of the day. The Rev. Joseph Bennett of Woburn, while speaking in his funeral sermon of the deep sensation which the death of Dr. Spaulding had produced among the people of the neighboring towns, remarked : ' They have long known his amiable disposition, his sprightly talents, his pleasing manners, his social qualities, his peculiar activity in business, and his rising reputation and usefulness as a physician, as a statesman, a citizen and a Christian.'

Dr. Spaulding possessed an unusual share of public spirit, and always took a great interest in all matters appertaining to the affairs of the state and nation. In the year 1841, he was chosen a member of the Executive Council, and was again re-elected in 1843, which office he held at the time of his decease. It is believed that few individuals ever manifested in a stronger degree, or more disinterested manner, the elements of true republicanism and patriotism. He was also a firm believer in the doctrines of evangelical religion, and in his last illness was remarkably sustained by the consolation of that gospel which he had so long possessed. And though the messenger of death came unexpectedly, in the midst of urgent business and great usefulness, in the very meridian of life, and with the most flattering prospects, he was perfectly resigned to his situation, and awaited his final dissolution with a calmness and composure becoming the Christian. Dr. Spaulding was admitted a fellow of the Mass. Med. Society in 1819.—*Dr. Homans' Address before the Mass. Med. Society*, 1843.

DR. JOHN SPENCE died May 18, 1829, at his residence in Dumfries, Va., near the banks of the Potomac river, aged sixty-three years, one of the collaborators of the American Journal of the Medical Sciences.

This gentleman, for nearly forty years, enjoyed in the section of Virginia in which he lived, the highest reputation as a judicious and successful practitioner, and has contributed in no small degree to the present scientific state of medicine in this country, by presenting the example of an indefatigable and accomplished student, almost to the close of his existence ; and by his original contributions to the pages of American Journals.

Upon the first introduction of the vaccine disease into the United States, his attention was closely bestowed upon it, and in a short time he became satisfied of its really possessing those prophylactic powers attributed to it by its renowned discoverer. His zeal in the cause, his general intelligence and polish as a scholar, and his established reputation in medicine, inspired the public with such confidence in his judgment, as soon enabled him to extend the benefit of his convictions, not only throughout his own region, but to the more distant points of Virginia, and of the adjoining states. He was on this momentous occasion, while public opinion yet remained undetermined, a luminary in the path of science ; and though he reflected a light derived from a more lustrous source, yet he contributed in no small degree to its extension. The journals and publications of that day attest sufficiently the spirit of apostleship with which he was inspired by the new doctrine, and his efficiency in the cause. He remained to the time of his death a devoted believer in the same cause, and from repeated and varied experiments, had satisfied himself so fully on the subject, that the slightest doubt of genuine vaccine being a protector from variola, was to him a heresy in medicine of the most monstrous and unpardonable kind.

His next considerable contribution to the profession was the report of a trial in some cases of pulmonary hemorrhage, of the remedial efficacy of digitalis.

In the year 1806 he carried on an interesting correspondence with the late Dr. Benjamin Rush, on the successful treatment of a case of puerperal mania. This correspondence is published in the Medical Museum of Philadelphia.

Last year he presented a valuable paper to this

journal on the efficacy of a sea voyage in arresting pulmonary consumption in his own person when a young man. Having given this brief and imperfect sketch of his scientific labors which are generally to be found in the Medical Museum of Dr. Coxe, and in Miller's Medical Repository of New York, we may proceed to say something of his personal history.

Dr. Spence was a native of Scotland, and spent five years in the University of Edinburgh when its reputation was illustrated by the lectures of Cullen, Black and Monro. Being fully qualified to graduate, he was prevented by symptoms of pulmonary consumption, and was advised by his physicians to take immediately a long voyage. The *res angustæ domi*, which have been so efficient in the nurture of genius, prevailing in his domestic circle, prevented him from adopting a course more gratifying to his feelings, and he was induced to accept, in the year 1788, the offer of a private tutorship in a family residing in Dumfries, in Virginia. At the same moment he had an offer of a promising professional appointment in St. Petersburgh, which has since turned out very advantageous in reputation and emolument to its occupant, but the alarming situation of his health induced him to prefer the more genial climate of the United States. His accomplishments as a Latin and Greek scholar made him a very respectable member, as tutor, in a numerous family, the head of which felt the full value of bestowing a good education on his children.

The voyage saved his life, and upon the expiration of his engagement, he assumed, in 1791, the practice of a profession in which he had been highly educated, and to which he was much attached. From many of his countrymen residing in the place, and most of the families being of Scottish descent, he was in a short time fixed in a highly advantageous business. Dumfries, though now deserted by commerce, and in decay, was at that time in the full tide of prosperity from a most valuable tobacco trade to Europe, and especially to Glasgow. The rational feelings of the Doctor's countrymen, and their liberal remuneration of his professional services, secured for him in a few years an independence.

His well merited distinction, together with a consideration for the circumstances under which he left the University of Edinburgh, induced the Medical Faculty of the University of Pennsylvania to concur unanimously in an application to the board of trustees to confer upon him the honorary degree of Doctor of Medicine, which was accordingly complied with at the commencement, in July, 1828.

As a practitioner of medicine, he was attentive and sympathizing, and knew perfectly the deportment which suits the physician in the presence of a patient. In the instance of a professional brother, who visited him during his illness, and whose attention was withdrawn during the visit, and its attendant interrogatories, to some unimportant and irrelevant object in the room, he said afterwards to a friend, 'that man has not yet learned how to behave in a sick room.'

The fruits of his professional experience were diligently recorded; he has, therefore, left many valuable manuscripts, the digest of which it is to be hoped will be presented to the public before long, by a competent hand.

A few weeks before his death, the gloom of a sick chamber was rendered still more melancholy by the death of a favorite son in the progress of his education. His punctuality as a correspondent ceased with this unexpected blow to his hopes as a parent, and sinking finally under the pressure of infirmities and grief, the next intelligence from him was through a connexion, who communicated the tidings of his having died without a struggle. He has left a widow and a small family of children to deplore his loss.

W. E. H., in the Am. Med. Jour.

DR. WILLIAM SPOONER was born on the 24th day of March, 1760, a few days after the great fire of that year. His parents lived in Washington street, then Cornhill, Boston. On the night of that fire, the house that they occupied being in danger, it became necessary to remove his mother ; in consequence of this exposure and her subsequent confinement, she died. At the age of nine years he was placed under the charge of the celebrated Mr. Lovett, for many years the master of the Latin school. In the family of this venerable teacher he continued to live until July, 1774, when he entered College. In the following April the battle of Lexington took place. Cambridge now became the seat of war, in consequence of which the scholars were dispersed ; and he went to Sherburne, where with several others he lived with Ex-President Locke. In October, 1775, the scholars were ordered to Concord, and were restored to Cambridge in October, 1776. He graduated in 1778, having lived as chum, during his whole collegiate course, with the late Samuel G. Amory, Esq.

On leaving college, he immediately entered upon the study of medicine under the charge of the late Dr. Samuel Danforth, who at this time lived at the north part of the town. The reputation which this distinguished physician afterwards enjoyed, was not at that time acknowledged among the richer classes of the community; but he was extensively called upon by the poor, which gave to his pupil ample opportunities to see his practice. Having pursued the study of medicine for three years, in 1781 Mr. Spooner entered a man of war as surgeon, and continued to act in this capacity until peace took place—having during this time made three cruises in three different vessels, in one of which he was captured and carried into Barbadoes.

In April, 1781, immediately upon his return from his last cruise, peace having taken place, he embarked for Europe. The following winter he entered the medical school at Edinburgh. This school at that time was the most distinguished in the world. Among its professors were Cullen, Monro and Black.

In 1785, he received the degree of Doctor of Medicine. On this occasion he presented a dissertation, ' *De Ascite Abdominalis*,' which he afterwards published, and which has been commended by com-

70

petent judges for the correctness of its style. In
this treatise he describes some experiments made by
himself and two of his fellow students in January,
1785, on the top of St. Arthur's seat near Edinburgh. Some accounts of these experiments may
be found in Thompson's work on Inflammation, in
the chapter on Frost-bite, pp. 453, 497, 498. The
summer of 1786 he spent in London, and with Dr.
Wistar of Philadelphia pursued a course of anatomical dissection. With this gentleman Dr. Spooner
contracted a friendship, which was ever afterwards
maintained.

Dr. Spooner arrived in Boston in October, 1786,
and settled as a practitioner in medicine. The peculiar advantages of his education, the polish of manners that he had received abroad, and the distinction
of family and wealth, gave to him a very flattering
reception into the first circles of society. In the
course of the following winter he was attached as
surgeon to the regiment fitted out from Boston to
suppress Shays' rebellion. But as the news that this
insurrection had been quelled met this body of troops
soon after they left town, he was not called into actual service. In 1804 he was elected a member of
our State Legislature, and continued to be re-elected for seven successive years, for five of which he
was chosen senator. In his politics he was a decided federalist, although there were few men in public
life, during that exciting period of our history, who
exhibited less of the character of a partizan than he
did. He was always ready to do justice to the cha-

racters and the measures of his opponents, and to check the excesses to which the measures of his own party, at times, seemed to tend.

Dr. Spooner was an efficient member of the Massachusetts Medical Society—of the American Academy of Arts and Sciences—of the Massachusetts Historical Society, and the Humane Society. For many years he acted as one of the medical Censors of our State Society, and as a member of the Committee for awarding the Boylston prizes. He also served on the school committee for this town, and for a long time was the oldest member of the Board of Overseers of Harvard University. The ease of his pecuniary circumstances on starting in life, and the absorbing interest of politics in which he afterwards became engaged, were not favorable to that devotion to professional pursuits which can alone ensure full success. Still, for several years, he had a good share of medical practice ; and until late he continued to enjoy as a physician, the confidence of some of our most respectable families. He was decided and successful as a practitioner. In the early stages of disease he depended almost entirely upon evacuants, and in the more advanced stages of acute, and in all chronic cases, he made a much more free use of stimulants than is common at the present day, always paying attention to the state of the alimentary canal.

In his manners he was affable, respectful, and even courteous ; he was a remnant of that old school, which with him seems almost entirely to have passed away. In his feelings he was benevolent and truly public spirited ; he was always willing to give his time, and to contribute from his means, to all objects intended to promote the public good. There are few institutions of public utility established during the active and prosperous periods of his life, which will not find his name in the lists of its benefactors. He died at the age of 76 years.—*Boston Med. and Surg. Jour., vol.* 14.

Dr. JOHN STONE was born at Rutland, Worcester county, in the State of Massachusetts, in the year 1763. He received a good academical education, and commenced the study of medicine with the celebrated Dr. John Frink of Rutland, a distinguished member of the Massachusetts Medical Society. After the close of his pupilage he commenced practice at Greenfield, in the county of Franklin, Mass., where he soon obtained an extensive business. An attack of hæmoptysis induced him to relinquish the practice at Greenfield, and to establish himself in the city of New York, about the year 1805, where he remained about two years, and became an active member of the New York Medical Society, and did considerable business. His health was at this time reinstated, and he was induced once more to return to Greenfield, where he remained until 1819, when he sold his place and privileges to Dr. Seth Washburn, who died in the year 1825. He then removed to Providence, Rhode Island, where he remained a year or two, and then took up his abode at Springfield, Mass., where he engaged in extensive and lucrative business, which con-

JOHN STONE, M.D.

W. C. Sharp's Lith. Boston

tinued till near the time of his death, in 1838, at the age of seventy years.

He joined the Massachusetts Medical Society in 1803, and continued an active member of it from that time till his death. For many years he was a counsellor in the society, in which office he discharged his duties with fidelity and zeal. At the recommendation of his professional brethren, who knew his worth, the honorary degree of Doctor of Medicine was conferred upon him in the year 1824, by the authority of Williams College, then in connection with the Berkshire Medical Institution. He educated a number of pupils in the profession, among the rest Dr. Alpheus F. Stone of Greenfield, a distinguished Fellow and Counsellor in the Mass. Med. Society; and an only son, who afterwards entered the army as an officer, and died at the South. His library was large and respectable, and he kept pace in the purchase of books, with the great and important improvements of the age. His business was extensive as a consulting physician, and he enjoyed the confidence of his professional brethren by whom he was surrounded.

In his manners Dr. Stone was a perfect pattern of a gentleman; and no one could approach him, however humble his sphere and condition, without receiving a share of his urbanity and particular attention. A neighboring physician once observed of him that 'that polite how do you do?' of his, took away his business. This expresses all I could wish to say of him in this respect. In his person he was tall and erect, and he was proverbially one of the neatest and most fashionable men in his dress in the country. He was always ready at the call of any one, and there are but few physicians living who could, or did do a greater amount of business in a given time. His faculties continued bright till the close of his life, and he was able to transact business till within a short time previous to his death. He died universally lamented.

My Address before the Mass. Med. Society.

DR. HENRY STUBER. The individual merit, the extended information and general service rendered the cause of science and humanity at an early period of our country's progress in intellectual culture, demands that Dr. Stuber should receive a passing notice in this volume. His name, moreover, is indissolubly associated with that of Franklin, as his biographer, inasmuch as we are largely indebted to him for that valuable account of the illustrious sage which accompanies his autobiography, and for his historical record of Franklin's discoveries in electricity. The materials are indeed scanty for our object, scarcely a trace of the career of Dr. Stuber being found in print, and the long period which has elapsed since his death forbids our deriving any particular information concerning him from his scattered cotemporaries. To my friend, Dr. John W. Francis of New York, I am obligated for all I have to say, as the brief notice which I now insert is taken from the life and writings of Franklin, by Jared Sparks. Dr. Francis' communication to the learned editor may be found in the 10th volume of that extensive work.

' Dr. Stuber was cut off too early in life,' says Dr.

F., ' to afford materials for much beyond the ordinary record of an obituary register. He was descended from German parents, and was born in Philadelphia, as nearly as can be ascertained, in 1770. The traditional accounts concerning him, are eminently favorable as to his natural capacity, his various attainments, and his moral worth. He evinced throughout his brief career an ardent love of literature and science; and though his circumstances were narrow, he pursued them more with the desire of promoting useful and benevolent designs, than with a view to selfish remuneration. He acquired the rudiments of the Greek, Latin and German languages under the direction of the learned Dr. Kunze, at that time connected with the University of Pennsylvania, and was one of his favorite pupils when Dr. Kunze left the city of Philadelphia for New York, in 1784. Those languages he acquired with a remarkable facility; they were, however, but auxiliaries to his investigations in almost every branch of human inquiry, to which he seems to have directed his energies. His store of knowledge, which he thus accumulated, laid a broad foundation for his intended career. His acquaintance with the different branches of physical and mental research now led him to a close study of medicine, and he graduated with honor in that profession. His health, however, forbade him more than a very partial exercise of its responsible trusts. Very early thereafter, peculiar opportunities presenting, he obtained a situation in one of the public offices of the United States government; and deeming Law more

available to his new pursuits, he commenced the study
of that science with unabated ardor, when he was
arrested by a disease of the pulmonary organs, which
at an earlier period had given rise to alarming apprehensions among his friends. He died when he had
just passed the age of his majority.

'The consideration in which his memory is to be
held, arises not alone from his numerous attainments
in letters and philosophy. Various contributions to
the periodical journals of the time attest at once his
powers in his native language, the solidity of his acquisitions, and no mean force of original thinking.
The only literary effort by which he will be remembered, is his continuation of the life of Franklin.'
'The most important part of Stuber's continuation,'
adds Mr. Sparks, 'is that in which he gives an historical account of Franklin's discoveries in electricity.'

DR. THOMAS H. SWABY. Mr. C. M. Crittenden,
the former Preceptor of the Academy at Seneca
Falls, N. Y., and now Principal of the Academy in
Deerfield, Mass., has politely handed me the following
facts in relation to his estimable friend.

'The life of a young man necessarily affords comparatively but few materials for biography. But when
integrity, benevolence, cultivation, manners, and promising indications of future professional eminence are
manifested, it is fit and important that the memory of
those, (however young) who have exhibited such
qualities, should be perpetuated in a manner that shall

render it more extensively and permanently useful, than when only preserved in the affections of friends and personal acquaintances.

Dr. Thomas H. Swaby, the subject of the present memoir, was born at Pontefract, England, March 12th, 1817. In 1822, he came to this country with his parents, who settled in Columbia county, Penn. He pursued the studies preparatory to his profession, under Dr. Meigs, in Philadelphia, and graduated at the Pennsylvania Medical University about the year 1838. From Dr. Meigs have been received flattering testimonials as to the gentlemanly deportment and favorable prospects of the future professional success of his young student. After traveling a year in the southern and northern states, he settled at Seneca Falls, and commenced the practice of his profession. In this he was eminently successful, and was fast rising to a high rank in his profession. Ever ready in the discharge of his duties as a physician, his services were never refused even to the most humble ; and by this class especially of his fellow citizens, will his loss most deeply be deplored. Gratifying testimony is afforded that the poor not only received his professional services without compensation, but were more frequently further aided by his private charities. Gentlemanly in his deportment, and affable in his manners, Dr. Swaby received the respect and esteem of all who had the pleasure of his acquaintance and intimacy. In his death his friends and the community at large have sustained an irreparable loss. He died November 12th, 1843, aged 26 years.'

71

Dr. J. Greely Stevenson died June 5th, 1835, at the White Springs, Virginia, aged 36.

He was born in Boston, March 28th, 1799. Having received his preparatory education in the Public Writing, Grammar and Latin School of his native town, he was entered at Harvard in 1812, being 13 years of age. He graduated in 1816, and began the study of medicine under the direction of the late Dr. John Gorham. The friendly and affectionate interest taken by Dr. Gorham in his pupil continued unabated to his death, and on that event many of those who had been under his professional care, transferred their confidence at once to his pupil who retained it undiminished during his life.

Dr. Stevenson died at an age when the individual, if ever, takes his place amongst men; when the mind manifests its power, and the conduct through the discipline which is the lot of self-dependence, and he had passed it honorably and successfully. He was not a man to regret that such had been his lot. Its discipline is severe, and the demands it makes great, and sometimes hard to be borne. Still he felt that in its path, however narrow, occasions were always to be met with which a man may make useful both to himself and others. The great opportunities for individual progress furnished by such a beginning of life, is the labor, the moral and intellectual labor it imposes; and success comes to some with such deep, such true enjoyment, as to those who have been, through their whole course, the ministers to their own good progress. In our brief history of his life may be seen

how successful he had been. Feeble health, which
took him occasionally from necessary occupation, did
not depress him. He submitted with almost unexampled cheerfulness to the painful and discouraging, and
his efficiency always returned along with power.

More than a year ago Dr. Stevenson was seized
with an obscure disease, resembling in many of its
symptoms continued fever, and having complicated
with these others of less easily determined character.
He was confined to his bed some weeks, and during
convalescence was from home, and continued in the
country until health was tolerably restored. He suffered from severe pain, and at times great swelling
of one of his legs. His stomach was frequently so
irritable as not to tolerate food for a day or more,
rejecting whatever might be taken, unchanged, and
with hardly the least previous nausea. He had also
headache at times, soreness of throat and increased
difficulty of breathing, occasionally accompanied by
cough. His nights were sleepless, and his days or
most part of them filled up with professional and
not unfrequently hard labor. The winter passed by,
and as the spring returned it was judged by his
medical advisers that he should leave home in this
very harsh season in New England, and pass some
months at the south. Under this advice he went to
Charleston, S. Carolina. He gained nothing while
there, and finding some of his complaints to be
increasing, left Charleston for the White Sulphur
Springs, in Virginia. His journey was full of suffering. Dropsy which had been confined to one limb,
soon extended itself over the whole body. The

difficulty of breathing amounted at times almost to suffocation. In his letters he sometimes spoke of his extreme suffering from this cause. But when he did so and gave his symptoms in the fullest details, it was after such a manner that you might easily suppose he was stating professionally the case of somebody else, and not his own. So remarkable was this in his letters, that a friend in writing to him remarked particularly upon it, and added that this gave him the strongest hope of his ultimate recovery.

His powers of mind remained unweakened to the very last. He was sitting up on the day of his death, and a friend seeing how exhausted he was, and believing from sure signs that he was dying, urged his lying down. He consented, but said he had no other reason for doing so than gratifying his friend. He had in fact that day spoken of making arrangements for proceeding in a carriage to a more elevated spot, where he thought he should certainly breathe more easily. He laid himself down on his bed, closed his eyes as for sleep, and never opened them again. His death came by approaches, at last so gentle, that he knew not of its coming; and sunk into his everlasting rest, as tranquilly as if he only slept.

The following is the epitaph on his grave-stone:

'Jonathan Greely Stevenson of Boston, died 5th January, 1835, aged 36 years. Were his grave in his native city it would require no epitaph. The inscription of his name, there universally known, would suffice to tell that beneath it repose the remains of a highly gifted, just and generous man—a pre-eminently learned and skillful physician—a most active and judicious philanthropist; and a son, a husband and a father, a brother and a friend, than whom none was ever more devoted, or more devotedly beloved.

He lived in the exercise and died in the hopes of the faith that though 'the dust shall return to the earth as it was, the spirit shall return to God who gave it.'—*Bost. Med. and Surg. Jour., vol.* 13.

DR. JAMES THACHER. After the principal part of this work was prepared for the press, intelligence was received of the demise of this venerable patriarch in the profession of medicine. Although this event was to have been anticipated from the great age to which he had advanced, and from many of the infirmities consequent on it, yet although he had passed his ninetieth year, he was still engaged in some of the active duties of his profession, and especially those duties which pertain to the domain of mind. Even in his declining years he devoted his attention to the cultivation of the sciences, and particularly to the study of medicine. So recently as the year 1831, he published an Essay on Demonology, Ghosts, Apparitions and Popular Superstitions, and in 1832, a History of Plymouth, the second edition of which was published in 1835. It is well known that in the year 1828, he published a work upon American Medical Biography in two volumes with plates, which received the approbation and sanction of the principal physicians in America. That work has long been out of print. Having ascertained that he would not publish a new edition of that work and that the infirmities of age prevented his publishing an additional volume, which the number of deaths among eminent physicians in America, since that period, had rendered necessary, I was induced to engage in the undertaking, and I submitted the plan of my work to Dr. Thacher, who cordially assented to it, and advised me to persevere in the prosecution of it. In my manuscript I dedicated the work to him, hoping that the shaft of death might be averted till long after the publication of the volume, and that he might live and be useful, like the venerable Holyoke, to whom he dedicated his work when he had arrived almost to the age of one hundred years. But none can withstand the all-conquering sword of time. The little time which is presented me before the publication of my biography prevents me from collecting such ample materials in relation to his life and character as I could have wished, and must be my apology for the imperfection of this memorial of his life.

Dr. Thacher was descended from a line of illustrious ancestors. I find no less than sixteen graduates of the name in the triennial catalogue of Harvard University from 1671 to 1832, nine of whom were clergymen. Of his immediate ancestors, I know but little. He was born at Barnstable, Mass., in 1754, and died in May, 1844, in the 91st year of his age. His mother was the daughter of a Mr. Norton of Martha's Vineyard, and grand daughter of Gov. Coggshall of Rhode Island. He early devoted his attention to the study of medicine, but of his preparatory education I know nothing. He studied the profession with the celebrated Dr. Abner

Hersey of Barnstable, a very celebrated physician, who died in the year 1787, aged 65 years. At the close of his pupilage, in the year 1775, at the age of 21 years, our beloved country was about to be involved in all the horrors of civil war. His youthful heart beat high with patriotic ardor for his oppressed country, and he resolved to enter the army as an assistant surgeon as soon as he could procure a commission for that service. From his Military Journal, a third edition of which I find is to be published by the Harpers of New York, revised by his grandson, Mr. James F. Hodge of that city, I extract the following paragraphs, showing the embarrassments under which he labored in procuring the appointment. Soon after the battle of Bunker-hill, when the country was nerved for war, he says : ' Participating, I trust, in the glorious spirit of the times, and contemplating improvement in my professional pursuits, motives of patriotism and private interest prompt me to hazard in this noble conflict, with my brethren in the Provincial army. From the critical and embarrassing situation of our country, numerous and almost insurmountable difficulties are opposed to my view ; and I am too young to possess a maturity of judgment, but yet unable to resist the impulse of enthusiasm which characterizes the times. My friends afford me no encouragement, alleging, that as this is a civil war, if I should fall into the hands of the British, the gallows will be my fate. The terrors of the gallows are not to be conquered, but I must indulge the hope that I may escape it. Hundreds of my superiors may take their turn before mine shall come.   The tories assail me with the following powerful arguments, ' Young man, are you sensible you are about to violate your duty to the best of kings, and run headlong into destruction ? Be assured that this rebellion will be of short duration.   The royal army is all-powerful, and will in a few months march through the country and bring all to subjection ; for they are experienced in war and expert in discipline.   There remains no rational alternative but a reconciliation to our lawful government ; or we shall soon experience their just vengeance.   What is your army but an undisciplined rabble ?   Can they stand against an army of regulars ?   Where are your cannon, your fire-arms, your bayonets, and all your implements of war ?   Above all where is your treasure, and where can you look for a barrel of gunpowder ?   The whole country can scarcely afford a sufficiency for a battle of an hour.' Not a small portion of their reasoning I feel to be just and true.   I am not certain, however, but much of it may prove erroneous.   The result of the late battle at Charlestown should convince the most incredulous tory, that our soldiers will face the regular troops, and that we are blessed with the smiles of Heaven on our exertions.   It would be presumption in me to determine as to probabilities and prospects ; but the voice of liberty cannot be stifled, while the welfare and happiness of more than three millions of people now in America, and of unborn millions, are involved in the issue.

Our rulers are the most competent judges, and under their banners I will venture, I hope not rashly, to enlist and trust my destiny in the hands of a kind and overruling Providence. My contemplated enterprise it is true, requires the experience and resolution of riper years than twenty-one, and qualifications which I do not possess, to ingratiate myself with strangers and those in authority. Having consulted Joseph Otis, Esq. of Barnstable, on this occasion, he immediately applauded my enterprise, and politely furnished me with a letter to his brother-in-law, James Warren, Esq. of Plymouth, who is President of our Provincial Congress at Watertown. Imagination could not fail to paint my prospects in bright colors, and I proceeded July the 3d, with alacrity to the seat of Congress. I was not disappointed in my interview with Mr. Warren; my letter procured for me a favorable and polite reception. He honored me with his friendship, and introduced me to his lady, whose father's family and my own have, for many years, been on terms of friendship and intercourse. The office which I solicit is one in the medical department in the provincial hospital at Cambridge. A medical board, consisting of Drs. Holton and Taylor, are appointed to examine the candidates; and they added my name to the list for examination on the 10th instant. This state of suspense continuing several days, excites in my mind much anxiety and solicitude, apprehending that my stock of medical knowledge, when scanned by a learned committee, may be deemed inadequate, and all my hopes be blasted.

On the day appointed, the medical candidates, sixteen in number, were summoned before the board for examination. This business occupied about four

72

hours; the subjects were anatomy, physiology, surgery and medicine. It was not long after that I was happily relieved from suspense, by receiving the sanction and acceptance of the board, with some acceptable instructions relative to the faithful discharge of duty, and the humane treatment of those soldiers who may have the misfortune to require my assistance. Six of our number were privately rejected as being found unqualified. The examination was in a considerable degree close and severe, which occasioned not a little agitation in our ranks. But it was on another occasion, as I am told, that a candidate under examination was agitated into a state of perspiration, and being required to describe the mode of treatment in rheumatism, among other remedies how he could promote a sweat, and being asked how he would effect this with his patient, after some hesitation he replied, ' I would have him examined by a medical committee.' I was so fortunate as to obtain the office of surgeon's mate in the provincial hospital at Cambridge, Dr. John Warren being the senior surgeon. He was the brother and pupil of General Joseph Warren who was slain in the memorable battle on Breed's hill. This gentleman has acquired reputation in his profession, and is distinguished for his humanity and attention to the sick and wounded soldiers, and for his amiable disposition. Having received my appointment by the Provincial Congress, I commenced my duty in the hospital July 15th, 1775. Several private but commodious houses in Cambridge are occupied for hospitals, and a considerable number of soldiers, who were wounded at Breed's hill, and a greater number of sick, of various diseases, require all our attention. Dr. Isaac Foster, late of Charlestown, is also appointed a senior hospital surgeon; and his student, Dr. Josiah Bartlett, officiates as his mate; Dr. Benjamin Church is Director General of the hospital.

On the 18th of Feb., 1776, Dr. John Morgan of Philadelphia was appointed by Congress Director General of our hospitals instead of Dr. Church removed. Since his arrival here, a new and systematic arrangement in the medical department has taken place; the number of surgeon's mates in the hospital is to be reduced, and vacancies in regiments are to be supplied. I have been subjected to another examination by Dr. Morgan, and received from him the appointment of surgeon's mate to Dr. David Townsend, in the regiment commanded by Col. Asa Whitcomb, stationed in the barracks on Prospect Hill.'

I cannot omit mentioning in this place a little incident showing the method of treatment adopted by Dr. Thacher and two medical attendants, in the case of the bite of the rattlesnake. The treatment, however, was not altogether new. In the month of August, 1776, his regiment was ordered to Ticonderoga. Soon after his arrival at Skenesboro', near that place, 'a soldier had the imprudence to seize a rattlesnake by the tail; the reptile threw his head back and struck his fangs into the man's hand. In a few moments a swelling commenced attended with severe pain. It was not more than half an hour when his whole arm to his shoulder was swollen to twice its natural size, and the skin became of a deep orange color. His body, on one side, soon became affected in a similar manner, and a nausea at his stomach ensued. The poor man was greatly and justly alarmed; his situation was very critical. Two medical men beside myself were in close attendance for several hours. Having procured a quantity of olive oil, we directed the patient to swallow it in large and repeated doses, till he had taken one quart; and at the same time we rubbed into the affected limb a very large quantity of mercurial ointment. In about two hours we had the satisfaction to perceive the favorable effects of the remedies. The alarming symptoms abated, the swelling and pain gradually subsided, and in about forty-eight hours he was happily restored to health!'

After the surrender of Burgoyne to the army of Gen. Gates, Dr. Thacher, with the other medical attendants, was busily engaged in the hospital attending to the arduous and painful duties of his profession, after a series of protracted and sanguinary battles. He says: 'The hospital is now crowded with officers and soldiers from the field of battle; those belonging to the British and Hessian troops are accommodated in the same hospital with our own men, and receive equal care and attention. The foreigners are under the care and management of their own surgeon. I have been present at some of their capital operations, and remarked that the English surgeons performed with skill and dexterity, but the Germans, with few exceptions, do no credit to their profession; some of them are the most uncouth and clumsy operators I ever witnessed, and appear to be destitute of all sym-

pathy and tenderness toward the suffering patient.
Not less than one thousand wounded and sick are
now in this city, (Albany). The Dutch church and
several private houses are occupied as hospitals. We
have about thirty surgeons and mates; and are constantly employed. I am obliged to devote the whole
of my time from eight o'clock in the morning to a
late hour in the evening, to the care of our patients.
Here is a fair field for professional improvement.
Amputating limbs, trepanning fractured skulls, and
dressing the most formidable wounds, have familiar-
ized my mind to scenes of woe. A military hospital
is peculiarly calculated to afford examples for profitable contemplation, and to interest our sympathy and
commiseration. If I turn from beholding mutilated
bodies, mangled limbs, and bleeding, incurable wounds,
a spectacle no less revolting is presented, of miserable objects, languishing under afflicting diseases of
every description—here are those in a mournful state
of despair, exhibiting the awful harbingers of approaching dissolution—there are those with emaciated bodies and ghastly visage, who begin to triumph
over grim disease and just lift their feeble heads from
the pillow of sorrow. No parent, wife or sister, to
wipe the tear of anguish from their eyes, or to soothe
the pillow of death, they look up to the physician as
their only earthly friend and comforter, and trust the
hands of a stranger to perform the last painful duties.
Often have I remarked their confidence in my friendship, as though I was endeared to them by brother-
ly ties. Viewing these unfortunate men as the faithful defenders of the liberties of our country, far sepa-

rated from their dearest friends, who would be so lost
to the duties of humanity, patriotism and benevolence, as not to minister to their comfort, and pour
into their wounds the healing balm of consolation?
It is my lot to have twenty wounded men committed
to my care by Dr. Potts, our Surgeon General; one
of whom, a young man, received a musket ball
through his cheeks, cutting its way through the teeth
on each side, and the substance of the tongue; his
sufferings have been great, but he now begins to ar-
ticulate well.   Another had the whole side of his face
torn off by a cannon ball, laying his mouth and throat
open to view.   A brave soldier received a musket
ball in his forehead; observing that it did not penetrate deep, it was imagined that the ball rebounded
and fell out; but after several days, on examination,
I detected the ball lying flat on the bone, and spread
under the chin, which 1 removed.   No one can
doubt but he received his wound while facing the enemy, and it is fortunate for the brave fellow that his
skull proved to be too thick for the ball to penetrate.
But in another instance a soldier's wound was not
so honorable; he received a ball in the bottom of his
foot, which could not have happened unless when in
the act of running from the enemy.   This poor fellow is held in derision by his comrades, and is made
a subject of their wit for having this mark of a cow-
ard.

Among the most remarkable occurrences which
came under my observation, the following is deserving of particular notice.   Captain Gregg, of one of
the New York regiments, while stationed at Fort

Stanwix, on the Mohawk river, went with two of his soldiers into the woods a short distance to shoot pigeons; a party of Indians started suddenly from concealment in the bushes, shot them all down, tomahawked and scalped them, and left them for dead. The captain, after some time revived, and perceiving his men were killed, himself robbed of his scalp, and suffering extreme agony from his numerous wounds, made an effort to move and lay his bleeding head on one of the dead bodies, expecting soon to expire. A faithful dog who accompanied him, manifested great agitation, and in the tenderest manner licked his wounds, which afforded him great relief from exquisite distress. He then directed the dog, as if a human being, to go in search of some person to come to his relief. The animal with every appearance of anxiety, ran about a mile, when he met two men fishing in the river, and endeavored in the most moving manner, by whining and piteous cries, to prevail on them to follow him into the woods; struck with the singular conduct of the dog, they were induced to follow him part of the way, but fearing some decoy or danger, they were about to return, when the dog, fixing his eyes upon them, renewed his entreaties by his cries, and taking hold of their clothes with his teeth, prevailed on them to follow him to the fated spot. Such was the remarkable fidelity and sagacity of this animal.' This event has been rendered into poetry, and the elder readers of this memoir will recollect the concluding stanza of that poem in the American Preceptor, a standard book at the commencement of the 19th century.

> ' My dog, the trustiest of his kind,
> ' With gratitude inflames my mind,
> ' I mark his true, his faithful way,
> ' And in my service copy Tray.'

' Captain Gregg was immediately carried to the fort, where his wounds were dressed ; he was afterwards removed to our hospital and put under my care.   He was a most frightful spectacle ; the whole of the scalp was removed ; in two places on the top of his head the tomahawk had penetrated through the skull ; there was a wound on his back with the same instrument, besides a wound in his side, and another through his arm by a musket ball.   This unfortunate man, after suffering extremely for a long time, finally recovered, and appeared to be well satisfied in having his scalp restored to him, though uncovered with hair.   The Indian mode of scalping their victims is this,—with a knife they make a circular cut from the forehead, quite round, just above the ears, then taking hold of the skin with their teeth, they tear off the whole hairy scalp in an instant, with wonderful dexterity.   This they carefully dry and preserve as a trophy, showing the number of their victims, and they have a method of painting on the dried scalps, different figures and colors, to designate the sex and age of the victim, and also the manner and circumstances of the murder.'

About the 20th of December, the sick and wounded soldiers under his charge at Albany having recovered, Dr. Potts, the Surgeon General of the army, as a compliment for his attention, skill and assiduity to his patients, awarded him a generous and valuable present, and he obtained a furlough for forty days for the purpose of visiting his friends in New England. Soon after his return to the army, he was stationed at the Highlands, near West Point, where he remained a very considerable time.

Dr. Thacher was at West Point in 1780 at the time of the treason of Arnold and the capture of the ill-fated Andre. He has given a thrilling description of the execution of the latter, on which heart-rending occasion he was present, in his Military Journal, but my limits will not allow me to detail it.

He was present at the surrender of Lord Cornwallis with his army on the 19th of October, 1780, which terminated the struggle between the mother country and her colonies. He says, ' this event reflects the highest honor on our combined arms, it will adorn the pages of our history, and we fondly hope it will be attended with the most favorable consequences in bringing this long, protracted and distressing war to a happy termination. It will be to me a source of inexpressible satisfaction that I have had an opportunity of participating in the siege and capture of a British army. It is among the blessed privileges and richest incidents of my life. I have for several days been afflicted with inflammatory rheumatism, attended with excruciating pains. Having no other covering than canvass tents, and the weather being extremely cold, my sufferings have been almost insupportable ; but I have much less

73

reason to complain than to be grateful to a kind Providence, that I have enjoyed uninterrupted health during my seven years of military service.' The Journal of Dr. Thacher, with the Revolutionary Annals and the biography of the distinguished General officers of the American army, is one of the most interesting volumes upon the subject of our revolution which has yet been published, and will repay the reader for an attentive perusal.

At the termination of the revolutionary war he settled in the town of Plymouth as a physician and surgeon, where he resided till the day of his death. He was an eminently successful practitioner, enjoying the entire confidence of his fellow citizens, and of the community where he resided.

His practice during the greater part of his life was extensive and laborious. He devoted much of his time and attention to antiquarian researches, and was a member of the Pilgrim Society of Plymouth. He was also a member of the American Academy of Arts and Sciences, of the Massachusetts Medical Society, and of several others. In 1810 he received the honorary degree of Doctor of Medicine from Harvard University.

For many of the latter years of his life he was afflicted with a difficulty of breathing, which deprived him in some measure of the pleasures of social intercourse, which he highly estimated. He, however, did not repine at his lot. This defect might have been favorable to the great literary eminence to which he attained, as it might have induced him to devote himself with greater assiduity to his favorite studies. He was one of the most elaborate and voluminous writers in the medical ranks in New England, and his works have always been sought after, and read with great avidity. The following is a list of some of his publications, and it justifies me in making the above remarks.

1. Observations on the art of making marine salt from sea-water, by evaporation produced by the sun's heat, with a description of the works and the several processes used in preparing medicinal salt and magnesia. Communicated to the Academy of Arts and Sciences in 1802, and published in their volume.

2. Observations on the natural production of Iron ore, with a description of smelting furnaces, and some account of the manufacture of iron in the county of Plymouth, accompanied by several specimens of iron ore. Communicated to the Historical Society of Massachusetts and published in their 9th volume.

3. American New Dispensatory, 1810, 4th edition, 1821.

4. Observations on Hydrophobia, 1821.

5. Modern Practice of Physic, 1817, 2d edition, 1821.

6. American Ochardist, 1822, 2d edition, 1825.

7. Military Journal kept during the Revolutionary War, 1824, 2d edition, 1826.

8. American Medical Biography, 2 vols., 1828.

9. Practical Treatise on the management of Bees, 1829.

10. Essay on Demonology, Ghosts, Apparitions and Popular Superstitions, 1831.

11. History of Plymouth, 1832, 2d edition, 1835.

12. Various communications in the Medical Periodicals.

'In his private character,' Dr. Winslow Warren, a fellow townsman of Dr. Thacher, from whom I have many of the facts in relation to his life, says 'he displayed many estimable traits. As a citizen he was public spirited, a lover of order, and a warm supporter of the civil and religious institutions under which he lived, and in all the relations of life he was guided by a spirit of benevolence, kindness and disinterestedness, which gained him the attachment and regard of many friends.'

DR. T. H. THOMPSON was son of Dr. A. R. Thompson of Charlestown. He was educated at Harvard University, where he also took his medical degree in 1826 or '7. He was then settled in practice in Rockport, Me., where he remained only a short time. He was there very highly respected for his many excellent qualities, both moral and intellectual, was in high repute as a skillful physician, and his friends parted from him with great regret. Dr. Thompson then commenced the practice of his profession in this city where he remained about eight years. His practice here was never much extended ; and about two years ago he removed to Appalachicola, where he died in the course of the last summer.

The memory of Dr. Thompson is cherished by those who best knew him. Of strong and cultivated mind, well stored with useful knowledge, of excellent judgment, and with an extraordinary power of discriminating the true from the false in the character of others, with an imagination remarkable for wit and playfulness, his society was much sought for and valued by his friends. He was modest and unassuming, it may have been even to a fault; and it was this trait in his character which circumscribed his circle of practice, and not any deficiency in those qualities of the head or heart, nor of the necessary medical attainments, which are indispensable in a good physician. Those whom he attended professionally in this city were strongly attached to him by his goodness of heart, as well as by his valuable services to them. He was honest in the truest and strongest sense of that word. For this trait he was peculiarly distinguished; neither by word or action, would he ever deceive in the slightest degree.

At Appalachicola his character appears to have been well appreciated, and in various forms there have come to us the strongest testimonials of the very high esteem in which he had been held in that place. His death is lamented as a loss to the city. And here there will be long cherished the recollection of his kindness of disposition, and of his many agreeable and valuable qualities.—*Bost. Med. Jour.*

DR. CALEB TICKNOR. The Boston Medical and Surgical Journal observes: ' With feelings of profound sorrow we announce to the profession the recent death of Caleb Ticknor, M. D., of the city of New York, who has been taken away in the meridian of his usefulness, at the age of 36. Dr. Ticknor was extensively known in this country and in Europe. His Philosophy of Living, a work generally admired, gave him a reputation wherever the English language is spoken. He was talented, industrious and philanthropic, and devoted to the science of medicine because it gave him an opportunity of doing good. He was a native of Salisbury, Connecticut, and one of three brothers who were physicians. One of them is an eminent surgeon in the naval service, and the other still resides in Salisbury. The lamented subject of this brief notice received his professional education at the Berkshire Medical Institution—a circumstance of which the friends of that school may well be proud.

Very many papers have appeared in the Journals which were from the pen of Dr. Ticknor, though, perhaps, rarely known to have been from that source. Such was the fact in relation to articles in this Journal. We were expecting a critical essay from him about which letters have been interchanged, when the melancholy intelligence of his death was accidentally discovered in one of the daily papers. He had engaged, too, to prepare several pages on the statistics of homœopathy in the United States, for the next volume of the Medical Almanac. A hope is entertained that the undertaking was completed before death closed his labors. Dr. Ticknor became a thorough convert to Hahnemanism from an honest conviction that it was a rational system, notwithstanding the ridicule it so often excites. The idea of profiting by what is usually considered a hallucination of a portion of the civilized world, never once entered his mind. He was honest in his intentions, and dared to brave the public sentiment which at one time set with a strong flood against him. This is gleaned from his own letters to the editor. Although we differ from him entirely upon the merits and claims of homœopathy, the circumstance interposed no barrier to friendship. We esteem him for his integrity and sterling worth of character, and now mourn his early death as an irreparable loss to the republic of letters, to science and humanity.

It should be the immediate business of those who are favorably circumstanced, to collect the various productions of Dr. Ticknor's hours of study, and append to them a memoir of his life, which, if published, would be an acceptable offering to the friends and admirers of that excellent man.' See in addition, an Address at his funeral, a notice of which is published in the 23d vol. of the Boston Med. and Surg. Journ.

DR. ELI TODD. Dr. Samuel B. Woodward, Superintendent of the Massachusetts Lunatic Asylum, at Worcester, Mass., has furnished me with the following graphic memoir of this eminent philanthropist in the cause of the victims of insanity. It will be seen that he was the great pioneer in the establishment of the admirable Retreat for this unfortunate class of our fellow beings, in the State of Connecticut, and that for several years he devoted his life to the subject of insanity with unwearied assiduity.

'Eli Todd, M. D., who was extensively known as
the distinguished Superintendent of the Retreat for
the Insane at Hartford, Connecticut, was born in New
Haven on the 22d of July, 1769.   His father, Mi-
chael Todd, a respectable and wealthy merchant, died
when his son was five years of age, leaving him to
the care of his mother, and an elder brother by a
former marriage, from whom he received every kindness which it was in his power to bestow.   He had
two sisters younger than himself, one of whom married the Hon. Samuel Crafts, formerly Governor of
Vermont, and now a member of the Senate of the
United States.

At the early age of six years, young Todd was
placed under the care and instruction of his great
uncle, Jonathan Todd, D. D. of East Guilford, Connecticut, and from him as he said, he received 'the
milk of his education.'   He here commenced the
study of the Latin language, and other branches preparatory to a collegiate education.   At the age of ten
he left this venerable man and was placed under the
instruction of Elizur Goodrich, D. D. of Durham,
Connecticut, a man alike distinguished as a divine
and as a teacher of youth.   With him he continued
till he was fitted for college.   He entered Yale College in 1783, at the age of fourteen.   Dr. Todd ever
retained the highest respect for these two excellent
men, and whenever he visited the places of their residence, the scenes of his childish sports and early associations, he sought every thing interesting and dear
to him, and especially the graves where the remains
of these venerable teachers were deposited.   The

E. Todd. M.D.

writer once traveled through the town of Durham with him, where he spoke with deep feeling of the kindness and solicitude of the sainted Goodrich for him in the days of his pupilage and childhood and the anxiety which he manifested that he should receive a public education, having doubtless some forecast of the distinction to which he might arrive if well trained and suitably educated.

Dr. Todd graduated in 1787, at the age of eighteen, with the usual collegiate honors, ' distinguished for his literary and scientific attainments.'

Both before and while in college, those noble traits of character which ever endeared him to all his acquaintances, made him the object of general regard and affection to his teacher and associates. He was ever beloved where he was well known.

After his graduation Dr. Todd visited the West Indies with the intention of extending his travels to Europe and even to Asia, then the theatre of interesting events to the lovers of liberty, when the native tribes under Tippoo Saib were attempting to resist the well disciplined forces of Great Britain. He was, however, taken sick with yellow fever in the Island of Trinidad, and after recovering from extreme danger, was advised to return home. Circumstances soon occurred which induced him to commence immediately the study of the profession which proved to him the path of great usefulness and renown.

His father left him a handsome patrimony which was in the hands of his elder brother. While on a voyage from the West Indies to this country, this

74

brother was lost, the ship and the whole of the cargo being sunk in the sea. The fortunes of this family were thus swept away before they came in possession, and young Todd was thrown upon his own resources. He now commenced the study of medicine, with Dr. Ebenezer Beardsley, a gentleman of high repute in his native city, as his preceptor. After a due course of medical study, Dr. Todd commenced the practice of his profession in the town of Farmington, Conn., in 1790, before he was fully twenty-one years of age. He soon acquired business and a reputation for talents and skill which were honorable to his character, and evinced research and tact of which his seniors might have been proud. He had an extensive private practice, and early in life was extensively consulted by his medical brethren in cases of difficulty and danger.

Few men carry to the bedside of the sick the philanthrophy and philosophy which Dr. Todd exhibited. His whole soul as well as all the energies of his well stored mind was awakened to the interests of the sick. His examination of symptoms was thorough and critical, at the same time blended with so much kindness as to secure the confidence and affection of the physician who needed his counsel, and of the patient who received the benefit of his skill.

Dr. Todd was married August 9th, 1796, to Miss Rhoda Hill of Farmington, a lady who possessed a most amiable disposition and great good sense, and who proved to him a most excellent wife. She died in March, 1825. In November, 1828, he married

Catherine Hill, sister of his former wife, who still lives to bless his memory, and imitate his example of doing good.

After practising his profession in Farmington about twenty years, and gaining a reputation which reached far beyond the limits of his circle of practice, he was invited to move to the city of New York. Here he remained but a short time, not being pleased with a city life. He was induced to return to Farmington by the earnest solicitations of his friends and employers, who made him liberal pecuniary proposals. His return was hailed with joy by a large circle of friends, who justly appreciated his worth as a man, and his abilities as a physician. He frequently said that one of the reasons which induced him to leave New York, was the gloomy spectacle of a funeral procession with a *single* mourner! a feeling strikingly illustrative of his benevolent and social nature.

He continued in Farmington ten years longer, enjoying the confidence of the community, which afforded him a lucrative business, and forming strong and lasting attachments.

In the autumn of 1809 he removed to Hartford, where his consultations had previously extended. Here he also gained a good business, and soon became the most extensive consulting physician in the city.

The intercourse of Dr. Todd with his brethren was always rendered pleasant by his kind and social character, which always inspired respect and confidence. The junior members of the profession loved him as a friend, and at the same time confided in his skill and guidance in all cases of professional difficulty. The character of the young physician was always safe in his keeping; however different their views of the case might have been, he managed to secure to them the confidence of their employers, while at the same time he often wholly changed the prescription; thus laying them under obligations which usually resulted in firm friendship.

In 1821, the number of cases of insanity in Hartford and the vicinity excited more than usual attention to the want of a suitable place for their treatment and cure. Doctor Todd saw most of these cases alone or in consultation, and felt, perhaps more keenly than any other man, the difficulty of managing the insane in private practice. He did much to awaken the attention of the profession and the public to the necessity of an institution for the safe keeping and cure of the insane, and to him, probably, more than to any other person, is that State indebted for the Retreat for the Insane at Hartford, an institution conducted by him for ten years with unrivalled success and approbation.

The attention of Dr. Todd had for many years been especially directed to diseases of the brain and nervous system. He was of a very susceptible nervous temperament; his father died a victim of insanity; his only sister who survived infancy was periodically insane, and finally died by suicide; and he had a fearful presentiment that he might ultimately become insane. These circumstances, together with the number of similar cases which had been led to seek his counsel by the patient interest which he manifested in their examination, had caused his mind to investigate this class of diseases with unusual attention and interest, and he understood them better than most men of his time.

When the Retreat was ready to go into operation the attention of the whole community, and particularly that of the medical men who had interested themselves in its establishment, was turned to Dr. Todd as its physician and superintendent. The committee of the Medical Society who were designated to make the nomination, unanimously named him for the officer, and the Board of Directors with the same unanimity approved the appointment. Such was the characteristic delicacy of his feelings, so apprehensive was he that the public would attribute his strenuous efforts for the establishment of the Retreat to selfish desires of place and honors, that he resisted long and firmly the pressing solicitations of his friends to accept the appointment. He finally yielded to the importunities which met him on every side, and entered upon the duties of the place with a zeal and disinterestedness which augured favorably of the success to which he finally attained.

Few institutions in the world have been managed with more success than the Retreat while under the care of Dr. Todd. He took it in its infancy without patients, and almost without resources, at a time when public sentiment was far from being favorable to such institutions, he adopted a course of management peculiarly his own, carried it into successful operation, and gave to the Retreat a character for the comfort and care of its members, not surpassed in this or any other country. Here, too, he raised himself a name for intelligence and philanthropy as imperishable as the cause of humanity.

Dr. Todd's devotion to the Retreat did not prevent him from doing much business abroad, particularly in consultation with his brethren in different cases.

His high reputation as a physician, and his good standing with his brethren of the medical profession, led them to confer upon him the highest honors in their gift. He was repeatedly elected Vice-President and President of the Medical Society, and he received other marks of distinction in associations of medical men, which evinced their confidence and esteem.

Political honors were also tendered him. He was for a number of years a candidate for Congress, selected by his political friends, who were then a minority in the state. He never sought political preferment, but chose to spend his life in a way more congenial to his nature, in the exercise of the high virtues which adorn and dignify human nature, and benefit the human family.

He was at one time solicited to take the charge of the Bloomingdale Asylum, near New York, and afterwards was selected as Superintendent of the State Lunatic Hospital at Worcester, both of which institutions were more lucrative than his office at the Retreat, but he declined them both, preferring to spend his life in his long cherished and favorite institution. Till the last hour of his life the welfare and prosperity of his own Retreat was the subject of his constant solicitude.

During the last three years of his life, Dr. Todd had distressing paroxysms of disease in which the heart participated largely. The last year the symptoms of fatal lesion of the organs of the chest were successively developed, and paroxysms of pain like angina pectoris were attended with a copious discharge from the pulmonary cells of a thin and bloody fluid. It was uncertain what organ suffered most, and a post mortem examination exhibited less of organic change in any than was expected.

Till late in the season he devoted his attention to his health. He traveled, visited the watering places and the sea coast, but gained no relief. When cold weather approached he returned home, too well acquainted with the nature and tendency of his disease to mistake the issue. He was fully confident that it must terminate his life. He awaited the event with Christian fortitude, and died November 17th, 1833, aged 64 years.

A medical gentleman who was well acquainted with Dr. Todd for more than thirty years, thus wrote after his death :

' He was a man take him for all in all,
' Eye shall not look upon his like again.'

' We feel ourselves utterly incapable of attempting an eulogium upon the deceased. The records and printed reports of the Retreat demonstrate that greater success has attended Dr. Todd's practice in recent cases of Insanity than has been heretofore known of any other institution of the kind, either in America or Europe. He was perhaps equally able in every other department of his profession in which he engaged. He was also as much distinguished for his virtues in the various relations of life. He had a chivalrous sense of honor and integrity, softened by the most exquisite feelings of humanity and philanthropy. His professional life was a series of most benevolent acts, and from his eminent talents as well as his particular station, he was enabled to mitigate a greater proportion of the corporeal and mental ills of humanity than falls to the lot of most men. A peculiar suavity of manner and an unaffected sympathy in the distresses of others justly inspired greater confidence of his patients in him than in any other physician we ever knew. For many years he has very generally been considered at the head of his profession in the State.

The death of such a man is a loss to the whole community. It makes a chasm which leaves us in doubt and uncertainty whether it can be filled. From his being at the head of one of the most important institutions, a whole State are his mourners.'

In the circle of his acquaintance it is, perhaps, generally known that Dr. Todd, in early life, was sceptical as to the truths of the Christian religion. He entered on the stage of active life at the commencement of the French revolution. It is well known that the misguided efforts of that nation in the cause of liberty were preceded by the speculations of the philosophers and learned men on the abuses in government, and in religion, by which they have been so long oppressed.

A lover of liberty and naturally addicted to philosophy, Dr. Todd, like many others of a similar character, embraced the principles of the philosophers who gave impetus to that revolution, and became a sceptic in religion.

He was never a scoffer at Christianity, for he had witnessed its good fruits and respected the men who taught its precepts for their moral worth and good deeds. He had too much benevolence to undervalue the influence which Christianity exerted in the cause of humanity, and too much candor to deny its legitimate claims to a large share of the good that was effected in the various channels of Christian philanthropy. He had sympathy with every man who had the good of his race at heart.

Many years before his death his views of religion were changed and continued to become more favorable till the time of his death. With the writer he had many familiar conversations on this subject, and till the last year of his life, when we were separated, probably no one knew better the views and sentiments of this good man. Without adopting any exclusive sectarian views, he felt the influence and was guided by the precepts of pure Christianity. He had always been strictly conscientious, and his moral character was pure and spotless. A respectable clergyman said of him that 'he was the best man he ever knew.' A physician who knew him intimately, and who, being himself a religious man, was capable of appreciating religious character, said of him, 'take him as a whole, body, mind, and moral and religious principles and conduct, he was the most perfect man

75

I ever knew.' Such would be my testimony after fifteen years of most intimate acquaintance.

During the last year of his life his religious character shone brighter and brighter to the end, when he left the world, giving confidence to his friends that he died in the prospect of a full fruition of heavenly bliss, of which he had a foretaste, to use his own language, ' a beginning of the heavenly enjoyment on the earth.'

There is no circumstance connected with the life of Dr. Todd more to be regretted than that he left so little on record of his vast experience and acquisitions in knowledge, all of which was so well digested as to flow from his lips with eloquence such as few men possessed. As his memory was exceedingly retentive, his resources of practical wisdom were ever at command to direct and guide his prescriptions; but he has left little for others to glean from those ample stores of intelligence which his active mind was able to turn to valuable account at the bedside of his patients.

To his friends and medical associates he was ever ready to give his opinions and the result of his experience with a freedom which showed conclusively that he had no desire to secrete his skill and deprive them of the benefit of it. On the contrary he was always ready, as he was fully able, to impart instruction to those who would listen to him, and no man could hear him without admiration and delight.

He had a great aversion to writing, even his correspondence was too much neglected on account of his dread of taking up his pen.

His first report of the condition of the Retreat

shows what he was able to do, and what he might have done, had he accustomed himself to writing. A single extract from it will serve to show his ability as a writer, no less than the correctness of his views, and the benevolence of his feelings.

While speaking of the system of management adapted to the institution he says: ' The law of kindness which in this institution constitutes the pervading and plastic power of its moral discipline, does not at all countervail or interfere with the important policy of impressing patients with a due sense of authority, neither does the impartial, unimpassioned and regulated exercise of wholesome authority irritate them, or diminish the grateful sense they generally feel of that unrivaled gentleness and respect which is required to be maintained towards them by every member of the institution. It is thus that those necessary restraints which they violently resist at home, and consider as capricious and vengeful acts of tyranny, they submit to hear and regard with a degree of loyal feeling, as imparted regulations, essential to the well being of their little community.

On the whole, therefore, the physician of the Retreat making due allowance for the forlorn character of a great majority of cases admitted, and also for the embarrassment peculiarly incident to the infancy of all institutions, cannot but be satisfied with the results, which are far more favorable than he had ventured to anticipate, and which he believes will have the effect of animating the immediate friends and patrons of the Retreat with a sanguine hope of ultimately accomplishing the design of this noble institution, which has been reared and fostered by them, with the benignant purpose of consecrating it to the relief of the deplorable calamity that strikes at the fountain head of every blessing of existence, that stands in the catalogue of human sufferings with a sad pre-eminence of claim over all others upon our commiseration, but which in truth has received the smallest share of our assistance.

All other sufferers seek relief from their sufferings, and successfully appeal to the kindly feelings of man for sympathy and aid. But unlike all others, the maniac who most needs tenderness and care, is neglected, because he shuns the care and tenderness which he needs, repels the hand stretched out for his relief, and would fain bar the doors of charity against himself.

But through the Divine influence of Him, who, touched with a sense of human infirmity, tempers the wind to the shorn lamb, his followers, in the temper of their master have sought out this forlorn and intractable sufferer and placed him under the guardianship of benevolence.

By the blessing of Heaven the public sensibility is at last awakened to this interesting subject. The legislature, as well as many of our citizens, have embarked in the cause with a fellow feeling and liberality calculated to animate and fortify our confidence in human nature. They have contemplated the victims of insanity with a profound but considerate compassion, that promises to be as lasting as it is rational. This is not one of those sudden gusts of sympathy that is exhausted by its own violence, that expends itself in idle regrets, or exhales in passive pity; it is the steady action of a sentiment at once wholesome and practical, and which with a tonic efficacy rouses and supports every energy of will and power to co-operate in behalf of its object.'

Among the papers of Dr. Todd was found a manuscript in his own hand writing, giving his plan of the treatment of the insane, which must have been written soon after the Retreat was opened for the reception of patients. I am sorry my limits do not allow me to extract from it.

No man was ever better qualified to derive and carry into effect a system of management for the insane, than Dr. Todd.

His personal appearance was dignified and commanding, at the same time exhibiting condescension and urbanity. His form was symmetrical, and his activity and strength proverbial. He had a good constitution, was capable of great endurance, with an appearance of health, vigor and stamina that indicates a long and active life. His manners were easy and agreeable, he was at home with the most refined society, and with the most learned and polished men; he was also gentle, affectionate and civil to the younger, the timid, and the humble. His countenance was strongly marked, expressive of vigorous intellect, and beaming with benevolence and kindness. Dr. Spurzheim remarked, after looking at his head, that 'he had a bushel of benevolence.' His conduct was always marked by the strictest and most scrupulous delicacy. He had an unusual flow of spirits, facetiousness and raciness of conversation, un-

common colloquial powers which charmed and instructed the listener beyond any other man I have
ever met.   At the same time he was modest and unassuming; never spoke of himself when he could
avoid it, but always spoke well of others when he was
able to do it.

'Being eminently skillful as a physician,' says Dr.
Rockwell, 'he was well qualified to adopt a system
of remedies, which would result in restoring the patient to physical health.   He possessed a happy tact
and ingenuity in discovering those obscure and latent seats of diseases which are frequently the causes
of insanity.

Well acquainted with the reciprocal actions of the
mind and body on each other, and possessing a profound knowledge of the secret motives of human
action, and the numberless and diversified considerations by which the mind of man may be arrested,
awed and conciliated, he skillfully and successfully
applied those medical and moral means which sooth-
ed and quieted the raving of the furious, raised and
encouraged the hopes of the desponding, and never
failed in gaining the confidence and affection of
both.'

He had a philosophic mind.   In his investigation
of a subject, whether professional or not, he was
always direct and discriminating; he saw it in all
its bearings and remote connections, and rarely failed to arrive at correct conclusions.

His taste was always as correct as his judgment.
In the fine arts of painting, statuary and music, he
was a connoisseur and critic.   He was a skillful per-

former on several musical instruments, and thought much of the favorable influence of music on the mind, whether rational or insane.

Whatever could benefit his fellow men always gave him pleasure. In his intercourse with society, in his visits to the sick chamber, in his care and guardianship of the insane, this motive was the ruling principle of his conduct. His opportunities of doing good in these several ways, were unusually great.

' In every relation to society he exhibited those qualities of the head and heart which never fail to receive the friendship and respect of mankind. But

> ' Nothing in his life
> ' Became him like the leaving it. He died
> ' As one that had been studied in his death.'

DR. AMASA TROWBRIDGE, JR. was the son of the celebrated Dr. Amasa Trowbridge, one of the most eminent surgeons in Western New York, and Professor of Surgery, &c., in the Medical department of Willoughby University of Lake Erie. The following notice of the death of this excellent young man, and a slight notice of him is from a newspaper of the day, June, 1841.

' Dr. Trowbridge was on his return, on horseback, from a professional visit to the upper part of Watertown, Jefferson county, N. York, and was overtaken by a pair of horses with a lumber wagon on the full run ; the pole of the wagon brought up against the Doctor's horse, throwing both horse and rider to the ground, and crushing the skull of the latter, by the fall, in the most frightful manner. Several persons who were near and witnessed the transaction, hastened to render assistance, but on raising Dr. Trowbridge to a sitting posture, the blood gushed from the eyes, ears and nose in great profusion. Several physicians were in immediate attendance, and the skull was bared by Dr. Crawe, preparatory to operating; but the frightful manner in which it was crushed, told too plainly that no human power could save him. He died in about forty-five minutes from the time of the accident, and as may be supposed, was insensible from the time it occurred.

Dr. Trowbridge was the son of Dr. Amasa Trowbridge, Professor in the Willoughby Institute, Ohio, formerly of this village, (Watertown), and well known as a skillful, accomplished and successful surgeon. The son was reared in our midst, and bred a surgeon and physician by his father, under whom he studied, and with whom he some time practised. He was a bold, skillful, successful operator; and at the time of his death, 27 years and some months old, had obtained a high professional reputation. Cut off in the very morning of his usefulness, his death is regarded as a public calamity, and it has diffused a general gloom over our village and county.

The funeral solemnities took place on Thursday last, and brought together a larger concourse of people—among whom we noticed many of our most esteemed citizens from different and remote parts of the county—than was ever before convened on a similar occasion in this village, and the ceremonies of the day were peculiarly solemn and appropriate. During the funeral solemnities the stores and shops in the village were closed, in token of respect for the deceased.

The following additional notice of this excellent young man, is from the Jeffersonian, Watertown, Jefferson county, N. Y.

The life of Dr. Trowbridge presents to the young aspirant for professional skill and eminence, a useful lesson and example. Under the guidance and instruction of one whose own reputation stands so high in his profession, with all the ardor of youthful inquiry, steady perseverance and industry, united with a ready perception and keenness of observation, he early gave promise of that eminence towards which he was so rapidly rising. Adopting the best maxims of his professional brethren, he was ever in quest of whatever useful discoveries and improvements were introduced by the skillful experiments of the age. He studied not only the practice of his profession, but became easily initiated into its theory, and whatever subjects were calculated to throw light upon the causes or nature of disease were made the objects of his closest examination, and the well filled shelves of his library evince the variety and copiousness of his reading, and its adaptation to the rationale and pratique of the accomplished physician. He compared every unusual case with the opinions of the best authors, and brought to bear in his whole surgical practice the fruit of practical experience, and the wisdom of others, and while possessing the cool self-possession of the operator, he never forgot his feelings as a man. The variety and success of his operations in every branch of surgery, have rendered him too well known

76

to need a mention. In his intercourse with his professional brethren he was gentlemanly and respectable, and secured their esteem not less by his acknowledged abilities than his modesty and courtesy. In private life his kindness and qualities of the heart had endeared him to all, and the simple but expressive eulogy has often been pronounced of him that 'he knew not enmity.' And to those who were intimately acquainted with him he had maintained a friendship for years, the strong ties of which death alone could sever. In all the relations of life it is not too much to say that few excelled him. Liberal in his opinions and feelings he was never the slave of prejudice or superstition, and although never neglecting the calls of professional duty, he found much leisure to gratify a refined taste in the study and the collection of the treasures of the earth, the sea, and natural history. As a physician he secured the confidence and affections of those with whom his duty brought him in contact, and never did he allow himself for a moment, from motives of present convenience, to excuse himself from attendance to however lowly or miserable a bedside he might be called. Out of our whole community none could have been taken whose loss would have been more severely felt, and there were none whose prospects of life and future usefulness stood fairer.'   B.

Dr. John Wagner of Charlestown, South Carolina, died May 22d, 1841, after a protracted illness.

Few have passed from existence whose lives have

been more checkered with vicissitudes and trials. At an early age he was attacked with rheumatism, to which he was subjected the remainder of his life, often prostrating his plans, embittering his existence and rendering necessary a resource to means to procure present ease, at the expense of the general constitution. Oppressed in bodily health, his mind reacted on every occasion, and in the intervals of pain was directed with considerable energy to his intellectual pursuits. Unsatisfied with the ordinary education at that time afforded in our city, he sought the opportunities furnished from older institutions. To Yale College he was sent, where, after passing the prescribed time in the diligent and zealous prosecution of his studies, he received the honors of that institution, the degree of A. B. being conferred on him in 1812, and that of A. M. in 1815.

With a mind thus prepared he entered upon the study of medicine under the direction of Dr. Post of New York. Under the superintendence of that gentleman he remained three years, devoting himself to the different branches of his profession with the most persevering industry, and acquired a knowledge of the practice of physic and surgery rarely equalled in so short a time.

The health of Dr. Post declining, he sought relief in a visit to Europe. During this time the subject of our notice, dissatisfied with his opportunities, resolved to visit the schools of London and Paris.

On his arrival at Liverpool he accidentally met his preceptor, who with suprise inquired into the object of his visit. I was doing nothing in New

York, was his reply, and resolved to come here. He was immediately furnished with a letter to Mr. Astley P. Cooper, and, by a fortunate occurrence, which superior devotion to his profession rendered available to him, became a dresser in Guy's hospital, undertaking the laborious duty of dressing, noting and recording the diseases of fifty or sixty patients. Here he remained twelve months, performing the above duties and perfecting himself in the practice of surgery and anatomy, and making preparations as a dissecting pupil. At the same time he was in attendance on the lectures on Surgery of Mr. Astley P. Cooper, delivered in the year 1815, '16 and '17.

Of his extraordinary diligence the voluminous manuscripts, carefully compiled and neatly executed, bear unequivocal evidence. They will always be referred to by his friends with pride and pleasure, furnishing the strongest testimonials of his devotedness to the cause in which he was engaged. Two large folio volumes on surgery and anatomy, closely written remain as records—besides his notes on various diseases, and remain a register of the most important cases.

About to leave London, he was furnished by his preceptor with the following gratifying testimonial: ' I cannot suffer Mr. John Wagner to quit England, without expressing my admiration of the zeal which he has shown in the pursuit of his profession, and the ability which he has manifested in the acquirement of a complete knowledge of it. America, which is making a rapid progress in professional science, will be proud to rank among its citizens a man so clear in his intellect, highly informed in his profession, and so kind and gentle in his manners.'

To this flattering expression of regard was added the desire that he should remain in London to promote his fortunes in that great metropolis. As a further evidence, he was presented with a bust of John Hunter, an additional incentive to diligence, and the man he delighted most to honor. He returned to America, married in New York, and settled himself a practitioner in that city. After a few years he removed to Charleston, S. C. His well-earned reputation had preceded him, and his reception was such as to furnish the most sanguine expectations of his future success. Without the apprenticeship to practice, the fate of so many, he was consulted in the most important cases, and admitted into the first families. His decision and perfect acquaintance with his profession, the kindness of his disposition, at once acquired for him the most implicit confidence, and his advancement was proportionately rapid.

With him a new era in surgery, in our city, may be considered as having commenced, and opportunities were soon afforded for the exercise of his skill in his favorite pursuit. Many of his brethren will remember the exhibition of surgical ability in a case of osteo sarcoma of the lower jaw, in which nearly half of that bone was removed. It was the third operation of the kind which had been performed in the United States, and two of them by the surgeons of Charleston—all present were pleased with his great composure. and dexterity, the rapidity of his movements, the perfect use of either hand, his kindness to his patient, and the masterly manner in which the whole was performed. Other operations of importance were undertaken—the amputation of the arm at the shoulder joint, the tying up the artery in popliteal aneurism, &c., with many others in which his perfect skill in the use of the knife, and an intimate acquaintance with the structure of the parts was manifested. In many respects he was not unlike his distinguished prototype, Sir Astley P. Cooper, of whom it was said, that his operations were like the graceful efforts of an artist taking a drawing. His practice increased rapidly, and he was soon among the established physicians of the city. In the winter of 1826 he commenced a course of dissections and demonstrations in Practical Anatomy, with the art of making and preserving anatomical preparations. The surgical anatomy of all parts concerned in the important operations were also dissected and demonstrated. His success in this undertaking was such as met his reasonable expectations, and the impressions left upon the minds of his pupils, of his great accuracy, and the skill, in anatomical demonstrations, such as few have equalled. In the art of making and preparing anatomical preparations he was rarely excelled—the specimens which remain exhibit the greatest neatness, display in the most striking manner the particular lesion of the parts, and furnish models for instruction and imitation.

In 1829 he was appointed Professor of Pathological and Surgical Anatomy in the Medical College of South Carolina. A professorship embracing the above topics was new in this country, and originated with the medical faculty of this city. Its limits were comprehensive. Treating upon topics which could not be considered under any of the established college courses, the successful discharge of this duty required much research and practical information. The syllabus which he published, exhibits his enlarged views, and his resources drawn from his valuale manuscripts, and that still more valuable storehouse which he possessed—his experience.

In 1832, after a closely contested election, he was appointed to the Chair of Surgery, vacant by the death of Dr. Ramsey. He continued connected with the institution until his death, performing his duties often under great bodily suffering, and mind embarrassed with cares.—*H. R. F., in the Am. Med. Jour.*, 1841.

DR. DANIEL D. WALTERS, for many years extensively engaged in the arduous duties of medical practice in the city of New York, was the son of Anthony Walters, and born in Putnam county, in that State, in the year 1773. He received a limited English education at his native place, and when arrived nearly at the age of manhood, repaired to the city of New York with a determination to become a member of a liberal profession. His natural energy and independence of mind induced him to select for the future business of his life, medicine, the study of which science he prosecuted under the direction of the late Dr. Valentine Seaman. He attended the lectures of Post, Hamersley, Rodgers, Hosack, Stringham and Mitchill, of the Faculty of Columbia College, the requisite legal terms, and the clinical instruction of the New York Hospital; and having complied with the collegiate regulations of the school, in order to assume the practice of his art, defended as his inaugural thesis a dissertation on Inflammation in 1803. During the time of his entering on the practice to the close of his career in 1824, he acquired great consideration for his clear views as a clinical prescriber and for his dexterity as an accoucheur, in cases of great difficulty. His only publication is his Diary of the occurrence of the first month of the Yellow Fever, which prevailed in the city of New York in 1822, with facts and observations relative to the nature and character of that disease, which was addressed to the Board of Health of that city, and printed in the New York Medical and Physical Journal, edited by Drs. Francis, Dyckman and Beck, vol. 1. In this able and most interesting paper, Dr. Walters contends on the broad basis of facts, for the distinctive character of yellow fever; that it originates from a poison *sui generis;* that it is of foreign origin, and cannot be deemed an aggravated form of bilious or domestic fever. As he was ever foremost personally in combating the pestilence, he was authorized to give his opinions with the authority of clinical knowledge.

Dr. Walters suffered repeated attacks of hemorrhage of the lungs, and died of pulmonary consumption, in New York, in 1824. His remains were interred in the burial ground of the Society of Friends, of which religious denomination his family were members. For independence in opinions, decision in emergencies, and frankness in professional intercourse, he was equalled by few. During the latter portion of his life he was much interested in disquisitions of a religious nature. Primitive Barclay he held higher in estimation than any other writer of sectarian theology.

J. W. Francis, M. D.

DR. HENRY WELLS. I regret that I have it not in my power to give a more particular account than I now can, of this truly great and eminent physician. I am indebted to Dr. Bachelder of Royalston, a former pupil of Dr. Wells, and late Vice President of the Massachusetts Medical Society, and to Dr. Richard Wells, late of Canandaigua, a son of Dr. Wells, for many of the facts mentioned in this memoir.

Dr. Henry Wells was born in the city of New York in the year 1742. He entered Princeton College at the age of ten years, and graduated at the age of fourteen. He studied medicine four years with the celebrated Dr. Hull of Connecticut. He afterwards studied medicine three years in the city of New York. I have been informed, but I will not vouch for the correctness of it, that he studied divinity for a short period after this. He afterwards kept an apothecary's store in the city of New York. His father, I understand, was a tory during the revolutionary war, and his property was confiscated. Dr. Wells removed

to Brattleboro', in Vermont—about the time of, or
just before, the war—where he resided several years.
As this was a rough country for his practice, he removed to Montague, in the county of Franklin, Massachusetts, where he supposed his business would be
less laborious. He was often called to patients at Albany, N. Y., Hanover, N. H., and various parts of
Connecticut, Vermont, New Hampshire and Massachusetts; and he had the confidence of all his professional brethren throughout the country. He was
much extolled by Dr. Nathan Smith, Dr. Twitchell,
and many other of our most respectable physicians.
He united himself with the Massachusetts Medical Society in the year 1785, and continued his fellowship
till his death in 1814, a period of twenty-nine years.
During a considerable portion of this time he held
the office of Counsellor in the Society. He received
the honorary degree of Doctor of Medicine from
Dartmouth College in the year 1806.

His habits and manners were conformable to what
were called the old school of gentlemen, and he has
been very appropriately called 'a nobleman of nature.' His dress was in Quaker-like simplicity, and
much in its form and color like theirs. He either
wore the velvet or buckskin small clothes or breeches,
the long jacket with flapped pockets over the thighs,
and the broad-brimmed, low crowned hat, as long as
he lived. He was broad chested, and a little inclined
to corpulency. I never saw him when I was not re-
minded of the portrait of the venerable Dr. Franklin. A miniature portrait which I have seen of the
Rev. Dr. Smith of Princeton, New Jersey, so nearly

resembles him that his family have pronounced the likeness correct. Notwithstanding his peculiarity of dress, and general appearance, his address rather excited familiarity than awe. Many of his patients almost worshipped him, and his presence has often smoothed their passage to the tomb. I am sorry that I have it not in my power to give more particular instances of the beneficial influences which his presence inspired in many incurable as well as curable complaints. A stranger laboring under a mortal complaint was induced to send for him, hoping that he might do something towards alleviating his distress, though he had no expectation that he could cure him. The doctor spent several hours with the patient, and when he left he was able to sit up and write a letter to his family physician, stating that the presence of Dr. Wells, his urbanity, cheerfulness, attention, and good sense, as evinced in his conversation, had so completely enraptured him and enchained his attention that he had almost forgotten his complaint. He was so much pleased with him that he observed he would rather have given a fortune than not to have seen him.

One of his patients in Montague, while he resided in Brattleboro', remarked that his presence was like that of an angel. After his removal to Montague, she observed that she saw him so frequently that his visits had lost some of their charms. This verifies the assertion that 'far fetched and dear bought,' is the most esteemed, and 'that a prophet is not without honor, save in his own country,' an observation which is many times true in the life of a country

physician. Even the most illiterate pretender will
often obtain the ascendency over modest, humble
worth, however learned and worthy the possessor
may be. Even Dr. Wells was destined to know and
to feel the truth of the remark in his declining
years. Gratitude for services rendered by an eminent physician is often as transient as the dew of
the morning. The elder members of the profession
whom I now address can doubtless remember many
instances where they have been highly extolled by
their patients in one sickness, whilst in a succeeding
one they have been superseded by charlatans or un-
fledged pretenders, thus reversing the sentiment of
' *vox populi, vox Dei*' unto that of ' *vox populi, vox
Diaboli.*' When a physician has once obtained the
well earned confidence of his brother practitioners,
he always retains it ; and this reputation is of vastly greater importance than the bauble reputation
gained by wealth. The patronage and applause bestowed upon Dr. Wells by his professional brethren
remained through a long life ; and after death was
transmitted to his descendants, and follows as a rich
legacy, which can never be lost.

Dr. Wells was always facetious and cheerful with
his patients, when their circumstances would allow
of it, thus inspiring them with great confidence of
their recovery. Many cases might be mentioned illustrative of the truth of this remark, but I have
only time to mention the following : He was sent
for to a patient who was considered to be dangerously sick. He spent the evening at his bedside,
and, on his retiring to rest, before he blew out his

candle, a messenger entered his room with a boot-
jack in his hand, which he informed the Doctor the
patient had sent in to him for the purpose of enabling him to pull off his buckskin breeches. The
Doctor sent back word to him that he need be
under no fear of dying for the present. The effect
was most salutary upon the sick man.

Owing to an accident, which I shall presently
mention, we have no details of his practice on record. He was supposed to be successful in some
cases in the cure of hydrophobia. He once mentioned to me that he knew a case of hydrophobia
occur six years after the bite of a mad dog. I
think the remedy on which he principally depended
was a preparation of mercury. Happy would it be
for physicians, as well as patients, were we able to
place any dependence upon this article for the cure
of this terrific complaint.

An account of the accident, which deprived the
world of much of the recorded usefulness and information of Dr. Wells, will be found in the following extract from a letter from his son, Richard
Wells, M. D., late of Canandaigua, N. York. I
wrote to him for information concerning his father
in the spring of 1840. He replied to me in a letter
of March 30th, of the same year, that the proposition which I made to him of writing some account
of the life of his father, was peculiarly gratifying to
him, and that nothing could have afforded him greater satisfaction than to know that the circumstances
connected with the sphere of action in the latter part
of his father's life were carefully and accurately nar-

rated. 'Yet,' he says, 'should I attempt to enter upon or prosecute any plan to accomplish so desirable an object, I should feel myself greatly embarrassed for the want of sufficient data for the ground work you so ardently solicit. I have for many years had in my possession all, or nearly all, my father's manuscripts, which were always kept at my office. Amongst them were many cases which he had noticed in the course of his practice, where any peculiarity of symptoms presented. Also a common-place book, in which he had noticed new theories and contrasted them. If I was still in possession of them, it would add much to the interest of his memoirs. Of all these I have unfortunately been deprived. A crazy man entered my office one morning, the key being left in the door, and soon began his work of destruction, by stripping himself and burning every rag of his own clothing; next, all the wearing apparel he could find, coats, boots and shoes, of a hired man of mine, then the shop furniture, and all the books that were out of the cases, and every day-book and ledger from 1824 to 1832, all the loose papers, letters, orders, memorandums, and with the rest, the manuscripts above mentioned. It requires more energy of body and mind than I now possess, to communicate what I may on suitable reflection get up, on summoning my resolution.' Thus at one fell swoop were the principal part of the written mental labors of this great man buried in everlasting oblivion.

Dr. Wells was affected for many years with what was supposed to be Angina Pectoris. He often thought he experienced much relief in this distressing and painful affection from the tartar emetic lotion, carried to the extent of pustulation. I do not know the complaint of which he died, Aug. 24, 1814, but I believe it was not an affection of the heart.

My Address before the Mass. Med. Society.

Dr. John Doane Wells was born at Boston in the year 1799, and died in the year 1830, aged 31 years. From Professor H. H. Childs', now Lt. Gov. of Massachusetts, eulogium upon the character of Dr. Wells, before the Berkshire Medical Institution, the following facts are taken.

'A very brief sketch of the life of Dr. Wells, together with some striking features and prominent traits of character, which he exhibited in his rapid progress and elevation to distinguished eminence in his profession, may profitably occupy our attention at this time—animated by his example, and inspired by his success, may a zeal and emulation be enkindled in your breasts, which shall burn brighter till the lamp of life shall be extinguished.

For the pre-eminent distinction which Dr. Wells attained, even before the meridian of life, he owes nothing to the influence of birth or fortune; though of highly respectable parentage, he claimed no alliance to the aristocracy of wealth or power, adventitiously bestowed. From his youth his mind was imbued with sound principles; early convinced of the value of time, he rightly estimated the importance of diligently improving the opportunities and advantages of education, with which he was favored ; accordingly we find him early distinguished by his habits of industry and close application to study, and by the purity of his moral conduct.

In his classical studies holding a rank among the foremost, always respected and beloved by his associates, having finished his collegiate course, he graduated in 1817, (at Harvard, I believe. S. W. W.) and immediately commenced the study of medicine, pursuing it with the same zeal and perseverance for which he was already distinguished. Anatomy was his favorite study ; his interest in this fundamental branch of the profession amounted almost to *enthusiasm*. He promptly availed himself of all the means and opportunities which presented for improvement; his labors in the dissecting room—his demonstrations to his fellow students, and his entire devotedness to the study of his profession, exhibit an example honorable to himself and worthy of your imitation. How well he succeeded in the acquisition of anatomical knowledge, and the consequent superiority he enjoyed, is distinctly told by the bright prospects which soon opened before him.

In the year 1820 he received the degree of Doctor of Medicine from Harvard University, and soon after, the appointment of Assistant to the distinguished Professor, Dr. Nathan Smith, then attached to the Medical School recently established in the State of Maine. So well qualified was he for the duties which were required, and with so much ability were they discharged, that soon after he was appointed Professor of Anatomy at the Brunswick school. Incited by a laudable ambition to excel, he visited Europe under the most favorable circumstances. He was Professor of Anatomy in a new and flourishing Institution—he was already well grounded in the science—he had begun lecturing— he knew precisely what was wanting to qualify him for more extensive usefulness, and he possessed the zeal and interest for the accomplishment of his purpose. In Paris he spent most of his time when absent; for there he found the advantages superior to those of any other country. And there he perfected his knowledge of Anatomy. Properly appreciating his opportunities, he applied himself unremittingly to the study of his profession. There too, besides the acquisition of medical science, he obtained a style of lecturing not surpassed in any school in the United States.

While in Europe he purchased for the Maine Medical School a library, and a Cabinet of Anatomy, which, with the addition since made under his directions, constitutes one of the most valuable collections of books and preparations any where found in this country.

On his return, laden with the fruit of industry, he engages with untiring zeal in the discharge of his professional duties. To his Professorship is added that of Surgery. He enters upon the duties of his office. His success is complete. The high expectations of his friends are more than realized. Principally by his labors and his talents, the Brunswick

78

school becomes deservedly popular, and becomes conspicuous among the Medical Institutions of our country.

In 1826 Dr. Wells was appointed Professor of Anatomy and Physiology in the Berkshire Medical Institution. To many of you I need not say how well
he succeeded—all were satisfied—nay more—all were
delighted. None could fail of being greatly benefited
who attended the clear and able demonstrations which
he made—who listened to his eloquence and followed
the lucid argument and the consistent reasoning to
their inevitable conclusions. His fame was now no
longer bounded by geographical limits—within the
last year he received an appointment in the Maryland University. But with the increase of his fame,
a decline in his health was too visible. He had
tasked his constitution too severely—and while the
powers of his body were weakened, his spirits were
unbroken, his zeal was unabated. He repaired to
Baltimore, and gave his introductory lecture to an
audience of more than fifteen hundred. It was received with the highest applause. He delivered his
course of lectures to a large and attentive class.
Trustees, Faculty and Students listened with astonishment and delight to the torrent of eloquence with
which he accompanied his valuable instructions.
But the spirit which had sustained, and animated,
and carried him triumphantly on, had exhausted the
powers of the body, requiring greater sacrifices than
his constitution could bear ; his health failed ; disease and death, occasioned by too frequent and too
great exhaustion, terminated the short but brilliant

life of one whose memory will long be cherished, and whose character his friends will long delight to contemplate.

The zeal and interest which had urged him forward in his professional studies did not cease to influence him in his professional labors: but the ability with which he was prepared for their discharge, he both *deserved and commanded* success. His lectures on Anatomy and Physiology were clear and comprehensive; minute, yet full; judiciously discriminating, he gave to each subject belonging to those sciences the attention which the importance of each justly merited. In the science of Anatomy, which has occupied the lives of such men as Bell and Hunter, Beclard and Meckel, he knew all that was known. To whatever part of the science he directed our attention, he at once excited our interest. On the subject of Physiology, a science of less certainty and less demonstration, he wisely abstained from all visionary speculations.

With a full and clear anatomical description of the different organs of the animal system, he delineated their functions, enumerated the phenomena of life, recounting the experiments which go to establish principles, and assign laws for the government of actions connected with life. Thus while his course enlightened and enlarged the understanding, the minds of his hearers were guarded against any prejudice or bias, which would hinder future investigation.

The subject matter of discourse is stated; the important points candidly discussed; the whole subject clearly presented, and in such a manner as not to excite present attention, but to invite future reflection and investigation.

In the practice of Medicine Dr. Wells possessed the requisite qualifications for eminent distinction and usefulness—and in the intervals between his lecture terms he was assiduously employed. Besides holding the office of Dispensary Physician, he was also engaged in very considerable private practice.

With the same zeal and perseverance which belonged to his character as Professor, he applied himself to the practice of Medicine; attentive to his patients, affable and agreeable in his manners, generally beloved, and rapidly acquiring the confidence of the public, and an extensive practice.

The value of decision of character, as well as perseverance, was duly appreciated by Dr. Wells. He saw and experienced the powerful agency of this principle, producing a concentration of effort and energy of action, which with irresistible force bears down all obstacles, and triumphs over all opposition. Its vast power and influence on the character is observed in all those who are distinguished masters in the arts or sciences, and in the liberal professions, as well as in the enterprises of philanthropy and benevolence. In our own favored country, where all are equal—where the road of preferment is open to all—and where merit is the criterion to settle the reward, the best succeeds who best improves his time.

Would you properly appreciate the traits of character which constitute a great and good man, follow the example of him whose praise is in the mouths of all who knew him. In his youth, and in his studies; in his manhood, and in his practice, industry, decision and perseverance characterize his every stage of life. Unaided by affluence, or the patronage of influential friends, he was early thrown on his own resources, and his efforts corresponded with the importance of the achievements he was destined to make.

In the preparation and delivery of his lectures, nothing was omitted which could contribute to aid in producing the most powerful effect upon his audience. His uniform practice of devoting the hour preceding his lecture exclusively to the particular subject, is proof of his industry and faithfulness, and gave him a familiarity and ease in the performance, admired by all.

Highly distinguished as was Dr. Wells in his professional qualifications, their attainment costing him much time and labor, we could not withhold from him the *tribute* which literature and general science so cheerfully award, and so liberally bestow on his character.

A thorough classical education, with a mind well disciplined, formed a solid foundation for the erection of a rich and solid superstructure; his varied and copious learning; the expanded powers of his intellect presented conclusive evidence of his industry and perseverance, and justly entitle him to the reputation of a good *general scholar.*

But it was his *moral qualities,* added to his intellectual powers, which gave a beauty and interest to his character, and threw around it a fascination, endearing him to his friends, and captivating all who fell within the circle of his acquaintance. Governed by a delicate sense of honor—in his feelings actuated by a spirit of liberality—open and frank in his disposition—above envy—he disdained all hypocrisy—and in an unparalleled course of prosperity, he maintained a dignity and modesty of demeanor, which proved his *moral worth* of the highest order. No false philosophy darkened the clearness of his perceptions, or disturbed the purity of his sentiments; none contaminated the professional instructions flowing from his lips. While unfolding the complicated and wonderful structure of the human system, he omitted no opportunity of impressing upon the minds of his hearers the evidence of the divine agency and wisdom displayed in the formation of man, and of the power and benevolence of God constantly exerted for his preservation and continuance. In all the different relations he was called to sustain in life, he not only acquitted himself with honor, but his *example bequeathed* to his friends and the public an invaluable legacy. We have seen him in prosperity almost unexampled; we have seen him admired and honored above most others of his age, and we have not witnessed a corrupting or destroying influence either on the mind or conscience. The field of his brilliant prospects is opening wider and wider; his sphere of usefulness is continually enlarging; his professional reputation high and immovably established; his numerous friends sharing with him a well deserved and wide extending fame. In the prosecution of all that earth can proffer to her most favored sons, suddenly and unexpectedly a sad and mournful change occurs; he is stopped in his career of prosperity, and compelled to exchange all the delights of social and active life for the torture of pain, and the confinement of disease; here his trials begin, and now is to be tested the value of his character for true wisdom. With fortitude and patience he endures the most excruciating sufferings of body, while his mind reposes in tranquil confidence in the dispensations of an overruling Providence, acquiescing in humble submission, influenced by the truths of the Christian religion, which he publicly professed, his soul rises above all earthly objects and holds converse with the skies.

In prosperity he was not corrupted, and now in adversity he does not despair. In the near approach of death he was calm and resigned, while the bosoms of his friends were torn with grief and sorrow. We sympathize with those friends in this most afflictive dispensation, and we mourn the early departure of one whose promise of long continued usefulness seemed so sure, and whose life was so great a blessing; but we bow submissively to the inscrutable Providence of the all-wise Ruler of the Universe. And now, though dead, he yet speaks in the most impressive language, that of his own bright example, worthy the aim and ambition of the most devoted student, and not less worthy the imitation of the most distinguished Professor.

No language or advice, young gentlemen, can be more useful or comprehensive than this, that you make John Doane Wells your standard of excellence; that you follow the path he marked out, luminous with his effulgence; it leads with certainty *direct* to a temple consecrated to fame and honor, to usefulness and to happiness.'

I was an associate Professor with Dr. Wells for two or three years in the Berkshire Medical Institution, and can most cheerfully subscribe to the truth of all that Prof. Childs has said concerning him. He was admitted a Fellow of the Massachusetts Medical Society in the year 1826.

DR. JOSEPH WHITE, of Cherry Valley, New York. I am indebted to Dr. Menzo White of Cherry Valley for the following facts in relation to Dr. White.

Joseph White, the subject of this memoir, was born in Chatham, in the state of Connecticut, on the 26th of September, 1763. At an early age he had the misfortune to lose his father, who was said to have been an intelligent man and a surveyor. He was left an only child with a widowed mother, with scanty pecuniary means, to breast his way alone in the world, A stripling during the revolutionary war, he embarked on board of a public armed ship, and was in one or two naval engagements; but of this part of his life he was not in the habit of saying much. He remarked that the roar of the cannon affected his organs of hearing so intensely that he was nearly or quite deaf for several days after one of the battles.

From the necessity of the case his early education was defective, irregular, and miscellaneous. Yet from his habits of perseverance, and the distinction, which he subsequently attained in his profession it is inferred, that it was continually in progress, and that his acquisitions of knowledge were steady, if not rapid.

He early exhibited his fondness and preference for the medical profession; and studied under a Dr. Fuller, and a distinguished surgeon by the name of Percival, of both of whom he continued through life to speak kindly. His industry was such, that before he was 21 years old he was admitted to the practice, it is said, of the first State medical society established in Connecticut, at the close of the revolutionary war. His pecuniary means were so limited that, like many other distinguished professional men in our country, he kept school for a period to enable him to prosecute and complete his preparatory studies.

Soon after receiving his license to practice he came to the State of New York, tarried a short time in Catskill, afterwards staid about a year at Bowman's Creek in Canajoharie, Montgomery county; and as early as 1787 came to Cherry Valley, where he spent the rest of his active and useful life.

Cherry Valley, the settlement of which commenced before the revolutionary war, was then the extreme western verge of civilization in this State, and those born or commencing business at the present period of our power, comfort, and affluence, can hardly realize the hardships, discouragements and privations to which the most fortunate of the pioneers were necessarily subjected. Books, the scholar's best food, surgical instruments, then in our cities far from the perfection which they have now obtained, and many of the helps to a physician, which the discoveries and improvements of the last half century have made common, were scarce, difficult to be obtained, even by

79

the wealthy, and often forbidden to the enterprising and ambitious. But the genius and experience of Dr. White, then an ardent aspirant for usefulness and distinction, made every help known and attainable to his purposes. He took at once an elevated and enviable stand among his brethren of the profession, and through a long life continued to maintain it. The defects of his early education were more known to himself than to others, and he was continually supplying them by untiring industry, and a vigilance that experienced no slumbering. Though his life was one of action, he stole time when others were sleeping, to become familiar, through the medium of books, with the discoveries and improvements in the healing art, as promulgated by the best practitioners, both in this country and in Europe.

While he loved his profession with the ardor which those destined to adorn either of the learned professions must feel and cherish, he was also a patriot, and was alive to the welfare and prosperity of the republic that had risen into existence before him. In 1796 he was chosen senator for the western district of New York. In 1798 he was selected as a member of the council of appointment when that patriot without reproach, John Jay, was Governor; and in 1800, during his administration, was appointed first Judge of the Court of Common Pleas for Otsego county, of which court he had previously been a side or assistant Judge. This station he continued creditably and usefully to fill for more than twenty years, and till the amendments of the state constitution took effect in the year 1822. Through that long period of political change and party excitement, he discharged his duties as judge with scrupulous integrity and fearless impartiality. He was a federalist of the Washington school, and gloried in the name when its pure practices had ceased to be fashionable. He has often told the writer of this article, that when Mr. Jay met his council, when he was a member, he would say, ' Well, gentlemen, we must do right, and do it in such a way that it will appear right, too ;' a maxim invaluable to all clothed in power and authority.

But his fame must not rest on the basis of his attainments and services as a medical practitioner; and he would not be spoken of in this work aside from them. His industry, economy, which he practised to the hour of his death, and his extensive professional business soon placed him above want; and in 1793 he purchased a large and beautiful farm which remained his residence the remainder of his life ; and is now occupied by Jacob Livingston, Esq. who married his only daughter.

His perceptions were quick, but before he acted in his professional character, he carefully examined and noted all the symptoms, and his judgment was not formed or acted upon, until he made use of all the lights in his power. Hence his usefulness, the value of his opinions, and the confidence which his practice inspired. He filled a large space in his profession, and his calls and rides extended from Albany to Buffalo, about three hundred and fifty miles asunder, and no one acquainted with his character will pretend that this wide spread fame rested on any thing like quacke-

ry or empiricism. He was the friend and admirer of
the Baconian philosophy.   Induction was with him
the governing principle. Theory, however specious,
unsupported by facts, had no charms for him, and was
no guide to his practice. He read and noted with
care all genuine, useful discoveries; and it was wonderful, considering his numerous calls, some of which
he even neglected, how well and exactly he knew
what each modern had added to the science and practice of physic and surgery, and how readily he applied the acquisitions of each to his own business.

His surgical operations were numerous, and very
generally successful. In Lithotomy he had early and
extensive practice. Many cases of this kind, the efforts to cure which seemed desperate, he undertook
and performed, and the patients survived to bless and
venerate his name after he was gone. A record of
some of these would be interesting and probably beneficial to the profession, were materials left to state
them accurately and make the record perfect. But
such is not the fact. He was deemed a neat as well
as scientific operator, and excelled in judgment of the
time and necessity for every painful operation. Although always firm he was never rash.

As skill in surgery appeals directly to the senses, it
is apt to excite wonder and admiration more than
equal skill in the cure of diseases that lie hidden from
view, and beyond the reach of manual operation. On
this account eminence in surgery attracts popular applause more readily and freely than equal scientific
ability employed in the practice of physic; as the

success of the warrior is more loudly applauded and fully appreciated than the more silent labors of the statesman.

In 1817 Dr. White was chosen President of the Medical College at Fairfield, and Professor of Surgery in the College of Physicians and Surgeons of the western district of New York, located at that place. During that and several successive years, he lectured on surgery in that institution. His lectures attracted a respectable number of students thither, and in conjunction with learned and skillful coadjutors, among whom were Drs. Beck and McNaughton of Albany, he rendered the institution popular and useful.

Without pretensions to oratory he spoke clearly, and often forcibly. He also wrote well without studying, understanding or caring for the niceties of composition. Of him it may justly be said that he did much and thought profoundly, without speaking for distinction or writing for fame. He obtained the highest honors of the profession, and was for a period President of the State Medical Society.

At his death, which happened on the 2d of June, 1832, in the 70th year of his age, he left two sons, one of whom is, alas! now no more, pursuing his profession, and both in extensive and diversified practice. His departure, therefore, seemed to leave a less void in the profession than might have been anticipated. How popular he was as a physician and surgeon may be best known by a common observation in the wide circle of his practice, that the name of White alone, without any study or skill will do much towards obtaining an extensive and lucrative employment in the healing art.

His mode of traveling was on horseback. Few men could endure so great a measure of fatigue from this method of traveling. For the robust it is however the most eligible and healthy, and altogether preferable to the gig or the sleigh, which lead to habits of indolence and effeminacy. He at one time rode from Albany to his place of residence in Cherry Valley, fifty-three miles, without stopping. At another time he rode from Buffalo to Batavia, forty miles, before taking his breakfast.

DR. THOMAS WILLIAMS, my grandfather, was second son of Col. Ephraim Williams, of Stockbridge, who was of the third generation in lineal descent from Mr. Robert Williams, who landed at Boston, and settled at Roxbury in Massachusetts, in 1630, ten years after the landing of the pilgrims on the rock at Plymouth, and eight years after the first settlement of Boston. Thomas was born at Newton, Mass., April 1, 1718. I regret that I am not able to obtain more facts in relation to his history. He received the honorary degree of Master of Arts from Yale College about the year 1737, and studied the profession with Dr. Wheat of Boston. He settled at Deerfield as a physician and surgeon about the year 1739.

Dr. Williams was held in high repute, not only as a man of science, but as a physcian and surgeon, by the government of the country. In the French war, which commenced in 1743, he was appointed surgeon in the army, in the projected expedition against Canada, which failed. He was afterwards surgeon of the chain of forts which extended from fort Dummer, at Vernon, in Vermont, to fort Massachusetts, at Hoosac, or Adams. These forts were situated, one at Vernon, one or two at Bernardston, one at Colerain, one at Heath, one at Rowe, one at Adams and one at Williamstown. Perilous indeed must it have been to visit these forts in an uncultivated and almost uninhabited country, exposed to all the ravages and horrors of savage warfare. Little does the present generation know of the hardships and dangers which our fathers suffered in planting and defending the pleasant country we now occupy. Now that roads are established in the best possible manner in which they are capable of being made, across the back bone of New England, or Hoosac mountain, we think it a hardship to pass them. Think then of the difficulties which our fathers had to encounter in passing this mountain in a time of savage war, when there was no road but a horsepath, when the country was a forest, and when they were continually exposed to the attacks of the Indians. Dr. Williams must have often been imminently exposed, for he was frequently obliged to pass these forts. It is related of him that a day or two before the capitulation of Fort Massachusetts, at Adams, at the west side, and at the foot of Hoosac mountain, which happened on the 20th of August, 1746, for some reason he obtained permission of the commandant of the garrison, to return to Deerfield. At a little distance from the fort, he, with thirteen attendants, passed through a company of hostile Indians, who lay so near the road on each side of it that they could almost reach them with their guns; yet he never discovered them, and they let him pass unmolested. This fact was mentioned to him soon after the surrender of the fort, by an Indian. The fort capitulated soon after this, and had it not been for his absence, he probably would have been taken and carried to Canada, as were all the inmates of the garrison who were not murdered by the perfidy of the French and Indians. The reason they did not fire upon him, probably, was on account of their fear of alarming the garrison. He was at Deerfield at the Barr's fight, so called, which happened a few days afterwards, and dressed the wounded. (For an account of this action see my History of the Indians of this place, Gen. Hoyt's Antiquarian Researches, and Williams' Redeemed Captive.)

In the war of 1755, he was surgeon in the army under Sir William Johnson, at Lake George, and was present on the day of the bloody morning scout, on the 8th of September, 1755. Heart-rending must have been the news of the fall of a dearly beloved brother.* He was in the encampment at the head of Lake George, four miles from the scene of action. On the attack of Dieskau's troops upon the encampment the same day, he was incessantly engaged in dressing the wounded, and administering

---

* Col. Ephraim Williams, who commanded a detachment sent out against Dieskau, and was shot through the head early in the engagement. Col. Williams was the founder of Williams College.

medicine for their relief, and he was constantly exposed to the fire of the enemy, and their bullets continually whistled about his ears. Dieskau was wounded in the bladder about this time, and taken prisoner. Of this wound he ultimately died in France. Dr. Williams dressed his wound, and attended upon him while he remained in camp. He afterwards fell under the care of a French surgeon. The Baron, while at Albany, expressed his regret that he could not have the attendance of Dr. Williams, as he believed he would have cured him.

Dr. Williams' letters while at Lake George give a very interesting history of the campaign of 1755. In 1756 he held the office of Lieutenant Colonel in one of the regiments at Lake George. His correspondence that year also furnishes many interesting medical and military facts.

Dr. Williams always had an extensive practice in his profession. I have often heard our aged people speak of him with great respect and love. He was the only surgeon, in his day, in this part of the country. His ride was very extensive; of course his practice was extremely laborious. Dr. Pynchon of Springfield, and Dr. Mather of Northampton, were his cotemporaries. These were the principal physicians in the old county of Hampshire, which then included the county of Berkshire, in the State of Massachusetts. He was often called into the States of Vermont and New Hampshire, even as far as Claremont, several miles north of Charlestown, which was then called No. 4. His practice as a surgeon must have been very considerable. He procured all the important instruments which were then used in the profession. His reading must have been extensive. He sent to Europe for the most approved authors in the profession of medicine; and his miscellaneous and literary library, it is believed, was not surpassed in this section of the country. He left to his children, besides many other valuable works, a large edition of the Universal History, and twenty or thirty volumes of the London Magazine, one of the best works then extant.

He was held in high estimation not only as a man but as a magistrate. He held the office of Justice of the Peace under the crown, and also that of Judge of the Court of Common Pleas, and of Probate. For many years he had the office of Town Clerk, and many other important offices in the town. He educated several students in the profession of medicine, who became eminent and useful physicians. He was a firm believer in the truth of the doctrines of the Christian religion, but not in the dogmas or corruptions of it. He was a member of Rev. Jonathan Ashley's church, and was on terms of great friendship with him. His death was occasioned by a quick consumption, brought on by a severe cold which he caught in the discharge of his professional duties. It happened on the 28th of September, 1775, in the 58th year of his age. May his descendants emulate his virtues and imitate his good examples.

DR. WILLIAM STODDARD WILLIAMS was son of the foregoing, and was born at Deerfield, Massachusetts, Oct. 11th, 1762.

When men of eminence and worth are called to pay the universal debt, it is the duty of surviving friends to endeavor to portray their characters for the benefit of posterity. I therefore presume that the propriety of filial affection will not be questioned which attempts to delineate the character of a beloved parent, a faithful counsellor, and a skillful physician.

The character of Dr. Williams is extensively known, and his loss severely felt by a large circle of friends and acquaintances who have known his worth, and experienced the benefit of his skillful practice as a physician. To them his loss is a calamity which will not soon be repaired. To his family it is irreparable.

The subject of this memoir had the misfortune to lose his father in early life; but notwithstanding, his youth was devoted to study, and about the year 1780 he entered Yale College and continued there a year or two, but never graduated. In the year 1782 or '3, he commenced the study of physic with Dr. Sergeant of Stockbridge, one of our most eminent physicians, and for many years a worthy Fellow of the Massachusetts Medical Society. Dr. Sergeant was a pupil of Dr. Thomas Williams, and a classmate and intimate friend of Dr. Rush of Philadelphia. He continued his pupilage with Dr. Sergeant two years, the customary period at that time of professional study. He then commenced practice at Richmond, Berkshire county, where he remained nine months. Soon af-

ter, he removed to Deerfield, where, after contending
with many embarrassments and discouragements, he
established himself in extensive business and in honorable practice, which he held to the day of his death.
He was elected a Fellow of the Massachusetts Medical Society in 1800, and he always endeavored to be
governed by its rules and regulations, and was a warm
admirer and an active supporter of the laws of the
Society as long as he lived. He resigned his Fellowship in 1819, on account of the difficulty of attending
the meetings. He was appointed Surgeon of the 2d
Regiment, 2d Brigade and 4th Division of Massachusetts Militia, in 1794, and held his commission with
honor sixteen years. He received the honorary degree of Doctor of Medicine from Williams College
in 1823. He was commissioned Justice of the Peace
in 1800, and to show in what estimation he was held
as a jurist, he ever afterwards held that office. He
was one of the Trustees of Deerfield Academy from
its incorporation in 1797, and from the year 1803 he
was Secretary and Treasurer in that Institution. His
townsmen appointed him their Clerk for 19 years, and
an overseer of the poor, and to several other town
offices for many years. At the time of his decease,
and for several years previous, he sustained the office
of Clerk of the First Congregational Society in his
native town.

But it is with his character as a physician that we
are more particularly interested. The above facts
will show in what estimation he was held as a man.
Will it be invidious in a son to state that he was one
of the most attentive applicants to books I have ever

known? Many a time have I known him to return home late in the evening from tiresome professional duties, and pore over his books till after midnight, investigating the cases which occurred during the day. Educated of course in the Boerhaavian school, when no other system was taught, he nevertheless threw off the trammels of the humoral pathology, and to the day of his death he kept pace with the great and important improvements in our profession, and gave to his patients all the benefits of modern improvements and discoveries. His medical library was one of the most select and extensive in this part of the country, and he never purchased a professional book which he did not thoroughly study. At a time when the best standard medical works could not be procured in this country, he regularly sent to Europe for them, and continued to do so till the embargo and non-intercourse laws interrupted our commerce with foreign countries; since which our facilities for obtaining standard works in this country are much increased. His library was enriched by the Medical Extracts, by the European Medical and Physical Journal, by the writings of Beddoes, Trotter, Russell, Duncan, and innumerable others. In this way he was enabled to store his mind with those ample sources of information which so permanently established him as a physician, and which extended his reputation throughout this section of the country. He was more extensively employed as a counsellor than any other physician in the county. He was often called into the States of Vermont and New Hampshire, into every town in the county of Franklin, and into the counties of Worcester, Hampshire and Berkshire.

But it was his great attention to the sick that endeared him to his patients. Most of the time leaving some one at home who could attend to his calls, he was enabled to spend many hours, and even days, with his patients in the extremity of their distress, and with his own hand to minister to their wants. If any thing will attach a sick person to a physician, it is assiduous and patient attention to him during his distress. I have known him spend hours by the bedside of his patient, scarcely leaving his chair, except for refreshments, and in several instances I have known this attention continued for days. Great must have been his opportunity for watching the symptoms of disease, and for administering relief. All the families in which he has practised speak of this trait in his character with affection and love. Hundreds of people believe, and not without reason, that were it not for this most unparalleled attention, many a husband and wife, many a son and daughter, would now be mouldering in the silent grave.

His practice as an accoucheur was very extensive. Probably no man in this part of the country was ever called to more diversified and difficult labors. Thoroughly acquainted with the use of instruments, he nevertheless, probably, did not use them more frequently than other skillful physicians would have done in similar cases. He devoted much of his attention to the diseases of infants, and so far as I may be allowed to judge, his practice was certainly very successful.

He was well acquainted with theoretical surgery, and studied with attention all the latest and best surgical writers. Of late, however, he did not perform any of the capital operations in surgery. I have seen him amputate a thigh neatly and successfully, and I have seen him perform several other important surgical operations. His cotemporaries will do him the justice to say, that in dressing an amputated limb, in bandaging and dressing wounds, few men surpassed him. Often called upon to advise in cases of operations, his opinions have always been received with great deference and respect, and by his advice he has saved many a patient from a tedious and distressing operation. His motto used to be, that those were the best surgeons who prevented the necessity of operations.

It is a subject of deep regret that he has not left a record of more of his important cases. Called upon to advise in more diversified and difficult cases than any other physician in this part of the country, such a record would have been invaluable. One reason for omitting to do this might have been a want of time, and another, which might have operated more powerfully with him, might have been his reluctance to court notoriety by publishing the result of his experience. Whenever honors have been conferred upon him in his profession he has ever considered them as ' sounding brass, and tinkling cymbals.' He has, however, left in writing innumerable prescriptions and recipes, which will be of immense value to his successors.

His practice was in accordance with modern im-

provements, but he was never hasty in adopting in-
novations. In acute diseases he bled with a bold
and unsparing hand, though he never could agree
with many of his cotemporaries in abstracting blood
in the advanced stages of phthisis pulmonalis, and
in many chronic complaints. He believed that the
modern depleting practice in such cases was annually destroying thousands of victims.

He was firm and unyielding in his opposition to
quackery in all its forms, and never has he been
known to counsel or advise with a man who was not
esteemed to be honorable in his profession, and who
was not regularly educated to it. His charges were
fair and honorable, and he never varied them for the
sake of obtaining business.

He educated a great number of students in the
profession of medicine, all of whom proved to be
good physicians, and many of them are now highly
eminent in the profession. As an evidence of the
estimation in which he was held by his professional
brethren, it may not be uninteresting to state, that
in cases of dangerous sickness he has been employed in the families of almost every physician in this
section of the country. His whole life was devoted
to his profession with unwearied assiduity and to the
melioration of the condition of his fellow beings.

As a man he was upright and honorable in all his
dealings. He despised unmanly concealment, and
underhanded meanness, in his transactions with his
fellow men. As a husband, and a parent, he was
most affectionate to his family, and endeared to them
by every tender tie. His home was his paradise and

his altar, and he never appeared to be happier than in the bosom of his family. He was kind and affectionate to the poor. Probably few men have done more to meliorate their condition. As an evidence that he never distressed them, the fact may be mentioned that during more than forty-two years he never sued more than two or three persons, although many of his accounts were open for the greater part of that time. I mention this not as a pattern to imitate, but to show his benevolence. Physicians in the country are too apt to let their accounts remain unsettled. More than one third of his accounts never were, nor never can be, collected, and many of them he never expected to collect at any time. So punctilious was he in keeping credit for his employers, that many of them never pretended to keep any account against him, even in extensive transactions. In his living he was remarkably temperate. Although exposed to all the vicissitudes of the weather in all seasons, yet for nearly forty years he never drank a glass of spirituous liquor, and he rarely drank a glass of wine. As a religious and moral man, as a tender husband and an affectionate parent, as an honorable man and an eminent physician, his family, his townsmen, and the community, bewail his loss as one of no ordinary magnitude.

His last sickness, though short, was severe. About the middle of December, 1827, he was called to Taunton, in the county of Bristol, to an only and beloved daughter, who was dangerously sick. Before her recovery other members of the family became seriously unwell, and his attention was required continually, day and night for more than a month.   He had been subject to severe attacks of the sick headache; his stomach became deranged, and the pain in his head was almost incessant.   He returned to Deerfield about the first of February, and soon after complained of dimness of vision.   His sight before had been remarkably good, and although he was nearly 66 years of age, he never wore glasses.   A slight amaurotic affection attacked his eyes, which increased as long as he lived, and the latter part of his life he was entirely deprived of the pleasure of reading.   The affection of his stomach and head increased, he became emaciated, and his spirits declined.   His case is pretty accurately described by Good, under the article Climacteric disease.   He however continued to practice till after the 20th of December, when a violent cold seized upon his lungs, and pneumonia supervened, which was relieved by bleeding and other remedies.   Incessant vomiting attended upon the complaint, which was not relieved till the system was so far shattered as to be beyond the reach of remedies.   His nervous system became affected, attended with slight mental alienation, which continued till the 8th of January, when he expired. Notwithstanding the weather was extremely cold and unpleasant, his remains were followed to the grave on the 11th by a vast concourse of friends and citizens, and eighteen physicians from this and the neighboring towns.   Such is a brief and very imperfect account of the life and character of Dr. Williams.

Dr. Westel Willoughby. Just as the printers were completing the publication of these memoirs, intelligence was received of the decease of my distinguished and venerable friend, Dr. Westel Willoughby, of Newport, Herkimer county, New York. Dr. Willoughby was one of the most distinguished men in western New York. He was the founder of the Willoughby University of Lake Erie, Ohio, and the town in which it is located received its name from his liberal donations to that institution. He was also one of the founders of the College of Physicians and Surgeons in western New York. My associations with both these Medical Colleges as Professor and lecturer, led me to an acquaintance with the character of this estimable man. The following abridged notice of him is from the Christian Register of October 19th, 1844.

Hon. Westel Willoughby, M. D. It is seldom that we have to record the death of one so useful and so distinguished in usefulness in the community and of so wide a sphere of action and influence in other days. In early life Dr. Willoughby went to reside in Herkimer county, N. Y., in the town of Norway, and for upwards of forty years had his residence in that part which was set off from Norway as the town of Newport. Here he shared with the first inhabitants the many privations of the wilderness. Devoted to his profession as a physician, few can adequately appreciate the difficulties to be surmounted in visiting the sick, over almost impassable roads, and through pathless woods, by night as well as by day, in winter's

SAM^L WOODWARD, M.D.

Aged 72

W.C.Sharp's Lith^y Boston.

storms and summer's heats. At an early period and
for many years he served the town as a magistrate
and town clerk. He was repeatedly elected a member of the State legislature, and during several years
was a Judge in the County Court of Common Pleas ;
his fellow citizens chose him their representative in
the Congress of the United States, and he served with
honor to himself and advantage to them. When the
College of Physicians for the Western District went
into operation, he was elected Professor of Obstetrics, and annually delivered a course of lectures in
that department of medical science for upwards of
twenty-five years. The long duration of this term of
service evinced the value of his lectures, and the very
general satisfaction they afforded ; and he was finally
elected President of that highly useful institution.

Thousands of medical students have been benefited
by his studies and untiring labors to promote the extended knowlege and practice of the healing art. In
all parts of our country, where they pursue their useful and honored vocation, the name of Professor Willoughby is to them ' like precious ointment poured
forth ;' and their last interview with their venerated
and beloved instructor they will recall with emotions of
gratitude and delight.

In domestic life Dr. Willoughby was a dutiful son,
affectionate brother, faithful husband, and ever trusted
friend. Dr. Willoughby for upwards of thirty years
was a professor of the religion of the Gospel of
Christ. Eighteen years ago he united with the Unitarian Congregational Church in Trenton, Oneida county, N. Y., and the even tenor of his Christian exam-

ple has been beautiful, in its serenity of faith, and peace and love. He fellowshiped with all who breathed the spirit of Christ, and delighted in the exceeding beauty and peace of his reign in the heart. He invaded no man's liberty, political or religious; and nobly, and in a truly catholic spirit, maintained his own; he had long desired his departure from earth; the interests of this world were gradually unclasped from his heart, and his hope was laid up in heaven.

On Thursday, the 3d instant, the conflict of disease and death terminated, and his soul passed into the unseen state of being; there, as we have no doubt, to meet 'a smile of welcome' to the bliss of heaven. Dr. Willoughby was born in Goshen, Conn., and was nearly 75 years of age when he died.

DR. SAMUEL WOODWARD. Samuel Woodward, M. D., seventh son of Israel and Abigail Woodward, was born in Watertown, Connecticut, in the year 1750. He belonged to a family remarkable for their longevity. The average age of his parents and their nine children was 86 years.

His father was a farmer, who had brought up his children to some mechanical employment, apprenticed him to an older brother, who was a shoemaker and tanner, designing to have him pursue the same business. With this brother he remained till he was twenty-one years of age, when, by his diligent application to business and his sedentary employment, he lost his health. He then relinquished this business and commenced study, attending school in summer and teaching during the winter. Thus by economical management, industry and prudence he contrived to get a good education, and being naturally fond of books he spent all his leisure hours in reading. He resolved to enter College, and all the difficulties and disadvantages which he encountered only served as incentives to more persevering and determined action, till by great economy and untiring industry he succeeded in accumulating a little fund, and at the same time fitted for college at the age of twenty-six. He entered Yale College in the autumn of 1776, and was in the sophomore or junior class when New Haven was attacked by the British troops, and assisted in throwing up the hasty works of defence which the necessity of the case demanded. At this time the college was broken up, and the class of which he was a member went to Glastonbury, Conn., but such was its broken and disturbed state that the benefits of instruction were materially lessened, and being somewhat advanced in age, he, with several others, left the class in an amicable manner, and commenced the study of medicine. When he entered college it was his design, and the expectation of his parents, that he should be a clergyman. This was particularly the wish of his mother, who was a very pious woman, and who wished to see one of her numerous family preaching the gospel she so much loved. Whether his leaving college before he graduated, or some other considerations influenced his mind is uncertain ; but he changed his plan and commenced the study of medicine with Dr. Hastings, then a respectable physician, in Washington, Conn., a neighboring town, and afterwards completed his study with Dr. Daniel Sheldon of Litchfield. Having completed the course of study, he commenced the practice of medicine in the parish of Torringford. In 1779 he was married to Miss Polly Griswold of that place. After practising medicine ten or twelve years in Torringford, he accepted an invitation to remove to Watertown, his native place, and established himself in his profession there. He left Torringford in 1790, and remained in Watertown two years. He soon found that this change did not promote his interest or increase his reputation, and he returned again to Torringford. After his return his business rapidly increased, and became quite extensive.

Soon after his marriage he was elected a member of the legislature of Connecticut, and afterwards when re-elected, he was the ' father of the House,' as it is called, being the oldest member, and took the Speaker's chair to call the House to order for regular organization.

For many years he educated students for the medical profession. His ride was at this time very extensive and arduous, and he was more extensively employed in consultation than any other in the county, except, perhaps, Dr. Sheldon of Litchfield, his former preceptor. His health was at this time very firm, and he was able to endure any amount of labor that he was called upon to perform. Indeed his health was always good till he was upwards of 70. He was a careful man, and consequently during a life of uncommon length and constant exposure, he met with no accident of any magnitude, and hardly had a day's confinement till ten years previous to his death.

He continued steadily to practice in his profession till he was 72 years of age, when, by the request of his children, and many of his friends, he suddenly withdrew, and encouraged a young physician who had recently entered the place, thus saving himself the disappointment and mortification of losing the confidence of his patients, and having business gradually withdrawn from him. Until this time he had enjoyed the unbounded confidence of his employers, many of whom had never seen another physician, and by thus suddenly withdrawing from business he continued to enjoy the high reputation he had established in his earlier days untarnished in the decline of life, and he is now ranked among the first men of his day, both as a man and a medical practitioner.

For some years previous to his death he had a series of afflictions; a disease of the bladder, asthma, a difficulty of swallowing, together with a rupture, which had long troubled him. These deprived him of comfort, and at times caused great suffering. He was, however, patient, and seldom known to complain or murmur. At last he was attacked with lung fever, under which, together with his old complaints, he gradually sunk, and died January 6th, 1835, aged 84 years and two months.

Dr. Woodward lived at a time when the stirring incidents of the nation's history must have produced a powerful as well as lasting impression upon his vigorous and youthful mind. At the time of the Decla-

ration of Independence he was twenty-six years of
age, and though never called into actual service during the war, he volunteered and assisted to defend
New Haven at the time it was attacked by the British, and at the subsequent burning of Fairfield he
went with the troops collected in the adjacent country
to expel the invaders, acting as surgeon to one of the
regiments of volunteers. This was the only service
which he personally saw. He was not, however, an
idle spectator of the scenes which were transpiring.
His patriotism was too strong, and his opposition to
British aggression too deep rooted, to allow him to
remain silent when he could do any thing to forward
the noble cause, and to keep on the final end and aim
of the revolution. He lent to it all the aid of his
talents, his influence and his pen ; and young as he
was, he probably accomplished more than very many
who were his superiors in age and influence.

One anecdote will serve to show his ability as a
writer, and his modesty as a man. At a large political meeting at Middletown, attended by some of the
most respectable and influential men in the State,
some anonymous articles of his, published in the periodicals of the day, became the subject of conversation at the dinner table. After several distinguished gentlemen had given great praise to the unknown
author, one gentleman declared with great emphasis,
' I would go this night to the utmost boundary of the
State to shake hands with the man who wrote these
articles.' Although he was at the table at the time
and heard the conversation, he did not break the
secret of his authorship.

82

In his political principles he was a Democratic Republican, always jealous of rulers, and an unflinching advocate of the rights of the people. He was the first man in the Connecticut legislature, after the peace, who came out openly a thorough advocate of Democratic principles. At this time he gained considerable reputation as a politician, and was for some time a candidate of the democratic party for Congress. The party being at that time a minority in the State, he wasnot elected. During the latter part of his life he did not lose his interest in politics, and in all his communications on the subject showed that he still remained the firm and undeviating friend of the people. His political opinions, averse as they were to the majority of his employers, did not shake their confidence in him as a physician, or tend to his disadvantage in a pecuniary point of view.

He was always faithful in his attentions to the sick, and carried with him to the bedside of his patients much that inspired them with confidence in his opinions and prescriptions. Never was a physician more fortunate in this respect. He had by his successful practice gained such a reputation that the most faithless were inspired with confidence at his approach, and of his medical knowledge no one had a doubt. He saw through a case readily, and observing all the strong features of it, his mind reverted to a host of others of a similar kind, and the effects of practice upon these, strongly impressed upon his memory, led him to apply his successful remedies anew, and generally with the most favorable results. He accumulated knowledge by experience, and experience by close observation. The characteristic features of his mind were sound sense and correct judgment. These he brought into exercise in the practice of his profession, and probably no physician in the county where he resided, except Drs. Hopkins and Sheldon, were his equals in the knowledge of the medical profession, when in the meridian of his activity. He was fond of reading, and no less fond of conversing upon medical subjects. In his practice he used but few remedies, and those of an active kind, relying much on the efforts of nature to throw off disease. He probably taught not less than forty medical students, and was considered a very thorough and excellent teacher. His qualifications, both for native vigor of intellect as well as by superior education, were quite above those of most physicians in his vicinity, though his advantages were quite limited, and he was emphatically a self-taught man. He was celebrated for his prudence, industry and strict temperance, and was a man of great moral worth. He was also a thorough business man, was remarkable for his punctuality and perseverance, and till past the age of 70 was untiring in his devotion to professional pursuits. He was a man of great simplicity of character, his dress and mode of living were always plain and truly republican.

In all public enterprises he was a conspicuous actor, and was always ready to do his part in whatever project was designed to improve society and make men better. He was a firm friend of temperance and did much to promote the cause, both by his extensive influence and his example. His philanthropy prompted him to action ; his judgment approved the measure, his whole soul was in it, and to the time of his death he was an untiring advocate of the cause. He was for many years a magistrate and was often consulted as a legal adviser by his neighbors, and they rarely had reason to regret following his advice, as it was a favorite maxim with him, ' do about right, and the law is not far removed from you.'

His epistolary correspondence was very interesting and instructive, up to the day of his death. His style of writing was very easy and chaste, and his penmanship, even to the close of his life, excellent. Few men could boast of more or firmer friends, for scarcely a man could be found who knew him who did not respect and esteem him, both on account of his estimable character and moral worth and intellectual endowments. He lived for the community, and most of his life was spent in the service of the public.

He lived to see many good days and went to the grave full of years. Few attained to the age at which he arrived, and few have died more lamented. His loss was truly a public one, and was severely felt by a large circle of acquaintances and friends. They know his value, and his memory will live long in the hearts of those who best appreciate his noble character.—*S. B. Woodward.*

Dr. HENRY WOODWARD. Henry Woodward, M. D., son of Samuel Woodward, M. D., mentioned above, was born in Torringford, Conn., May 26th, 1795.

When young, he shewed indications of a vigorous mind, uncommon observation and readiness to learn. At the age of 16 he entered a store, with the intention of qualifying himself for mercantile employments, but soon found that he loved books better than trade. He then left the business, and commenced the study of medicine under his father, and pursued it with his elder brother, Dr. S. B. Woodward, now Superintendant of the State Lunatic Hospital at Worcester, till he received his degree at Yale College. He then took an excursion to the west, traveling into New York, Pennsylvania, Ohio, &c., with a view of settling permanently in that country. While at Steubenville, Ohio, his eldest brother, then residing at Wethersfield, Conn., wrote to him and invited him to return and enter co-partnership with him, which he did, and they purchased a druggist establishment and continued together four years. While there in 1818 he married Miss Chiffonette L. Tryon, of Wethersfield, who died the same year. In 1821 he married Miss Mary E. Henderson of Middletown.

After residing in Wethersfield four years he was invited by Dr. Tully of Middletown, who was then about leaving the city, to come into his place and take his business. He soon got into extensive practice in Middletown, and was highly esteemed and respected as a physician. He had powerful and active rivals in business, who were jealous of his enviable popularity, and would gladly have taken advantage of any mis-steps that might have diminished his reputation and been of advantage to themselves; but he gained the confidence of his employers, and was estimated the ablest physician in the place. For years before his death his business was equal to that of any other physician in the State, both for respectability and extent. He received the honorary degree of Doctor of Medicine from the Connecticut Medical Society at an earlier age than any other gentleman in the State; and no young man was more esteemed by the faculty in an extensive circle of acquaintance.

He was twice chosen to represent the city of Middletown, in the legislature of the State, and was at the time a candidate for higher advancement. In the public stations which he filled he always sustained himself with dignity and ability, and was considered one of the ablest members of the House of Representatives. He had not the advantages of a collegiate education, but had those opportunities which, with his own industry and application, gave him a good education. From his earliest youth he was distinguished for his inquisitiveness and a strong desire to know the cause and mode of application of every thing with which he met. He was a good scholar, always able to take precedence of boys of his age, and when a student of medicine he was very diligent and thorough. He laid a broad foundation for future life, which, although terminating in early manhood, afforded him opportunity to gain high reputation as a physician. While yet a young man he became the counsellor of those around him, whose hoary hairs gave evidence of considerable seniority in point of age.

His mind was of a philosophical character, and was

well calculated thoroughly to investigate the causes
of disease, and skillfully apply the appropriate remedies; he had also the talent and tact that were necessary to gain distinction in his profession. His mind
was well stored with science, and experience was far
more valuable to him than to many; had he been
spared to have accumulated this kind of knowledge,
he would have had few superiors as a bedside practitioner. His intercourse with the sick was peculiarly
felicitous and happy, his manners were in a high degree refined and polite, and he had a fund of humor
and ready wit which he applied very appropriately on
such occasions. His patients all loved him, and met
him with the utmost cordiality and affection. With
all his anxiety for his sick friends he never suffered
his countenance to exhibit dejection in a sick room,
and in all his addresses to his patients his manners
were strikingly tender and affectionate; and while it
inspired hope and confidence, never blinded the vision
to the real danger of the situation. Whenever he
had dangerous cases of sickness on his hands his
anxiety was great and his attention unceasing. He
sacrificed his life for the welfare of his patients.

Frankness was a distinguishing trait in his character, and this gained him great respect among the
members of his profession. He loved society, and
society loved him. He was an interesting companion,
not only by the resources of his knowledge and happy mode of communicating his ideas, but he possessed an unusual fund of wit and humor.

His moral character was above reproach. He was
a man of active benevolence, gave much in charity,

and took hold of the great moral enterprises of the day with true zeal. He was a regular member of the Episcopal Church, of which he was for some time vestryman and warden.

In the midst of his activity and usefulness he was cut down by a disease of the chest, which in a few months terminated his life by a rapid consumption. He died October 10th, 1832, at the early age of 37 years.—*S. B. Woodward, M. D.*

DR. THEODORE WOODWARD was born in Hanover, N. H., July 17, 1788, and died in 1840, at the Vermont Asylum for the Insane. He commenced the study of medicine under the instruction of Doctor Nathan Smith, whose character is already before the public. Dr. Smith was to him both a friend and relative, being his maternal uncle ; and to whom in some important traits, Dr. Woodward has since exhibited a strong resemblance. His term of study was completed with Dr. Adin Kendrick, of Poultney, Vermont.

Dr. Woodward commenced the practice of medicine at the age of 21, in Castleton, Vermont. Although very youthful in appearance, he soon acquired, to an unusual extent, the confidence and patronage of the public, which was continued and increased nearly to the end of his professional career.

During the course of his practice Dr. Woodward performed most of the operations of surgery which are regarded as critical or important, and was no less distinguished for his fortunate selection of the

proper time and medical treatment of operations,
than for his accurate knowledge of parts and manual
tact; hence he was unusually successful, and extensively employed as a surgeon. Indeed, few country
practitioners, even of a much longer professional life,
have had an equal opportunity of observing so great
an extent and variety, both of general and surgical
diseases; few have rendered the healing art more
practically beneficial; and few have profited by it to
accumulate a richer fund of experience.

Soon after becoming established in practice, Dr.
Woodward's attention was turned to the condition of
medical education in his adopted state. An extensive region in which he was located, was found destitute of a school of medicine, such as was already
regarded as necessary to afford to pupils demonstra-
tive instruction in certain branches, and that kind of
tuition intermediate between books and experience,
which is imparted by public lectures on all branches
of medicine. Many students of medicine, whose
means of private instruction were very limited, were
found, either necessarily or willingly, to forego the
advantages of public instruction, and to enter the
profession with qualifications much below the standard of education in the more favored States, and
quite inadequate to the responsibilities of their station. In these circumstances we find Dr. Woodward,
adding to his labors, his usefulness and his honors,
those of a public teacher of medicine. This he did
not aspire to do by seeking to enter some well endowed and honorable institution; his was the very
different and difficult business, by individual effort,

83

unaided by legislative patronage, to create, to collect and arrange the materials of an independent college of medicine, remote from many of the facilities and advantages enjoyed by such institutions in our cities. By the aid of his worthy colleague, Dr. Selah Gridley, and the contributions of some friends of the enterprise, he succeeded in founding and establishing the Vermont Academy of Medicine. In this effort he received the hearty co-operation of many professional friends, who, it is believed, concur in awarding to Dr. Woodward the chief merit of having placed the advantages of competent medical instruction within the reach of many hundreds of young men who were seeking the qualifications of a useful and honorable profession.—*P., abridged from the Boston Med. and Surg. Journal.*

MOSES ALLEN LEE, M. D.,[*] the fourth son of Samuel and Elizabeth Lee, was born in Salisbury, Conn., March 2, 1805. His grandfather was the Rev. Jonathan Lee, the first settled Congregational minister of that town. In early childhood he suffered severely from an attack of hooping cough, which reduced him so low that his life was despaired of by his friends, and for many years he remained in a feeble and delicate state of health. Owing to this cause, his early education was not pursued in so regular and

---

[*] After the printing of this volume in alphabetical order, an intimate friend forwarded to me the following memoir of this distinguished and deeply lamented young man. With great pleasure I append it to these memoirs.

systematic a manner as it otherwise would have been ; but he possessed so quick an apprehension, and such a ready memory, that his attainments at the age of fifteen far surpassed what is generally met with in boys of that age, who have enjoyed the best advantages. From his feebleness of constitution, and the evils to be apprehended from sedentary habits and a life of study, he did not receive a collegiate education, but pursued mostly under a private teacher the different branches (including the languages,) which are usually taught in our grammar schools. As his health gradually became more rugged, he commenced the study of medicine under the direction of his brother-in-law, Dr. Luther Ticknor, President of the Med. Society of Connecticut, and received the degree of M. D. at the Berkshire Medical Institution in the year 1826. He immediately commenced the practice of his profession in his native town; from whence he removed to Litchfield, Conn., in the course of the next year, where he remained about two years ; during which period he was married to Miss Adelia M. Merrick, daughter of Joseph Merrick, Esq., of Pittsfield, Mass., whither he removed about the year 1830. For two or three of the following years, his time was chiefly devoted to agricultural pursuits ; but he gradually became more engaged in the practice of medicine, for which he had an extraordinary attachment; although he continued to cultivate his farm, and became one of the most active and useful members of the Berkshire agricultural society, which awarded him many premiums, for the best stock, wool, grain, &c. Having formed a partnership in business with Dr. H. H. Childs, late Lieut. Governor of Mass., he rapidly grew in popularity, while his practice kept him almost incessantly employed. His father-in-law having died and left him in possession of a large property, as well as sole executor of his estate, much of his time was necessarily absorbed in attending to the settlement of this business; after a few months, however, he was again fully engaged in his favorite pursuit of practising the healing art, which he henceforth continued till attacked by the disease which terminated in his death.

In the spring of 1841, Dr. Lee was elected Professor of Materia Medica in the Berkshire Medical Institution, and in the autumn of the same year, delivered his first course, consisting of about 80 lectures, to a class of more than one hundred medical students.

During the latter part of February, 1842, Dr. Lee was called to attend several cases of epidemic erysipelas, in the Pittsfield Poor House, of a highly malignant character, and during his attendance upon them was seized with the usual symptoms of the same disease; but under the judicious treatment of his colleague, he so far recovered in a few days as to be able to walk about; but from some cause unknown, a relapse occurred, and after a series of protracted and indescribable sufferings, he sunk under the ravages of Phlegmonous Erysipelas, June 16th, 1842, in the 36th year of his age.

From the first attack of his painful disease, Dr. Lee had a strong impression that he should recover;

which he retained until within two weeks of his death. He bore his extreme sufferings not only with perfect fortitude and composure, but during a great part of the time with cheerfulness. He neither feared death, nor the pangs of death. Having for several years professed Christianity, and lived the life and enjoyed the hopes of a Christian, he now experienced its blessed consolations, and exhibited the strength of that faith, which robs death of its sting, and the grave of its victory.

Dr. Lee was a man of truth, and strict integrity. Nothing ever made him swerve from the right; or what he considered to be the right, and not a single instance can be found, during his whole life, where he did not rigidly adhere to what was perfectly honorable and just. He carried his heart in his hand; whatever he did, was open and above-board; there was no concealment about him; whatever he felt or thought he ever freely expressed. He was distinguished also for his eminent social qualities, and the warmth and constancy of his friendships. No one ever relished the pleasures of social intercourse more than he; and his uninterrupted cheerfulness, and sprightly conversation made him a favorite in all circles. He was ready to make any sacrifice for his friends; and whether prosperous or unfortunate in life, his attachment knew no abatement from change in external circumstances. He was never influenced by popular prejudice, or fashion, or any of those undue currents, which go to make up public opinion. He formed his own opinions deliberately, and he did not change them from trivial causes. He was eminently hospitable and generous. His house was open to all who wished to enter, and none were sent empty away. As a father, he was kind and indulgent; as a husband, tender and affectionate; as a son, dutiful and attentive; as a brother, devoted and loving; as a citizen, liberal and public spirited; as a christian, sincere, humble and devout.

As a physician Dr. Lee possessed more than a common degree of tact, judgment and skill. If there was any one department in which he excelled more than another, it was in diagnosis. His perceptions were all uncommonly quick and accurate; and his mental operations so rapid, that he seemed to arrive at a knowledge of disease as it were by intuition. His reading had been regular and systematic, as well as extensive, and his knowledge was always at command. His mind was of a highly practical cast. Every thing was brought to the test of practical utility.

Dr. Lee was remarkably successful in the treatment of disease, and his reputation had already extended throughout many of the adjoining towns, so that he exerted a commanding influence in that part of the State. He had no medical hobbies, and he never ventured an opinion, in a case of disease, until he had fully investigated it, and then his opinions were generally found to be correct. He was a close observer of the phemonena of disease, and nothing was too trivial to escape his observation. He was not a disciple of any particular sect or school in medicine, but a true *Eclectic*, choosing from every quarter whatever seemed to him to be based on sound and correct principles. In short he was a close student of nature, and followed in the footsteps of her best interpreters. For success in the treatment of chronic diseases, Dr. Lee had few if any superiors of his age in the State; and he will long be remembered for having restored those to health, who had been considered as laboring under incurable maladies.

Always cheerful, and possessing a rare fund of native humor, he diffused cheerfulness wherever he went. No physician was ever more beloved by his patients, for no one was more attentive in sickness, punctual to all calls and engagements, or sympathized more deeply and sincerely in the sufferings and afflictions of his fellow men. He was remarkable for energy and decision of character, as well as unwearied perseverance in whatever he undertook. Whatever plans were laid he never ceased his exertions till they were accomplished. When in health, he never refused to attend any calls, whether by night or day, from rich or poor, and many are the instances where he not only gave his attendance, but gratuitously furnished the necessary family supplies.

Had Dr. Lee lived, he would unquestionably have risen to great eminence in his profession. As a teacher of medicine he would have particularly excelled. Though summoned at comparatively short notice to deliver a course of lectures, he not only succeeded in giving perfect satisfaction to his class, but rose at once to a degree of popularity rarely enjoyed by those who have been for years engaged in public teaching. He had no taste for hypotheses, or theoretical speculations; every thing was estimated according to its practical value ; its importance as connected with the treatment of disease. Students who attended his lectures, uniformly declared that they never had derived a greater amount of practical information from any public teacher of medicine, than from Dr. Lee. With a fine person, graceful and easy manners and a melodious voice, he united all those mental accomplishments which are necessary for usefulness and popularity. In his death, the Institution with which he was connected, sustained an irreparable loss. There may be those who have pursued their medical researches to a greater extent, or who have cultivated particular branches of the science with greater minuteness, but there are few, if any, who to such solidity of judgment, such a perfectly well balanced mind, add such an amount of really useful knowledge—and manifest such power of discrimination, such tact and skill in applying it to the relief of disease. P., a friend of Dr. Lee, writes, ' I do not believe that he had an enemy in the world. He was a universal favorite in Pittsfield, and all his acquaintance may be numbered among his personal friends. His funeral was a scene of universal weeping. He left a dying message for all his acquaintance, and the burden of it was, ' tell them not to neglect their spiritual interests.' '

Thus lived, and thus died, *Moses Allen Lee, M. D.*, leaving a beloved wife and three children to mourn his loss.

NOTE AND ERRATA.

Several typographical and other errors escaped notice while examining the proof sheets, although they were carefully read. Perhaps some of them might have been occasioned by the obscurity of the handwriting, and overlooked. Many words, when written and printed, appear very much alike, such as 'Homer' for 'Horner'; 'desire' for 'deserve'; 'keep' for 'help.' The judicious and candid reader will readily correct these errors at a glance, and they will not injure the meaning of the sentence. Some of the most important, which may possibly mar the sense, are noticed below. Through an inadvertence on the part of the compositors, the name of Samuel B. Woodward, M. D. was omitted, as the author of the life of Daniel Sheldon, at page 516.

Traveler is spelled *traveller* in two or three instances, and counsellor is spelled *counselor* once or twice. Webster, and some other late lexicographers and writers, use but one *l* in either of these words.

In the preface for '*Thatcher*' read 'Thacher.'

Page 143, 11th line from the bottom for 'Homer' read 'Horner'.

Page 202 after the last line on page 201 add—'would be superfluous. Scarcely had the year 1829'

Page 520, 7th line from the top for 'desired' read 'deserved'

Page 578, 7th line from the bottom for 'breathing' read 'hearing'.

Page 589, 12th line from the top for 'officer' read 'office'.

Page 590, 7th line from the top for 'different' read 'difficult.'

Line 5th from the bottom of the same page for 'institutions' read 'situations'.

Page 649, 14th line from the top for 'keep' read 'help'.

Page 486, 14th line from the top for 'Bailey' read 'Bentley'.

INDEX

to

AMERICAN MEDICAL BIOGRAPHY

of

1845

PLACES

SCHOOLS AND SOCIETIES

AILMENTS, MEDICATIONS AND COURSES OF TREATMENT

MISCELLANEOUS